URW-Edition No. 2 · 4/87

Digital Formats for Typefaces

by Peter Karow

URW Verlag · Kreienkoppel 55 · 2000 Hamburg 65 · West Germany

Copyright © 1987 by Dr. Peter Karow
Reproduction and printing: Himmelheber, Hamburg
Printed in Germany
ISBN 3-926515-01-5
Original edition: ISBN 3-926515-00-7
URW Verlag Hamburg

Contents

Preface 11

1.   **Introduction** 15

2.   **Typeface terminology** 19

3.   **The display of typefaces** 34
3.1   Visual display devices................................ 37
3.2   Typesetting machines................................ 45
3.3   NC machines 53

4.   **Requirements of typesetting** 58
4.1   Type structure 58
4.2   Form setting 61
4.3   Hierarchical format structure 65

5.   **Formats** 69
5.1   Review of formats 70
5.1.1 Bitmaps (bytemaps) 70
5.1.2 Run lengths 75
5.1.3 Open vectors.. 77
5.1.4 Closed vectors 79
5.1.5 Curved lines 82
5.2   Other concepts 91
5.3   Special coding techniques 95
5.4   Listing of a selection of type manufacturers 100

6.   **The URW concept** 102
6.1   IKARUS 102
6.2   Format hierarchy at URW 104
6.3   The IK interpolation 107

7.   **The preparation of rasters** 113
7.1   Soft-scanning 114

7.2	Manual corrections	124
7.3	SC formats for laser printers	133
8.	**Conclusions**	136
8.1	Properties of formats	137
8.1.1	Electronic requirements for the generation of control signals	139
8.1.2	Storage requirements	141
8.2	Requirements to be met by formats	143
8.3	Recommendations for manufacturers	144
8.4	Time required for producing type	145

Appendices

A	Type classification	151
B	Characters of a typeface	157
C	Accents for Latin type	165
D	Dingbats	169
E	Explanations of optical effects	171
F	Short dictionary of type terminology	172
G	Data structure for typefaces	180
H	Data structure for graphics: IG format	192
I	Description of the IK format	211
J	Description of the DI format	224
K	Description of the VC format	236
L	Description of the VS format	252
M	Description of the VE format	267
N	Description of the SC format	280
O	Description of the SN format	290
P	Description of the BI format	302
Q	Description of the GS format	313
R	Data structure for spacing	322
S	Width table	327
T	Kerning table	330
U	Touching table	355
V	Overlapping table	356
W	Programs for converting IK→DI	357
X	Marking rules	375
Y	Digitization rules	382
Z	References, on typefaces in particular	392
	The author	395

Summary

This book is intended to be mainly of interest to all those people who intend or wish to develop new machines for the output of typefaces.

It is possible to distinguish between three groups of equipment for which digital alphabets are required – display devices, typesetting machines and NC machines. Up to now the development of typefaces has been too dependent upon the design of the respective machine used. This needs not be the case. The digitization of type should be undertaken in two steps: firstly, the preparation of a data base using hand-digitization, and subsequently the automatic generation of machine formats using soft-scanning, achieved through the use of computer-based programs.

The digital formats for typefaces are suited to systematic ordering, as are the coding techniques. The various formats are investigated, their properties discussed and the relative production requirements analyzed. The appendices provide the reader with additional information, mainly on the digital formats for typeface storage as introduced by the IKARUS System.

This book is set in Marconi. Marconi was designed by Hermann Zapf in 1976 and prepared, by Peter Käpernick, for typesetting on Dr. Ing. Rudolf Hell Company's Digiset machine in 1976/1977. Marconi is the first typeface prepared for electronic typesetting with the aid of the IKARUS system.

Preface

This book is aimed at both technicians in electronics, and users of typefaces in many and varied applications. It is more than just an introductory book; it touches on a whole series of areas involving the digital preparation of typefaces.

In the past, typefaces used in visual display terminals (VDT) were often developed by engineers. Not only did the level of technology at the time place limits on the creation of good letterforms, but also the joy of experimentation was sometimes a predominant factor in the creation of type using electronic media. The aesthetic consideration of the letters was secondary.

Many of the current digitally generated types are difficult to read, some ignoring all the basic rules of legibility. We should not forget that legibility is not an outmoded term. Our eyes and reading habits – leaving out OCR information for the moment – have not changed over the centuries.

Consider for example the type used in modern video communication systems or on TV transmissions. The word images, sometimes using unusual typefaces, and shown for only short periods on the screen, are often difficult for the average, quite apart from the aged, viewer to distinguish. The letters are usually too closely spaced, and the word images often blend into one another representing an additional handicap for the frustrated reader. If a sans-serif type is used and the r and n are too closely spaced an m may result; the letter c and an l too closely spaced may unintentionally produce the letter d and so on.

This tight typesetting is a product of fashionable thinking in advertising which often leads to the formation of word images with letters too closely spaced. Each reduction of the letter spacing in texts also leads to an inevitable loss of legibility. We should not forget that the rapid recognition of word images is the primary task of all type character reproduction.

The legibility of many visual display terminals could be appreciably improved if the lines were set slightly further apart and the letter spacing were allowed to revert to a normal constant.

In the days of hot metal composition it was normally impossible to print letters closer together. Only with the arrival of phototypesetting with its new possibilities did letter spacing reduce, and obtain the bad habits it has now.

Writing is the visual reproduction of the spoken word, its primary objective being to convey a text to the reader without difficulties, immediately, and without disturbing the flow of reading with unnecessary embellishments.

The letters have no self-fulfilling purpose, neither are they a medium for self-representation. Their most important task is to provide clear differentiation between individual characters. This applies not only to the letters. Bearing in mind the importance of numbers in a modern industrial society, consider how easily the numerals 3, 6 and 9 can be mistaken for the 8. In telephone directories – especially if printed black on white – it can rapidly become a problem to distinguish between these individual numerals in the very small type sizes used. This leads us to one of the important criteria for new types: clearly distinguishable and unmistakeable forms.

Everything which makes reading more difficult or lengthy, or is detrimental because of its unusual form, has to be avoided. When considering a typeface all of these factors have to be included right from the start. The drawing of letter forms should also be able to meet aesthetic requirements. Each eccentric character within a word image disturbs the reading flow, and therefore the rapid comprehension of the text.

This handbook from URW is intended to provide an introduction to the many problems of typeface creation and digital typeface preparation. Not everything to do with typefaces is rational and logical. There are many purely optical factors to be considered. They are the result of long development throughout the history of type, based on experience and knowledge, which should not be ignored.

The primary objective is not to produce incredibly attractive, artistic alphabets as in the past. The application and development of new alphabets, as approached in this book, require the optimum utilization of the technical possibilities available today, and those future methods of type reproduction already hinted at.

Our current task is not to copy old typefaces, e.g. Garamond Antiqua from the 16th century or a Bodoni from the 18th century. We now live in the era of technology and electronics. We should try and solve our current problems by contemporary methods.

Many early type fonts stemming from the centuries following Johannes Gutenberg were designed for printing on wooden hand presses and predampened paper. The technical possibilities of type composition – with all its limitations – also determined the form of the letters.

Text from Gutenberg's Bible

The infinite possibilities provided by today's electronics should be used to develop types of our time, without historical hangovers. Clear forms, but not cold or machine-like in appearance, which can lead to an unconscious rejection by the reader and an unwillingness to read longer texts.

In addition, we are currently at the start of an era of new developments in the digital application of type characters. Whereas previously we were satisfied if the lines were just legible on the VDT, the current trend of development is to produce innumerable variations from stored basic fonts with high legibility.

Typography has previously been limited to two dimensions. The future technology will take letters and produce three dimensional effects and images with perspective distortion.

URW's experience in the area of type generation with the IKARUS system now covers a period of more than 10 years. Peter Karow was able, using the IKARUS system, to develop a new method in a program for the mathematical classification of type characters with high aesthetic qualities for the first time. The multitude of possibilities provided by modification and interpolation led to new ways of developing whole type families. The results will benefit today's users.

The computer aided mathematical conversion of letter forms will soon lead to a creative process with which it will be possible to generate more and more new and attractive solutions using letters and single word images. The IKARUS system represents the start of a new era in the reproduction of type characters. It will also make its presence felt as new areas of application demand aesthetically pleasing types.

A font, stored on a chip and having high digital precision and quality of shape will then help us to convert the many, often primitive, type characters currently on our display screens and computer printouts into pleasant types, using fonts to which we have become accustomed over the centuries in the standards of the Gutenberg art of printing. The quality which was once taken for granted should also be the standard of the future in the digital field.

Hermann Zapf

1. Introduction

The invention of electronically controlled machines for text display and output led to the digital storage of type. These machines can be divided into three groups according to their usage:
- Visual display devices (VDT, graphic VDT, TV)
- Typesetting machines (CRT, laser, microfilm, matrix)
- NC machines (drawing, cutting, routing, engraving).

Visual display equipment is used for the rapid display of texts on TV monitors. As a rule this purely electronic display for a temporary and cost-effective presentation has led to the development of bad letter quality, not aiding legibility. Not particularly beneficial to mankind!

Typesetting machines create text on film, printing plates or paper which are of more permanence and often only to be read at some later date. The presentation of the letters is usually of a very high quality, excluding for the moment the dot-matrix printers used in data processing.

NC machines are used for drawing on paper, for cutting self adhesive materials, for cutting, routing or engraving wood, metal or plastic. In this field the quality can be sometimes very poor (for example, the letters produced by character generators in plotters), which is unforgivable, but also extremely high (e.g. on flat bed drawing machines cutting materials for display on hoardings, windows, vehicles etc.).

In the course of using digitally stored types we have discovered the following:
- The developments within these three groups are independent of each other. No one knows what the others are doing.
- Typesetting machine manufacturers have made great efforts to achieve high quality.
- No one has as yet attempted to integrate the work of the separate fields to produce type with good legibility and reproduction quality on the various electronically controlled equipment.

In addition one must recognize that most development engineers associate type with Latin, Arabic or Chinese symbols for the reproduction of words. But there is much more involved: it is the reproduction of whole messages (advertisements, signs, books, newspapers, journals, tables, plans, calculations, drawings). Thus, in addition to letter types one needs to be able to represent logos, symbols, vignettes, frames or line graphics, or elements for the generation of line graphics.

Note: Within the terms of this discussion, type is used to denote all elements necessary to reproduce a message within the framework of electronic communication, be it on the visual display unit, on paper or any other material!

Returning to the consideration of the equipment:

it is a fact that its developers are usually engineers who, working under the pressure of time, have to produce the next improvement of their machine, to make it cheaper, faster or more powerful. Hardly anyone gives any thought under such conditions to improving the reproduction of type. And yet it is so obvious; because all of these devices use type for communicating with people. It appears as if the engineers have extrapolated from their own handwriting, since it has generally been adequate for communication in the typing pool or in the private sphere: someone has always been around who could read it. So they assume that computer type doesn't need any beautification or further treatment.

Examples of poor quality

As a consequence, letters are considered to be a necessary evil and are prepared for digital storage with the minimum of time and financial expenditure.

Two examples make this behaviour clearer. One of the inventors of the electronic typesetting machines has said what amounts to the following on the matter of type: "We have now finished the develop-

16

ment of the typesetting device, there are scanners included in our supply program. So, our customers are getting a CRT typesetter with a scanner and should then be able to produce their own type." In the twenty years since then virtually none of the users has achieved this. A similar reaction was given recently by one of the developers of alphanumeric VDTs with proportional type. He had taken approximately two years to develop the hardware and software, and approximately three hours of this for the actual proportional type to be displayed. He literally added: "The type was really no problem," this was reflected in its quality. And by the way, for this developer there was only "the type". He obviously makes two classifications of type species:

Handwriting and computer type.

Let us hope that in future the producers of writing machines place more emphasis on the quality and variety of the reproduction of type!

Further consideration of the three most important areas of application of type in connection with computers and electronic control will lead the observer to conclude that all devices have the following properties:

- Type is always stored in such a way that its digital form can be converted as directly as possible into electric signals, and
- on the whole it is not possible for type to be loaded into the writing machine by the host computer.

This last point can usually only be resolved if all system components for an application are supplied by the same manufacturer.

These two characteristics can have disadvantages. Within the scope of a particular machine the type has a specific digital machine format plus a specific face. All developments show that the generation of digital formats always proceeds within the scope of this one machine, to be introduced into the market as soon as possible. No one has looked further than the production and completion of this one machine and no one has considered that in any dynamic company, the product of today is followed by tomorrow's development of the next machine. So, type has always been developed, digitized, corrected and stored within the narrow limits of specific formats. This is an expensive habit! Every subsequent machine then requires the repeated procedure of digitization, correction and storage of type – because as a rule one machine's format is not convertible to that of another machine unless one has used the same raster resolution in order to achieve the same type size.

This is also the reason for one of the bigger disadvantages of writing machines. Each particular machine has its own particular machine format, which as a rule can only be properly handled by the manufacturer. If a user of one of these machines wishes to run products from another manufacturer, a change of type is often unavoidable, i.e. a change of type format and the specific type appearance, and in some cases even the type font itself.

These disadvantages can be overcome by the following procedure: the digitization of type is carried out independently of any specific machine. This digitization has to be universal so that it can be adapted to any desired application. To put it another way: all machine formats are calculated by computer from one mother format.

The machine formats will be standardized and made accessible to all developers the world over. Manufacturers would be very happy about this – type would no longer represent a problem. Similarly, users would also be pleased; they could change setting machines without having to adjust or adapt to the new type font specific to the new machine.

In order to show how this objective can be achieved this book includes a detailed description and investigation of the various equipment classifications, several machine formats worth mentioning, coding techniques and finally the demands and problems imposed on type data formats by typesetting.

Subsequently, the properties of digital formats for type are illustrated and requirements developed for these formats.

In the final chapter, conclusions are drawn and suggestions made for the future course of progress in the manufacture of type data. Throughout this the reader should keep a critical eye on the quality of the text reproduction, which need not be neglected when using digital storage.

2. Typeface terminology

First the reader should be introduced to special expressions and terms used in the typeface world.

First of all, we shall consider the standard appearance of letters in normal print, black on white paper, i.e. letters physically present, and not stored digitally on some electronic or magnetic storage media, thereby no longer directly visible, but abstract. We are dealing here with terminology as used in the world of type designers and type producers.

Types are divided into two main groups: text and display.

The first refers to types used for the body of a text material in newspapers or books, the other is for titles and headlines.

Each type has its own special character and style. Currently, there are probably more than 10,000 different Latin typefaces available.

A simplified classification – following ATYPI (Association Typographique Internationale) guidelines – may be carried out as follows (see also appendix A):

Class	Typeface
Roman (Antiqua)	Baskerville
	Bodoni
	Garamond
	Palatino
	Times
	Optima
Sans serif (Grotesk)	**Futura**
	Helvetica
Black letter (Textura)	𝔚𝔞𝔩𝔟𝔞𝔲𝔪 𝔉𝔯𝔞𝔨𝔱𝔲𝔯
Script, Cursive	*Ariston*
Fancy, Free	**Goudy Fancy**

Many types are available in different fonts (complete assortments of characters of one size and style). These typefonts are also known as the type family. Such a family often consists of four upright and four italic type versions (differently weighted fonts). ITC (International Typeface Corporation in New York) produces four families a year according to this scheme, i.e. 32 different versions or fonts. ITC is one of the most active companies in the world developing new typefaces. The slanting angle of italics (slope to the right) is usually 12 or 12.5, rarely 15 degrees. The weight designations are as follows:

light	(mager)
medium	(normal)
demi	(halbfett)
bold	(fett)

A member of a typeface family is properly identified if one says for example "Optima demi italic". Previously, the type sizes were produced individually in hot metal composition and then set. There is no reason why these particular forms should not be retained, even in the age of digital type: we shall therefore continue with the concept as before, whereby from one font special versions were made in the various sizes of 6pt, 8pt, 9pt, 10pt, 12pt, 16pt, 18pt, 24pt, and 36pt (where pt = point).

First of all we can identify the individual letters using well known denotations. These are the letters "A" to "Z", the numerals, the punctuation marks (i.e. comma, full stop, question mark etc.) and language variations (e.g. ä, ö, ü, œ and ø). The marks over the letters are known as accents. Other accents are also available, e.g. ´ and ˆ for both upper and lower case letters. Currency symbols are also available, e.g. £ and $. Large letters are known as capital letters, caps, upper case. The small letters are known as lower case or minuscules. When capital letters are as small as the lower case letters they are known as small caps. And that isn't all.

Type experts have even more possibilities, there can be characters which are "raised" and "lowered", e.g. ^{0} or $_0$. The elevated characters are known as indices, superiors, superscripts or exponents, the lower are known as indices, inferiors or subscripts. Using both together one can produce fractions, e.g. ¼ or ¼. Most European languages require the use of accents to allow proper reproduction. This is very important. Only English no longer uses accents. Accents and special signs are a fairly large group, e.g. in

Czechoslovakian:	ÁáČčĎďÉéĚěÍíŇňÓóŘřŠšŤťÚúŮůÝýŽž
French:	ÀàÂâÇçÉéÈèÊêËëÎîÏïÔôÙùÛûÜüÆæŒœ
German:	ÄäÖöÜüß
Polish:	ĄąĆćĘęŁłŃńÓóŚśŻżŹź
Spanish:	ÁáÉéÍíÑñÓóÚúÜü
Swedish:	ÅåÄäÉéÖö

In appendix B you will find a summary of the letters in a Latin type-face with their designations, and in appendix C we have gathered together the accents for Latin letters. In order to gain an overall view we have included, not comprehensively or with pedantic accuracy, a few more terms worth knowing.

There are signs for formulae in mathematics, e.g. the root sign $\sqrt{}$ or the integral sign $\int$. Mathematics cannot, in fact, get by using only Latin letters, mathematical type includes Greek letters and Black letters among it's variants.

The type family AMS-Euler, a type for the setting of mathematics, was developed by Hermann Zapf in the Metafont system (see also chapter 5.2) together with Donald Knuth for the American Mathematical Society and Stanford University, and covers around 900 characters.

Other special typesetting elements:

Newspapers need a whole range of various line elements for producing line borders. Advertisement creation requires elements for embellishment and decoration. At this stage we have already moved away from type characters proper. In addition, special types (e.g. so

21

called Pi-fonts) are also required, which consist of decorative or swash elements or of ornamentation and special characters, and serve to hold the reader's attention. In appendix D we have included the "Dingbats" series from ITC, as designed by Hermann Zapf.

Ornamentation elements are also referred to as vignettes or embellishments, whereas a more pictorial representation, e.g. a tree, may be called a line graphic. Letters can also be reproduced as half tone or patterned. The letters – or rather their outlines – are filled with grey tone or grids of hatching or dots.

Before this text becomes too uninteresting for technicians, for whom this book of digital formats is mainly intended, we shall concentrate on individual letters and the formation of words.

In antiquity, letters were chiselled in stone or inscribed in clay (e.g. the Sumearian cuneiform). Letters were scratched, or written with a feather stylus (quill) and, in the western world after the middle of the 15th century, also appeared in printed form (Gutenberg in Mainz, Germany). All such letters have a certain thickness of stroke, for example the width of the basic stem of an "I". At the top and bottom this capital I has serifs. The "D" has one straight and one curved basic stroke, this can also be described as one straight stem and one curved stem. The lower case "n" has no ascender or descender, whereas the "h" has an ascender and the "p" a descender. The white inner spaces of lower case letters such as "o" or "n" are sometimes known as counters.

The "n" has an upper white "ink trap" where the second, initially curved stroke leaves the first straight stroke.

The "O" is approximately 1.5% higher than the "H", which is why it has an upper overhang. It also overhangs the base line (body line, type line), a base overhang. Curved lines have to be made larger in order to appear optically "of the same height".

The "H" has two vertical stems and one horizontal crossbar. These strokes appear to the reader to be of approximately equal thickness if the horizontal stroke has approximately 85% of the thickness of the two vertical strokes or stems, with respect to sans serif forms.

But not to worry, this book is not intended as a course in typography. However, technicians and programmers in the fields of typesetting machines and letters do require some knowledge of a few basic items. There are various books available (see appendix Z).

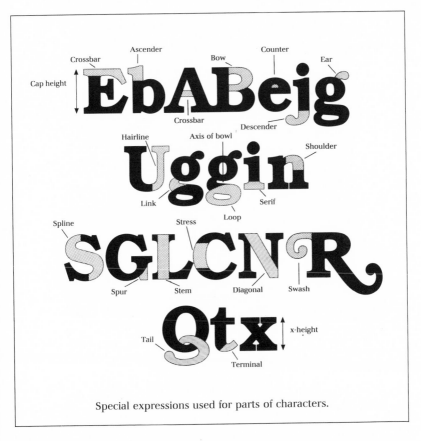

Special expressions used for parts of characters.

The transitions from straights to curves (e.g. in "m") are known as tangentials. Such transitions are optically more effective if one sets a clothoid on the straight. A clothoid is a type of spiral with a curvature starting at zero and increasing along the curve.

Motorway exits are often clothoid in design: when coming from the straight, one wishes to enter the curve without having to wrench on the steering. The turn of the steering wheel is a measure for the curvature of the carriageway. The same applies to the optical effect of tangential transitions in letters and logotypes. They too should be clothoid.

It is immediately noticeable if one takes a standing rectangle and places a semicircle above and below. One generates something which looks more like a bone than a rounded stem.

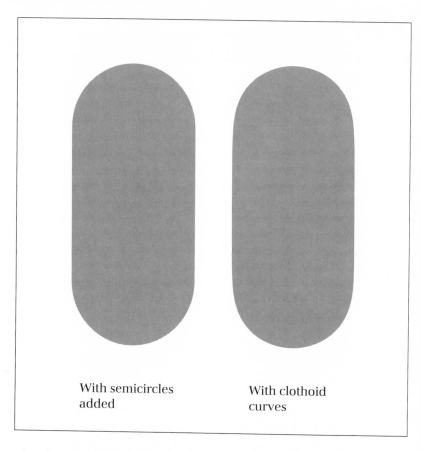

| With semicircles added | With clothoid curves |

The above mentioned optical effects would seem to me to be related to optical illusions. It is a well known fact that when recognizing or comparing forms and figures, mistakes of recognition occur.

As a small exercise we would like to confront the reader with a few basic questions.

1. Which rectangle appears to be a square? Please cross.

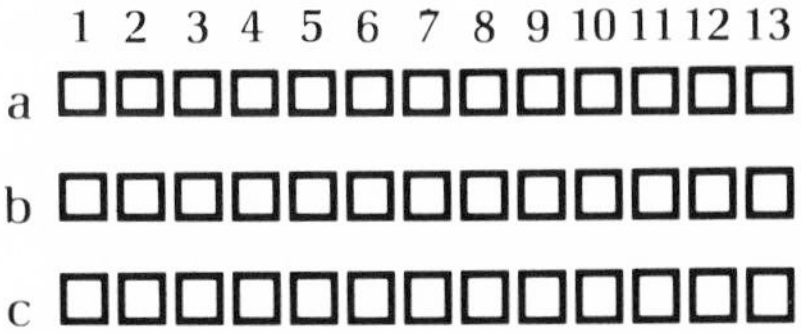

1 2 3 4 5 6 7 8 9 10 11 12 13

a ▯▯▯▯▯▯▯▯▯▯▯▯▯

b ▯▯▯▯▯▯▯▯▯▯▯▯▯

c ▯▯▯▯▯▯▯▯▯▯▯▯▯

---

2. Which ellipse appears to be a circle? Please cross.

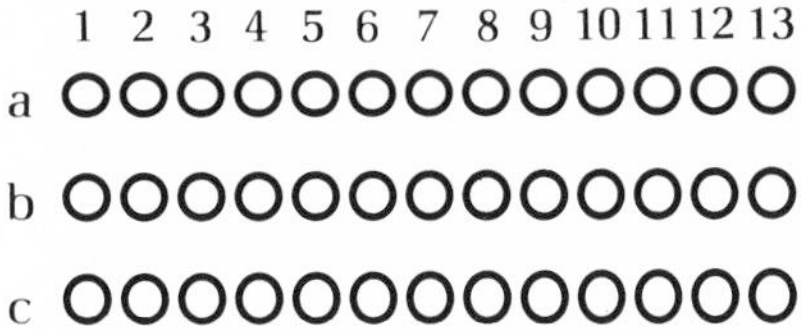

1 2 3 4 5 6 7 8 9 10 11 12 13

a ○○○○○○○○○○○○○

b ○○○○○○○○○○○○○

c ○○○○○○○○○○○○○

---

3. Which circle appears to be as high as the squares? Please cross.

1 2 3 4 5 6

a □○□○□○□○□○□○

b □○□○□○□○□○□○

c □○□○□○□○□○□○

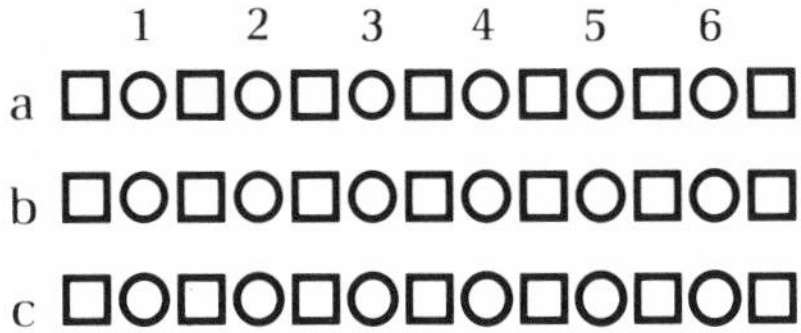

4. Which triangle appears to be as wide as the squares? Please cross.

1 2 3 4 5 6

a □△□△□△□△□△□

b □△□△□△□△□△□

c □△□△□△□△□△□

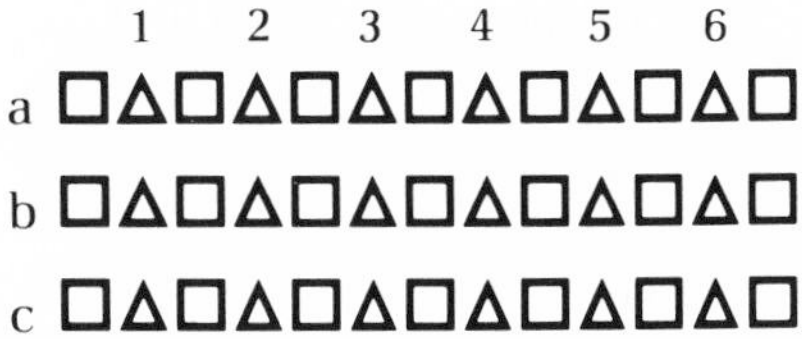

5. Which triangle appears to be as high as the squares? Please cross.

1 2 3 4 5 6

a □△□△□△□△□△□

b □△□△□△□△□△□

c □△□△□△□△□△□

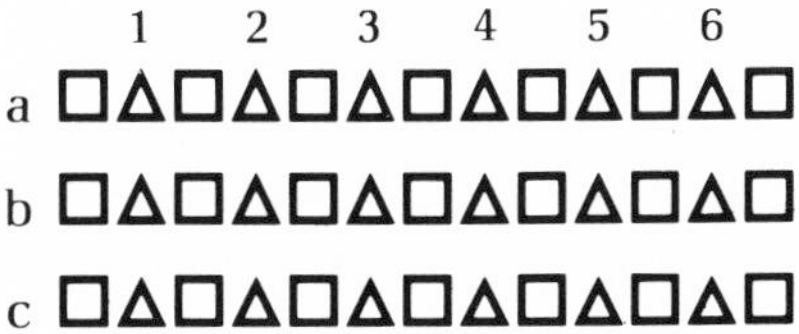

We have compiled our explanations and details of optical effects in appendix E. They are based on statistical averages as a result of an investigation involving 130 test candidates at URW in Hamburg.

In summarizing, we can say that a square only appears to be a square when it is 1% higher than it is wide, the same applies to circles. Furthermore, circles (curves) first appear as large as squares when their diameter is 3% greater than the length of the square (straight capital letters).

In the case of triangles (e.g. letters A and V) the height should be 3% and the width 5% greater than the corresponding square side length in order to appear as high as they are wide.

These percentages are mean values. The whole aim of this exercise is not to prescribe how one produces optically satisfying effects. We are merely trying to provide guidelines. Each particular typeface has, as might well be expected, its own individual effects and its own individual "excesses".

These and other optical effects can only be properly and correctly considered by experienced type designers. In future all technicians should bear this fact in mind. Let us hope that we have seen the last of those "computer typefaces in 3 hours".

Let us return to the terminology of letters. Some terms are from the era of hot metal composition.

A digitally stored letter has a mathematical reference point. In geometry this is known as the coordinate zero point, or the origin. This point is placed at the left hand lower corner of a squared box, into which all letters of a typeface will fit. This square is known as the "em square" or just "em".

The side length of the em square should be equal to the largest letter width in the font. The letter "m" is quite often the widest letter and is possibly the origin of the term "m square(d)". The height of the em is known as the "bodysize". The breadth of the letters is known as the width (measured in digital units), which is often relatively small for the letters "i" or "l" and often equal to bodysize in the case of "m" or "W".

The bodysize must also be large enough for accents, ascenders and descenders. The following is a commonly used division:

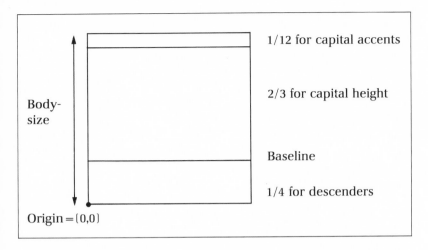

Body-
size

1/12 for capital accents

2/3 for capital height

Baseline

1/4 for descenders

Origin = (0,0)

Later in this book, in section 8.2, we propose a new em square, not to irritate friends, but rather to make life easier in the future.

Letters themselves rarely take up their total width, they have a left side bearing and a right side bearing (the white spaces on the left and right of the letter).

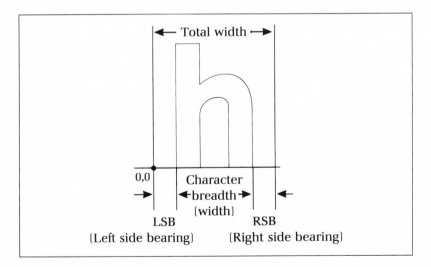

Total width

0,0

Character
breadth
(width)

LSB
(Left side bearing)

RSB
(Right side bearing)

The left and right side bearings are intended to allow the letter to appear optically balanced next to any other member of its typeface. In practice this is of course a compromise, because the spacing between letters is dependent upon the form of the preceding and following characters. Consider for example the A and two possible following neighbours B and T.

In hot metal composition we would have the following images, AB and AT. In the case of "AT" the T could be brought closer to the A, because the "A" is wider at the bottom and the "T" is wider at the top. In metal composition this is no simple matter, since the intervening metal has to be removed mechanically by hand. This is known as kerning (undercutting). Only then does "AT" appear as optically balanced as "AB".

Where groups of letters are combined, as for example ff, fi, fl, ffi, ffl, we have what are known as ligatures. They are combined and used as one character. Some examples of ligatures with hardly recognizable characters are the German ss – ß (**ſs**) and et – & (&⁀).

Subsidiary lines also run parallel to the baseline, as shown in the following diagram:

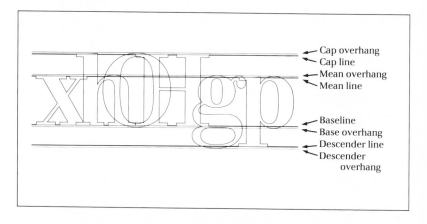

The thick lines are more important than the thin ones. The relative position of the thin to the thicker lines varies from face to face. There are no exact guidelines because their position depends on the type design. Digital storage for coarse resolutions sometimes requires a more rigidly specified positioning of the auxiliary lines than that required in the original typeface, which does not help to improve its appearance.

Typefaces may be modified, given an italic angle, expanded or condensed. The characters can be contoured, "antiqued" (artificially aged) or rounded. One may change the lower case height in relation to the cap height, blend whole words together, or give letters various shading, and in general create entirely new letter forms.

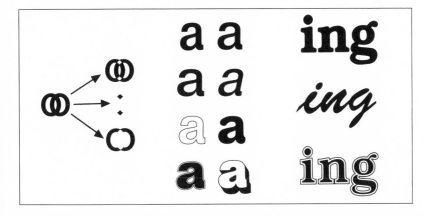

Using simple geometric operations they may be enlarged, condensed, rotated and distorted. Envisaging transformations like these is undoubtedly no problem for technicians. On the other hand, there is a whole series of devices which are incapable of doing this at all, for example most VDTs.

Nowadays most VDTs set " MONOSPACED ", i.e. all letters have the same set width. This is also termed "non-proportional". Typesetting machines set with proportional widths, which is a very great advantage. Setting can be further improved when not only the right side bearing is adjusted to the left side bearing of the next letter, but the space between any two letters is also adjusted specifically for that pair of letters, i.e. using the technique of digital kerning. Consider for instance:

Television

traditional

Television

kerning

Finally we have a few special terms associated with the digitization of type. All devices write with a certain line resolution, which is

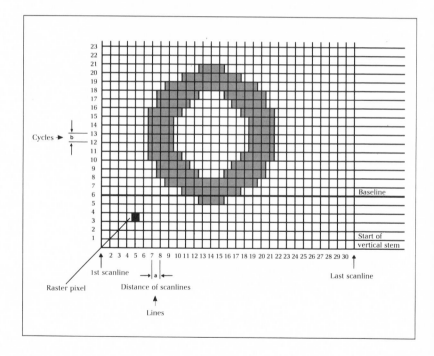

specified in either lines per inch or lines per millimeter. This means that the black faces of the letters are generated by the machine (e.g. typesetting machine) so that black lines of a certain thickness are drawn, line by line. A further limitation of digital technology is the line itself; the writing line can only be switched on or off in certain, electronically specified periods (cycles). This means that white or black sections of a line consist of a number of beats (pixels). The letters then appear as lines and dots on a horizontal and vertical raster (or grid). One talks of a 400×400 raster where the em square consists of 400 scanlines and 400 pixels per line in both the X and the Y direction. One may also describe this as an em with a 400×400 raster resolution.

We are of the opinion that describing a letter according to its em is the best way of picturing the digitization of type.

One Didot point = 1p is the generally accepted unit of measuring for type size. Previously, according to Didot 62 2/3 points = 23.566 mm. However, in Europe nowadays one normally works with the new Didot point and the dimensions 1p = 0.375 mm, whereas in America it is standard practice to use the pica point where 1pt = 0.351 mm. One inch (1 inch = 25.4 mm) has approximately 72 pts (more precisely: 1 inch = 72.27 pts).

Legislators would like to see a new dimensioning of capital letter heights (H-height) in mm, rather than bodysizes in points. At the moment typesetting machine manufacturers give measurements in both systems; the world of printing is very conservative, and the old units are often still in use.

Texts in newspapers usually appear in 9p ≅ 3.4 mm bodysize ≅ 2.25 mm cap height, 10p is also sometimes used.

Typewriters often have 9.5p ≅ 3.6 mm bodysize ≅ 2.4 mm cap height, others have 10pt = 3.51 mm bodysize.

If we consider the 9p em as standard size then we have:

| Writing resolution in | | Raster for |
l/mm	l/inch	the 9p em
7	180	24 × 24
9.4	240	32 × 32
11.8	300	39 × 39
15.7	400	54 × 54
32	813	108 × 108
64	1626	216 × 216
96	2438	324 × 324

If we place a 9p Didot em next to a 9pt pica em, both with eightfold magnification, one can recognize a difference in bodysize of approximately 7%, **but an H-height almost the same.** The pica em of most companies allows less room for descenders.

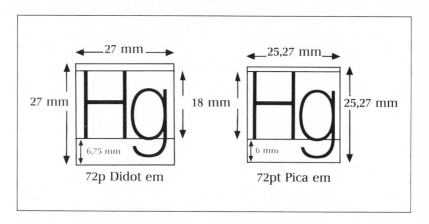

27 mm

27 mm

6,75 mm

72p Didot em

18 mm

25,27 mm

25,27 mm

6 mm

72pt Pica em

As the bodysize determines the line width of text, setting with pica points allows the presentation of English texts with the same cap height, but smaller line widths because there are no accents to collide with descenders of the line above. There is in fact a simple conversion method from Didot points (new typographic points) to mm: The ratio of cap height to bodysize is 2:3. Similarly, $1p \times \frac{2}{3} = 0.375 \times \frac{2}{3}$

=0.25 mm. Thus, one can arrive at the cap height in mm by dividing the bodysize in points by 4.

4p bodysize = 1 mm cap height.

The same is true for pica points as shown above.
Rasters of 50 × 50 and smaller are known as
– low resolutions,
Rasters in the 100 × 100 range and more are known as
– high resolutions.
Ask any typographer and he could greatly expand this chapter and go into much more detail. However, we shall stop with the traditional terms here in the hope that we have not generated too much boredom.
See appendix F for a short listing of English, French and German terms for and about typefaces.

3. The display of typefaces

Even though we really want to discuss digital formats we cannot avoid casting an initial glance at the devices which display the type characters. We would like to distinguish three separate categories, namely visual display terminals, typesetting machines and NC machines.

All machines have the following procedure in common when writing a letter: first of all the character is stored digitally somewhere in the machine or the system, either electronically or magnetically. All characters have a binary address, so that by electronic selection any desired figure can be accessed in any sequence.

The first step is the reading of the character, i.e. the storing of the digital data in a temporary, fast access memory. The processing unit then prepares the image data digitally so that either vertical or horizontal black line segments are produced. Such a digital line then consists, for example, of an alternating series of zeros and ones, known as the bits (see sketch).

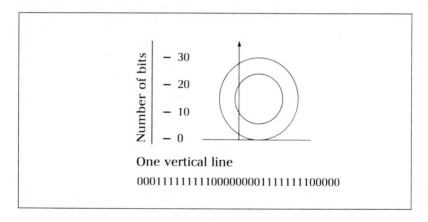

One vertical line

000111111111100000000011111111100000

From this sequence it is possible for the processor to generate an electronic signal for driving the writing mechanism, to produce out of the following bit line

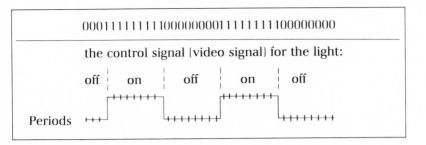

000111111111100000000011111111100000000

the control signal (video signal) for the light:

off   on   off   on   off

Periods

The beam of any particular machine has a certain thickness, determining line width and separation.

NC machines, and also some graphic visual displays prepare their control signals in a different manner. These machines can direct their writing devices from point to point in a horizontal and a vertical direction simultaneously. The stored digital data is used to generate two parallel control signals, one for movement in the X direction, the other for a simultaneous movement in the Y direction. The signals themselves contain the number of unit steps for the movement from point to point, whereby adding the path segments in the X and the Y direction together produces a short straight movement. These short straight segments are known as vectors.

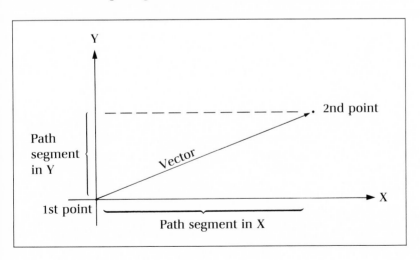

Visual display devices and typesetting machines, on the other hand, generate lines either parallel or perpendicular to the writing direction, and then move from line to line.

Thus: all three machine groups can describe a surface by generating signals for the X and the Y directions.

The point of greatest interest for us is what the machines write and how the results appear. For this reason we have generally abbreviated the electronic mode of function in each machine as follows:

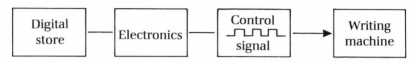

We have found a simplified illustration which shows how the control signals and light source interact in a laser typesetter (see below).

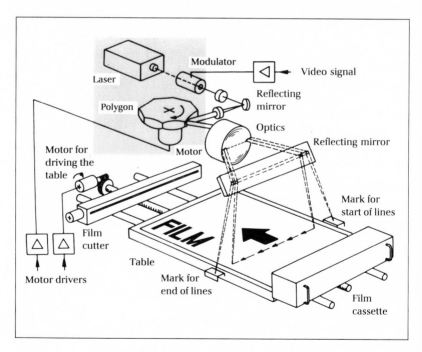

3.1 Visual display devices

In the case of visual display devices, the control signals are utilized to divert the electron beam of a cathode ray tube (CRT). The electron beam then impinges on a phosphorescent layer, the screen, and generates a bright point.

One can classify visual display devices (=VDT, video display terminals) into two groups: raster scan VDTs, which are similar to normal TV appliances and direct visual display terminals (direct VDTs) which are similar to oscilloscopes. The first use a system whereby the image is generated electronically line by line horizontally and displayed on the screen. This system first appeared in 1970 as a computer console development, and is mainly used nowadays as an alphanumeric data display terminal for data acquisition and monitoring, and also as a graphic display terminal of the second generation. In the case of the direct VDTs, the image is built up in a manner similar to that of an NC machine. The visual lines form the drawing or graphic. The movement of the electron beam is simultaneous in both the X and Y directions. Such graphic display monitors were already connected to computers in the early '60s, often had light pens attached, and were used in the manufacture of PC boards for example.

The use of direct VDTs (storage display) really expanded to a more widespread application in the early 1970s, and starting in 1975 the raster scan VDTs have found many uses as alphanumeric display terminals.

First generation display terminals

Such display terminals have a light beam which travels line by line from the left to right of the screen. Neighbouring raster points are joined to form one line, whose length corresponds with the number of points for which the electron beam was turned on. For the digital display of letters relatively small rasters for the em are used (e.g. 8×10).

In the following series of pictures, the pairs of images have the following relationship: the first photograph shows the full view of the graphic display terminal, the page composed or the paper drawing (depending upon device group). This produces different reductions.

The second photograph shows a 5:1 enlargement of four square centimeters of the original surface on which the letters are displayed.

The first pair, below, shows the image of letters on a normal display unit. The resolution is approximately 2 lines/mm or 50 lines/inch.

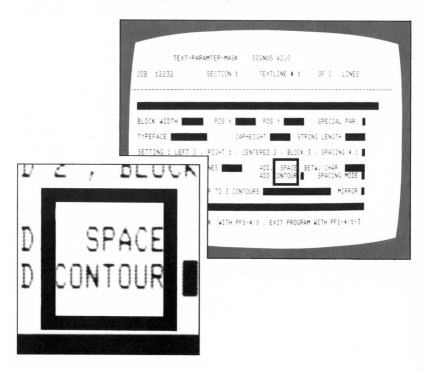

Second generation display terminals

Display terminals of this type operate basically in the same way as the alphanumeric raster display terminals of the first generation, except that they store 16 × 16 half bytes per letter, use more lines and need not necessarily write monospaced. The result of all these improvements is that the processing electronics have to work 16 times faster. The resolution is approximately 4 lines/mm or 100 lines/inch.

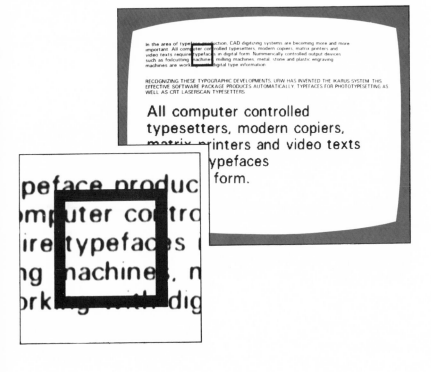

First generation graphic display terminals

Graphic display terminals of the first generation (direct VDTs or storage displays) have very fast line generators for the X and Y control of the electron beam. The data to be displayed is stored graphically as vectors. Each vector links two points (knots). The resolution may be up to 10 lines/mm or 250 lines/inch, the width of the electronic beam is, however, only 4 lines/ mm or 100 lines/inch.

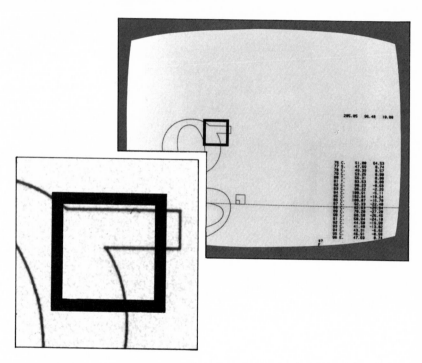

Second generation graphic display terminals

This class of graphic display terminal, the raster display terminals, generate their entire screen display (e.g. 600 lines each with 800 points) from a corresponding bitmap of 800×600 bits. These display terminals are gradually taking over from storage display terminals. The line imaging is slightly worse but they have less difficulty in filling in screen areas with black or white. Resolution is up to 4 lines/mm or 100 lines/inch.

Second generation graphic display terminals with halftone display

A relatively recent development is the raster display terminal which can display not only black or white points but also various intermediate gray tones. The image of the pixels is read from a quarter-byte, halfbyte or bytemap with corresponding four (quarterbyte), 16 (halfbyte) or 256 (byte) gray tones. Lines are well imaged. Resolution is up to 4 lines/mm or 100 lines/inch.

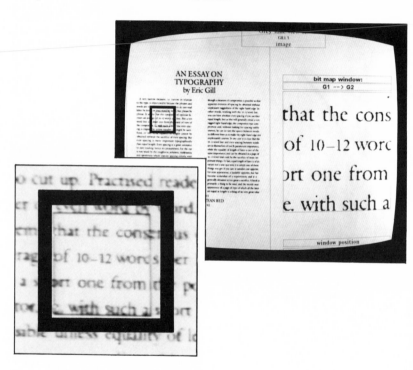

TV

The type displayed on normal TV screens has two main sources.
Either a TV camera focussed directly on the object:

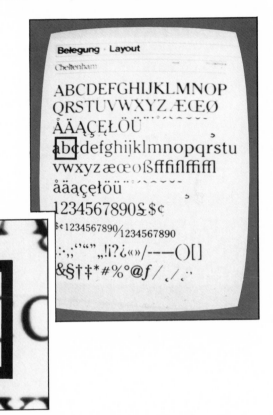

or the type is produced by a typesetting processor and mixed into the analogue videosignal. Standard resolutions are approximately 2 lines/mm or 50 lines/inch.

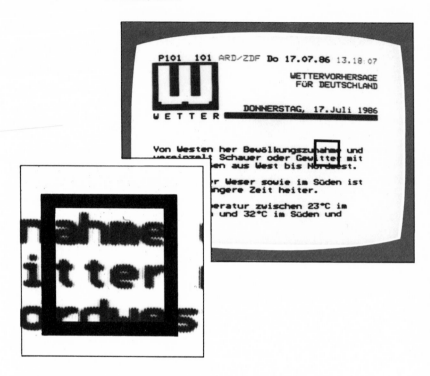

3.2 Typesetting machines

For the purpose of this book typesetting machines include: matrix printers, electrostatic printers, laser printers, microfilm devices, CRT machines, laser film recorders and other less widely used printing machines. The term typesetting machine has previously been more limited in context.

Typesetting machines for hot metal composition have been available since 1886 (Mergenthaler), e.g. Linotype or Monotype, and photo-typesetting machines for Latin letters have been available from 1949 onwards (Higonnet, Moyroud). Ever since 1922 various attempts have been made in different countries on forerunning machines; in Japan in 1923 a phototypesetter was invented for Kanji. The big breakthrough for phototypesetting had to wait until 1965. At this time, in 1964/65, Dr. Ing. Rudolf Hell had already invented the Digiset and presented the first fully electronic typesetting machine. These machines are known as CRT machines because they make use of cathode-ray tubes. From 1975 onwards, CRT machines have taken over the market and ousted hot metal composition.

Between 1974 and 1978 the first laser typesetters (Linocomp and Lasercomp) were produced and presented, and in recent times the displacement of phototypesetting and CRT machines by laser machines has become apparent.

All of these machines are described by the overall term "typesetting machine". However, as mentioned above, we will also include other devices, e.g. matrix printers, electrostatic printers, laser printers and micro filming devices under this term.

Matrix printers have been available since 1970 and have found widespread use as a cheap alternative to fast printers (which use metal type printing characters) for printing the outputs of electronic data processing.

Over approximately the same period, the use of electrostatic printers has become more widespread in the field of computer aided design (CAD) for the generation of drawings with text. Such printers compete to some extent with plotters and drawing machines.

Laser printers have been sold with some success by XEROX from 1980 onwards. Their first real breakthrough into larger market segments is as recent as 1984. These printers, connected with PCs (personal computers) will undoubtedly be the office typewriter of the future, and will be used in the field of desk top publishing.

The microfilming devices represent a special variant of typesetting machine. They produce film sheets which are viewed with enlarging devices. The increasing capacity of computers and data networks probably marks the end of the use of such devices.

In summary, we think that the only devices which have a chance in the future are high resolution matrix printers (24 to 36 needles for the bodysize), laser printers and laser film recorders (laser typesetters).

Matrix printers

Matrix printers have a printing head consisting of a row of between 9 and 24 needles, orientated perpendicular to the writing direction and controlled by the control signal. The needles press printing black or ink from an ink ribbon onto the paper, similar to a typewriter. The em consists of from 7×9 points up to 36×24 points on current machines. Monospace typesetting is the norm. Resolutions vary from approx. 2 to 7 lines/mm or 50 to 180 lines/inch.

When preparing the German edition of this book, the text was only available in the form of lists printed out using a matrix printer. Reading these proofs I failed to notice many mistakes, which I only found in the text when reading the final proofs (produced by a Digiset).

Electrostatic printers

Electrostatic printers are also known as electrostatic plotters. The control signals are used to produce electrostatic charges on lines running parallel to the writing direction, which then attract ink particles. These ink particles are absorbed by the paper and produce the print. Typical resolution values are 8 lines/mm or 200 lines/inch, newer machines are capable of 16 lines/mm or 400 lines/inch.

Laser printers

Laser printers work on a principle similar to electrostatic printers. Use is made of a well focused light beam which may be turned on and off and directed to produce electrostatic discharge of highly charged ink particles. In general, resolutions are between 12 and 32 lines/mm or 300 and 800 lines/inch in both X and Y direction.

Über eine wechselvolle Geschichte hinweg ist die Victoria heute zu einer der führenden Versicherungsgruppen herangewachsen. Durch unsere Kunden. Sie sind in diesen 130 Jahren immer Grundlage unseres Erfolges gewesen - über viele Generationen hinweg. Vom ersten Kunden, der sich 1853 bei uns ▭enteuer» einer Eisenicherte, bis zur Daten-'ung von heute: so ver-e Kunden und ihre indirüche, so verschieden

raten. [
Deutsch
europäis
Rahmen
rungspr(

Tun Sie
Frau als
Privat-H
schliess(
dann, w(
lich Sch
Unvorsi(

Microfilming devices

In microfilming devices the control signals are generated as in drawing machines. A very highly focused light beam writes the text in the form of small straight strokes. Resolution is indirectly about 300 lines/mm or 7500 lines/inch after photographic reduction.

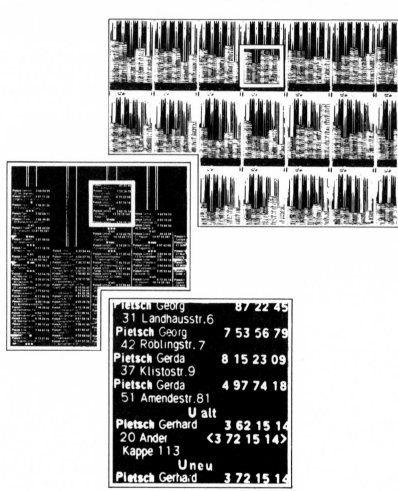

CRT machines

CRT machines are fully electronic phototypesetting devices which make use of cathode ray tubes (CRT). They differ from normal TV screens or display terminals in that the electron beam is extremely sharply focused. The light on the display surface is used to expose films. An optical lens system is placed between the display and the film. On film, resolutions of between 25 to 100 lines/mm are possible in both directions (vertically and horizontally), or 625 to 2500 lines/ inch. Type reproduction is very good. Typesetting speeds are anything up to 2000 characters/second.

CRT-Maschinen

CRT-Maschinen sind vollelektronische Lichtsetz Fernsehröhre (Cathod Ray Tube = CRT) verwend zum normalen Fernsehen oder den Sichtgeräten is strahl in diesen Geräten sehr gut fokussiert. Das Li schirm wird zur Belichtung von Filmen verwendet gerät und Film befindet sich eine Linsenoptik. Auf man eine Auflösung zwischen 25 bis 100 Linien/mi und horizontal) bzw. 625 bis 2500 Schrift ist sehr gut. Die Setzgeschv hen/Sekunde.

CRT-M

Fernse]

zum n

Laser film recorders

In laser film recorders laser light is used directly to expose films. The control signals move a light spot (or several) across the film and switch it on or off. Resolution and composing speed are comparable with those of CRT machines, although mostly they are faster. In conjunction with these typesetters we have, for the first time, a machine which can rotate characters arbitrarily. Other machines are also able to do this (theoretically), but as far as we know this has only been realized up to now in one machine. The resolution is typically between 50 to 100 lines/mm or 1250 to 2500 lines/inch.

Other typesetting machines

Typesetting machines are available with other methods of operation, e.g. ink jet printers or laser vaporization machines for direct exposure of printing plates.

At this point, however, we would like to limit ourselves to providing a brief summary of the ways and means by which digitally stored letters may be displayed, and would rather not go into details of the many variations.

It will become clear that all machines require their own particular type of digital coding. Correspondingly, the required resolutions favour certain coding techniques: for display terminals or matrix printers, bitmaps, for resolutions around 20 lines/mm, scanline coding, for very high resolutions, outline coding. This results from the necessity of keeping the type storage requirement in a machine as small as possible in all cases.

3.3 NC machines

The term "NC machine" (i.e. numerically controlled machine) was chosen as the group name for the following machines. For our purposes these machines operate on a very similar principle, they move a "pen" in the X and the Y direction simultaneously and one differentiates between the actual writing instrument:

Pen	– Drawing machine or plotter
Knife	– Foil cutting machine
Router	– Routing machine
Engraver	– Engraving machine
Flame	– Flame cutting machine
Laser beam	– Laser cutting machine or laser engraving machine
Water jet	– Beam cutting machine (pressure cutting machine)
Sand jet	– Stone engraving machine

The control signals all require the same treatment, similar to that of direct VDTs and microfilming machines. In the case of NC machines however, one usually requires relatively powerful motors to produce the actual movement in the X and Y direction.

On the other hand, having the same sort of control signal means that the digital storage of type is the same for all of these machines.

So, plotters are also capable of writing, but are extremely slow compared with laser composers. A "typesetting speed" of 1 character per second is common. Nowadays writing instruments can often be moved with speeds between 1 cm/sec and 1 m/sec.

The early 1950s saw the development of numerically controlled machine tools in the USA. The initial beginnings of large flat bed plotters from 1950 to 1960 may be traced back to Konrad Zuse and the ARISTO company. Whereas Konrad Zuse kept to a rigid digital development of the X and Y axis drives using stepping motors, at ARISTO DC motors were used on a digital-analog basis. In 1959 the first "ARISTO Coordinatograph with numerical continuous path control" was presented.

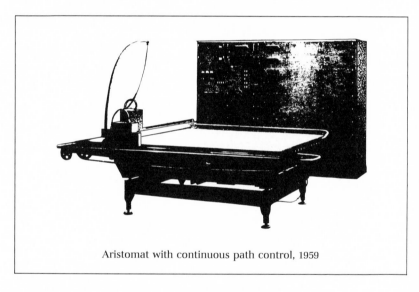

Aristomat with continuous path control, 1959

Flat bed drawing machines available today are a development of this and have working areas of about 1 m² up to 2 m².

These machines work at high drawing accuracies of 1/100 mm and are expensive for this reason. Smaller plotters are more reasonably priced. They have working areas corresponding to A3 format, and a drawing accuracy of 1/10 mm.

Three different NC machines are described on the following pages.

Plotters

The smaller plotters have a resolution of approximately 0.1 mm up to 0.025 mm or 0.004 inch up to 0.001 inch, which corresponds to 10 to 40 lines/mm or 250 to 1000 lines/inch.

Flat bed drawing machines

The larger flat bed plotters actually have earned the description "drawing machine". They do have resolutions of 0.025 mm up to 0.005 mm or 0.001 inch up to 0.0002 inch, corresponding with 40 to 200 lines/mm or 1000 to 5000 lines/inch. These are more than mere plotters!

Foil cutting machines

Most flat bed drawing machines can also be used to cut laminated films. As you can see, we have reproduced a very nice, large letter to show the precision which cutting can achieve.

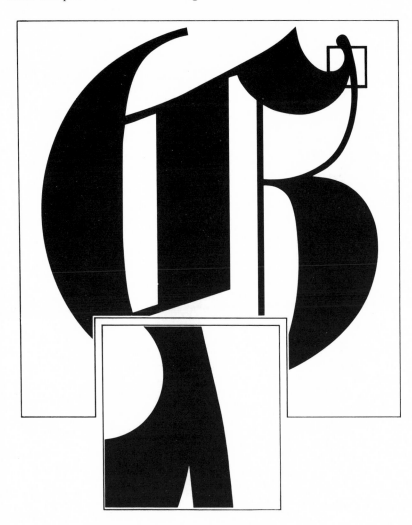

4. Requirements of typesetting

It is obvious that the different machines and the different electronic modules in the machines require different coding. In each case the digital storage for a certain machine has to be carried out in a manner whereby the type takes up as little space as possible, and can be read and processed as quickly and directly as possible. This is achieved by the optimum matching of the type code to the electronics used. The requirements placed by the machine on the digital format of the typefaces limit themselves for the most part to the code. The actual display of the texts, the typesetting, however increases the requirements.

4.1 Type structure

The initial requirement is that the data stored respective to each individual letter is accessible. To this end the letters have addresses and are listed in the letter index table.

Secondly, the left side bearings, right side bearings, and total widths of the characters have to be accessible independently of the image data. The widths are therefore stored in the form of separate data tables known as width tables. Accents present slightly more of a problem if they are treated as floating accents, related to the letters in the form of marked positions, and only arriving at these marked positions in the actual typesetting. This is possible using either a typesetting rule whereby an e and ` produce an è, or, with the aid of marking an e and ` the typesetting produces an è (` mark on e mark). We consider fixed accents to be better, i.e. extra letters for: è, é, ê, ñ, å, ë, ô etc; because accented letters are individual characters and should, as such, be checked by the type designers at the type design stage.

Ligatures are also important – as already referred to in chapter 2. They were created in order to produce an improved appearance for certain letter combinations, and can greatly enhance the overall appearance of well spaced text.

In addition, one has to deal with swash characters, e.g. an "ↄ" with an extended embellished stroke on its terminal, used at the end of a word instead of a normal "e", which is used at the beginning and in the middle of words.

These three examples – accents, ligatures, swash characters – create problems when entering text (on English keyboards for VDTs) where initially only the normal individual characters can be entered. Downline software is then used to find the new addresses for fixed accent letters, ligatures or swash characters. Not many text systems are capable of doing this at the moment.

It is now clear why a comprehensive description of a typeface (see also appendix B) is required.

It may be necessary to store particular number values, e.g.
– for superior indices (superscripts) and
– for lower indices (subscripts).

Furthermore, kerning and touching tables also belong to a particular typeface. The proper meaning of kerning has already been discussed in chapter 2.

Many producers of machines and type have not yet got around to dealing with kerning. Some companies – but by no means all – produce so-called aesthetic boxes, which provide correction values for certain important letter pairs. As an example, the illustration below is a list of letter pairs for which the Berthold Company is able to provide kerning values. As a rule these are negative values which are used to correct (reduce) the traditional letter spacing using set widths.

AT	AY	AV	AW	Ay	Av	Aw	A'	FA	F.	F,	TO	TA	Ta	Te
To	Ti	Tr	Tu	Ty	Tw	Ts	Tc	T.	T,	T:	T;	T-	LT	LY
LV	LW	Ly	L'	PA	P.	P,	VA	Va	Ve	Vo	Vi	Vr	Vu	Vy
V.	V,	V:	V;	V-	RT	RV	RW	RY	f'	WA	Wa	We	Wo	Wi
Wr	Wu	Wy	W.	W,	W-	YA	Ya	Ye	Yo	Yi	Yp	Yq	Yu	Yv
Y.	Y,	Y:	Y;	Y-	r'	r.	r,	r-	y.	y,	v.	v,	w.	w,
's														

At URW a completely different concept is used: the distance between any two letters is an individual value from first principles, i.e. at URW the kerning table for 100 characters, for example, has a length of $100 \times 100 = 10{,}000$ words, for 250 characters it has a length of $250 \times 250 = 62{,}500$ words. This means that aesthetic tables are a great deal smaller than the large kerning tables provided by URW. A special table is prepared for every type font.

In addition to the kerning values, there are also correspondingly structured touching tables allowing the spacing between letters to be reduced still further, letting them touch. Safety zones ensure that, for example with "HIH" in Helvetica, the letters do not touch.

Television
Traditional

Television
Kerning

Television
Touching

The overlapping table allows pairs of letters to approach each other so that they overlap – known also as sexy setting. Blending is where the black areas of the letters blend into one another and overlapping is where thin white edgelines outline the covering letter.

In everyday use, touching values are only required when setting "headline type" (cap height above 1 cm at normal reading distance) for correcting the kerning values. When doing so one uses the following rule:

The larger the letters the more kerning approaches touching.

Blending

Overlapping

Since 1983 URW has been using an algorithmic automatic calculation system which took three years to develop and which deals not only with traditional spacing but also kerning, touching and overlapping tables; a very complicated system. The results calculated are then checked using typesetting examples, and where necessary, are improved manually.

In appendix R we have described the data structure for all spacing, and in appendices S, T, U and V the set-up of the width, kerning, touching and overlapping tables.

4.2 Form setting

Form setting means the setting of lines not running in horizontal straight lines, i.e. the setting of sloping, circular, wavy and other lines.

A few examples of form setting are shown below:

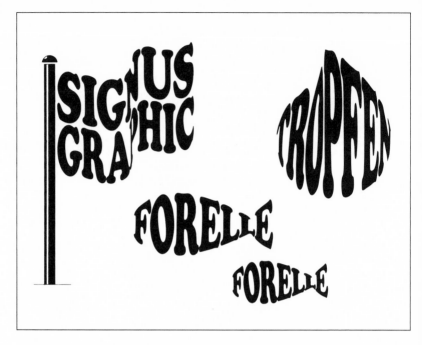

The term form setting also means however, the mathematical formula tables, table typesetting, the typesetting of graphic elements such as lines, frames, vignettes and in general all other possible requirements for the successful setting of advertisements. And furthermore, the setting of type along the contours of such geometric elements, or otherwise in combination with such elements may not be disregarded or forgotten.

Form setting therefore requires additional data:
- Body size in original data base
- Cap height
- x-height
- Stroke thickness of type (weight)
- Optimum size range for the typesetting,
- Width (traditional, kerning, touching, overlapping).

In addition, all codes must identify which inner edge relates to which outer edge, especially for contouring.

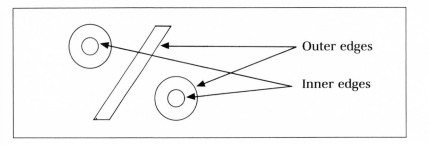

If the contour is to run outside the letter for example, then it lies outside the outer edges and inside the inner edges. This is known as
positive contouring, and results in a larger printing area.

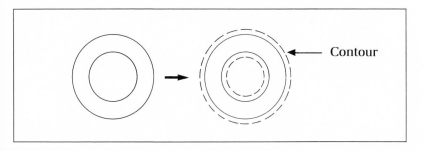

Consider type characters more complicated than Latin letters, e.g.
Japanese characters, symbols or logos; one soon discovers that so-
called outer edges can lie within so-called inner edges and inner
edges can be inside these as well, and so on.

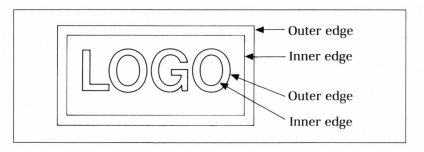

Shape setting thus represents an even greater demand on the digital format. It must be distortable, i.e. it must be adaptable to specified but, in principle, arbitrarily chosen external shapes. In the case of a circle, for example, the horizontal lines can be bent with the radius of the setting circle.

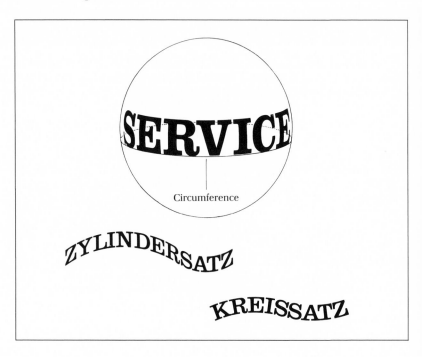

4.3 Hierarchical format structure

We have chosen the following structure:

Typefaces

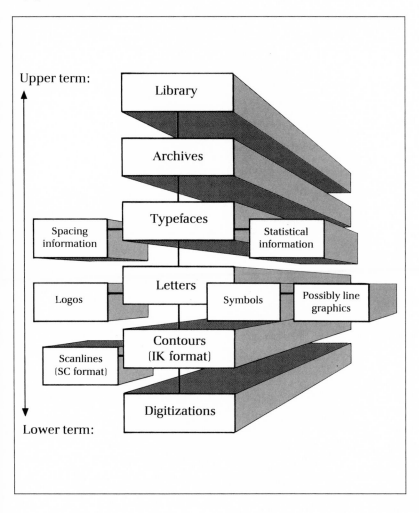

Upper term:

- Library
- Archives
- Typefaces
- Spacing information
- Statistical information
- Letters
- Logos
- Symbols
- Possibly line graphics
- Contours (IK format)
- Scanlines (SC format)
- Digitizations

Lower term:

Graphics

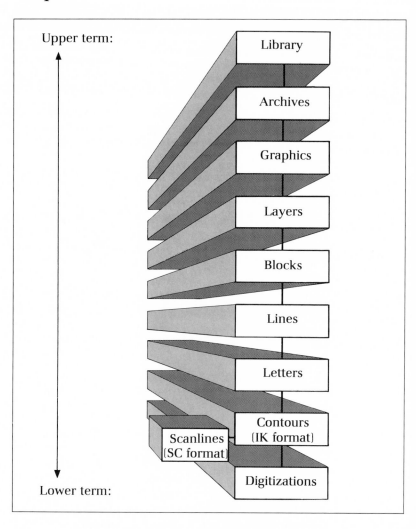

This data structure simplifies the manipulation of the related data. For example the copy, delete, insert and replace functions can be

applied especially to a chosen hierarchy plane, i.e. limited to the elements of one hierarchical level.

In appendix G there is an exact description of the typeface structure and in appendix H the structure of a graphic form in the IKARUS system.

In the framework of storing typefaces, a special structure is required for the "typeface" level and below. The actual host file management system should be used for the levels above typeface.

The storage of graphics requires a far more complex structure than that required for typefaces, though in other respects a graphic is treated hierarchically as a typeface or, if the graphic is simple, as a character.

In our experience the functions for typeface and graphic – as for example IKARUS modifications – are too slow if the files for the characters and graphics are not structured. Please note, we implement the IG format for this structuring, since we regard this format as the most suitable. This is the shortest of all available formats (see chapter 6.3).

At this point we would like to indulge in a little history – hopefully the reader will bear with us. Twelve years ago we were confronted with the problem of storing typefaces. We quickly decided on random access because of the quick disc access! Six years later we were posed with the problem of storing Kanji typefaces. Given the then available 5 to 10 MB discs our "random" philosophy was no longer suitable. We therefore decided to implement index sequential access method (ISAM). Unfortunately, ISAM was designed for commercial applications, and not for quick access to single characters of variable length.

Access to characters means above all loading one typeface into RAM and then processing many characters from this typeface, and not loading numerous individual characters from different typefaces from the disc. Normal ISAM file management systems are not fully capable of managing this relationship between characters and typefaces but are designed for searching for individual elements. Our element is – and this we learnt the hard way – the typeface, the large graphic, the collections of frames for images or line elements, and not every individual figure such as the character of a typeface, an element of a graphic, or a specific frame or line.

The developments in semiconductor memories and the advent of 32 bit microcomputers ideally suit our current, revised storage concept. At last we are able to store our critical mass, namely 20 to 100 KB for a Latin typeface as one unit, which was impossible with the previous 64 KB address barrier: a typeface is loaded as soon as only one character from this typeface is required. We then enclose the IK or IG structures with the typeface or graphic shells, enabling individual access to the desired hierarchical levels such as point, contour, etc. We recommend this procedure to all those who work with typefaces and graphics.

5. Formats

As the capabilities of electronics increased in the past so did the comprehensiveness of the digital information of the type data.

On the one hand, keeping the data compact required more highly developed control electronics, while on the other hand the greater requirements of the typesetting demanded more electronics and greater memory capacities for the type information.

Initially, the data was stored in the form of easy-to-deal-with bitmaps or run lengths, and later as outline codes; first the vector format, followed by more complex formats.

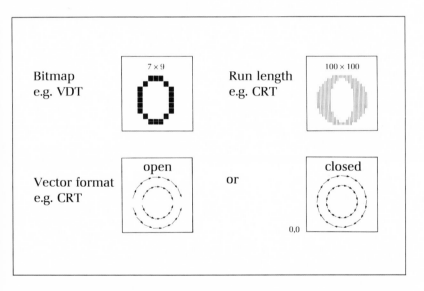

There are now a very large number of machines available using digital typefaces and thus a similarly large number of digital formats for typefaces. This variety demands categorization according to the following characteristics:

- method   bitmap
                     bytemap (halftones)

	run lengths
	vectors
	curves
	segmentation
	Metafont
– coordinates	absolute
	incremental
– code	simple
	complex

These last two characteristics – coordinates, code – do not necessarily mean a difference of format. In the first place absolute coordinates can be converted incrementally and vice versa, and on the other hand any complex coding can be calculated back to its simple original form (and of course vice versa).

In chapter 5.3 this is discussed in more detail. First of all let us consider the methods and try to establish a format review.

5.1 Review of formats

5.1.1 Bitmaps (bytemaps)
Consider the letter H for display on an alphanumeric VDT. Its bitmap has, for example, the form:

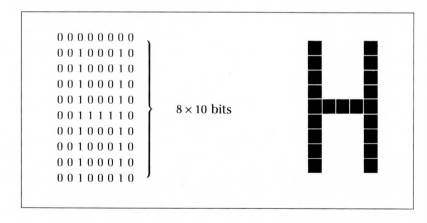

It would therefore seem obvious to store the 80 bits in 10 bytes and scan the bitmap from left to right horizontally, line by line from top to bottom. When doing so it is not important whether one sets the zeros equal to black and the ones equal to white or vice versa (video reverse).

The format of a typeface which is to be typeset monospaced on an alphanumeric VDT (first generation) is thus extremely simple: Every 10 bytes a new character starts. If the device can only display 128 characters, one needs a 1280 byte memory and the addresses for the image information are basically "ASCII value times 10".

With newer display terminals (second generation) and for TV captions one needs bytemaps instead of bitmaps. Depending upon the number of halftones at the edge between black and white, one may have quarterbytes (4 steps), halfbytes (16 steps) and bytes (256 steps). To transform a bitmap into a halfbytemap, 4×4 bits for example, are brought together, counted out and stored. There is, however, one limitation: 15 and 16 bits both produce a halfbyte of the highest value 15 (see also the following diagrams). The transformation of halfbytes back into their original bits is not possible (see lit. Warnock).

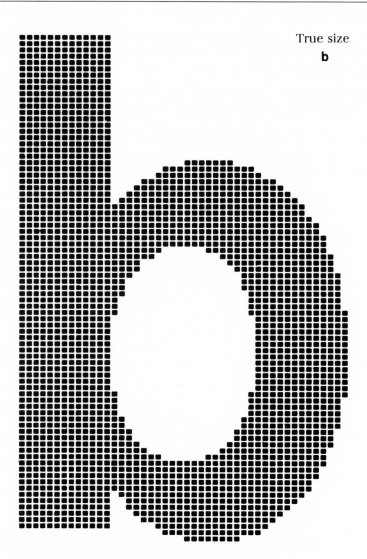

True size
b

Bitmap of lower case b at a raster of 100×120 for the em.

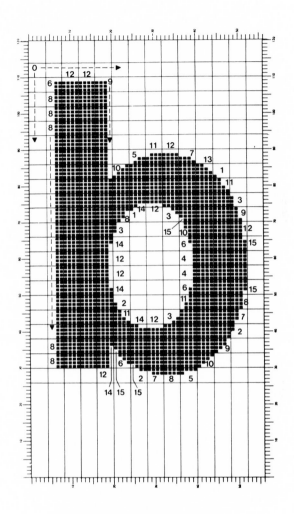

Preparation and calculation of a bytemap
at a raster of 25 × 30 for the em.

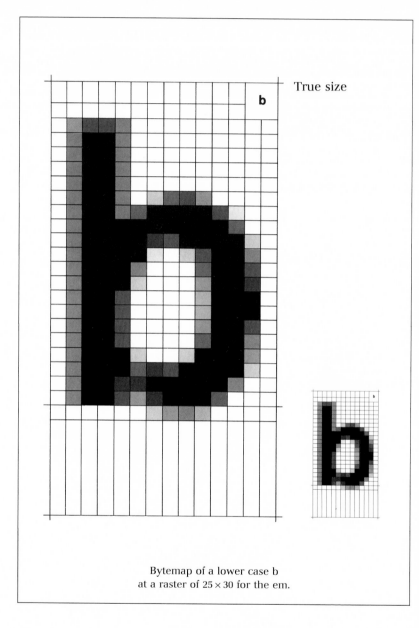

True size

b

Bytemap of a lower case b
at a raster of 25 × 30 for the em.

5.1.2 Run lengths

Bitmaps and run length codes are basically not very different. As bitmaps get larger and larger the question gradually arises of whether one should consider the successive zeros and ones in one line, i.e. count them out and code their number as a run length. When displaying letters by either horizontal or vertical lines (columns or rows) in a raster there are black and white alternations. With run length coding one assumes that the line starts externally to the letter and the first segment of the line thus always starts in white. Then black and white change at the transitions and one need not get involved in a special color coding for black or white.

On average, Latin letters have 3.5 transitions per scanline passing the em and fill approximately 43% of the em width. Thus, for a 32×32 bit raster one needs approximately $32 \times 0.43 \times 3.5 \cong 48$ bytes per letter plus $14 + 6 = 20$ bytes for the organization and handling of the scanlines (administration data), i.e. a total of 68 bytes. On the other hand the bitmap technique requires $14 \times 4 = 56$ bytes ($14 = $ average thickness of 32×32) not including the data required for administration. It is very soon apparent that from the above resolution levels upwards run lengths are a shorter form of coding than bitmaps.

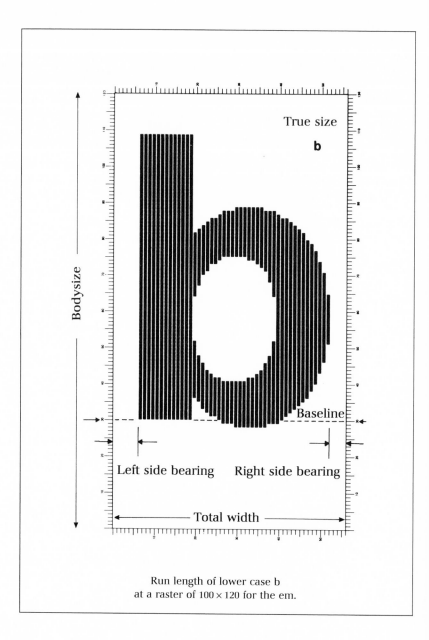

True size

b

Bodysize

Baseline

Left side bearing   Right side bearing

Total width

Run length of lower case b
at a raster of 100 × 120 for the em.

5.1.3 Open vectors

Transitions in neighbouring lines have a linear relationship in the first approximation.
Let us consider "H" in Helvetica:

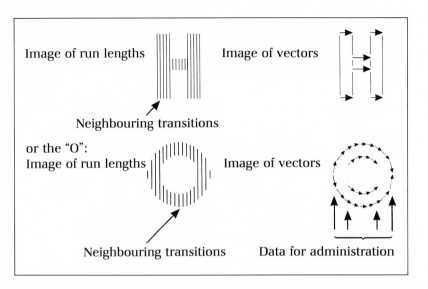

It is hardly necessary to mention that vector images consist of fewer straight lines than the corresponding run lengths, i.e. one therefore requires less data.

In order to describe a vector, in principle one needs the two coordinates of the starting point and the two coordinates of the end point. Often the end point of the preceding vector is also the starting point of the following vector. This means that per vector one only needs details of the end point. The description of vectors requires relatively more data in the "administration" than for run length coding, i.e. description data for start or finish of line pairs and also a little more electronics to generate the control signals.

Vectors are also used to generate letters for direct VDTs (graphic VDTs of the first generation), microfilming devices and plotters. Whereas before the vectors represented the edge of the black surfaces, here the vectors represent the middle of the basic strokes.

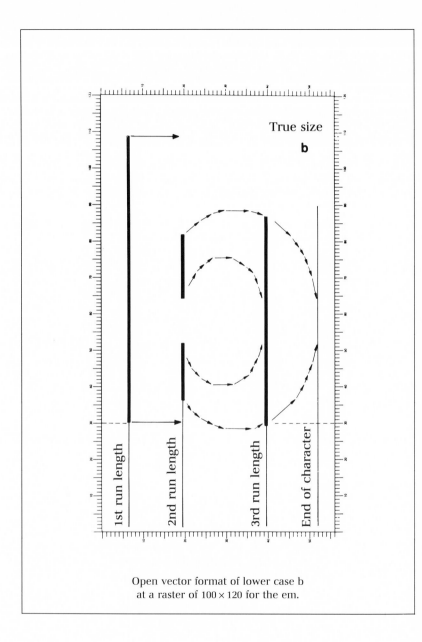

True size

b

1st run length

2nd run length

3rd run length

End of character

Open vector format of lower case b
at a raster of 100 × 120 for the em.

5.1.4 Closed vectors

Once data has been stored in the open vector format a great deal of electronic effort is required to make them rotatable. Up till now no manufacturer has actually managed this using the open vector format.

In the case of the closed vector formats this is easy to achieve:

In the closed vector format the vectors of each contour return to their origin. For example, an "O" consists of two closed line-paths, known as polygon paths:

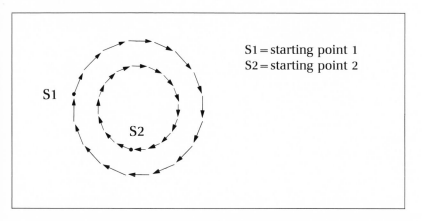

S1 = starting point 1
S2 = starting point 2

When dealing with closed vectors the position of the starting point for the line is unimportant; this means, letters stored in the form of closed vectors processed as such, can be easily rotated or deformed electronically because such transformations require that only the characteristic "closed" remains; there are no "openings" which are rotated or displaced.

In 1982 URW carried out simulating calculations and established that memory capacity requirement is lowest for typefaces coded with 4 bits for the X component and 4 bits for the Y component of vectors. The memory requirements of 3 bit coding and 5 bit coding are much higher. We consider this to be an astonishing and lucky coincidence, since 8 bit (2 × 4 bits for one vector) is an important figure in computers. URW uses a special code for the sign change in X or Y directions and also a special code for very long straights.

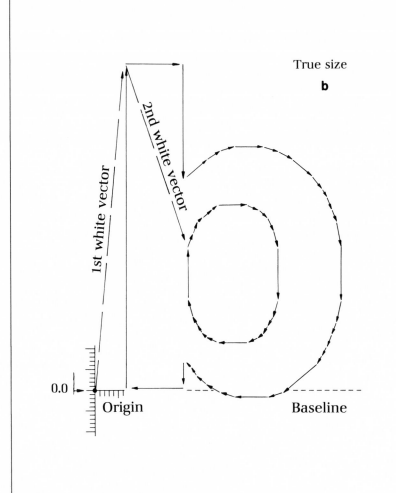

True size

b

1st white vector

2nd white vector

0.0

Origin

Baseline

VE format of lower case b at a raster of 100 × 120 for the em
(each coarser raster is calculable).

On the other hand the 4 bits are not so astounding because with 4 bits one is able, without too much effort, to code vector lengths between 1 and 13 (14 and 15 are reserved for special coding).

When considering bitmaps for different rasters between 100×100 and 400×400 per em, one sees that irrespective of the fineness of the raster at curves, hardly any vector components occur which are longer than 13.

Disregarding long straight lines, which are given a relatively long special coding, curves represent more than 90% of the total codes required!

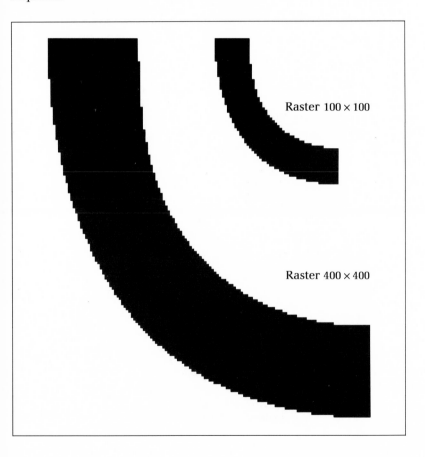

Raster 100×100

Raster 400×400

5.1.5 Curved lines

Curved lines is a slightly inelegant term which we use to distinguish all non-linear outlines. Curved lines is taken by us to be a description which may include elements such as:
- Straights and circles (Bitstream, URW),
- Bézier functions (Adobe),
- Spirals (Purdy, AM, Itek),
- Splines (XEROX and others).

Straights/circles

URW uses this format directly for drawing machines and graphic displays, other firms use this format for high resolution typesetting machines (60 to 100 lines/mm). It can be developed most directly and rapidly from the IKARUS format as mentioned later in this book. Basically, straight lines are used to link corners with each other and with tangent points, where we have a tangential transition of straights into curves. The curves are described as segments of circles which all blend into one another tangentially (see also 6.3).

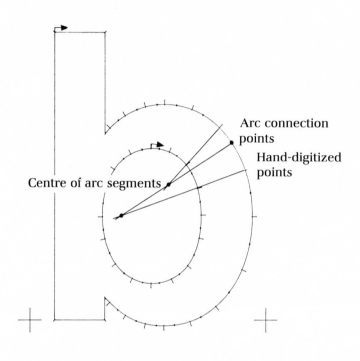

Arc connection points

Hand-digitized points

Centre of arc segments

DI format of lower case b at a raster of 15,000 × 15,000 for the em.
The combination of IKARUS and DI format is Bitstream format
(each coarser raster is calculable).

Bézier functions

Readers are no doubt familiar for the most part with straights and circles, but not necessarily with Bézier functions. The Bézier function runs between specified digitizations which are never reached, except for the start and final point. Mathematically it is similar to the spline function (a third degree polynom as mentioned later on).

Take, for example, 4 points, 1 starting point, 2 intermediate points (so-called control points) and 1 end point. We would then arrive at the following:

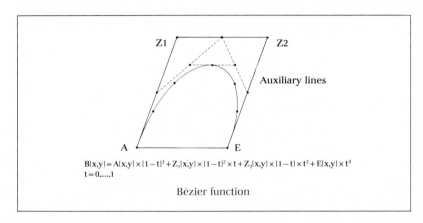

$$B(x,y) = A(x,y) \times (1-t)^3 + Z_1(x,y) \times (1-t)^2 \times t + Z_2(x,y) \times (1-t) \times t^2 + E(x,y) \times t^3$$
$$t = 0,....,1$$

Bézier function

We have marked in thin the auxiliary lines in order to demonstrate the position and construction of the Bézier line.

We have also included more figures below in order to illustrate the effect of the Bézier function.

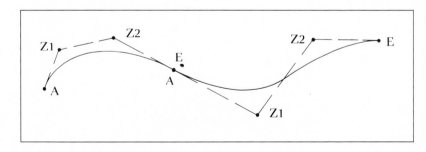

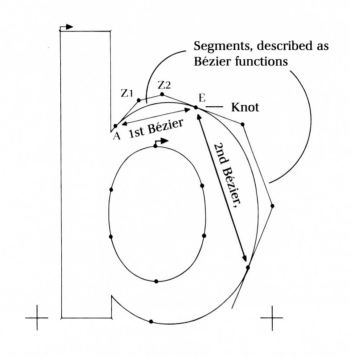

Segments, described as Bézier functions

Z1 Z2 E — Knot

A 1st Bézier

2nd Bézier,

Adobe format of lower case b at a raster of 15,000 × 15,000 for the em (each coarser raster is calculable).

In our opinion only automatically generated Bézier knots are of any usefulness. As far as hand digitization is concerned this method appears to us to be unsuitable, as it is a great deal more time consuming than for example the digitization using the IKARUS format. Bézier control points are located outside the outline and can only be easily found if one has a graphic display terminal which gives an immediate display of the Bézier function with any movement of the Bézier control points.

Graphic display terminals have a resolution of approximately 1000×1000 pixels per em, producing congruency to the original to within $1/1000$ per em. This is not a particularly good reproduction value. Furthermore, the trial and error method required to select good Bézier knots and control points is too time consuming. As a machine format, however, Bézier functions have their uses. The calculation of raster points is sufficiently fast when carrying out typesetting. It is approximately 6 times slower than using straights and circles. The same applies correspondingly to the spline function.

Spirals
Curve templates used to be known as French curves. They were made partly out of spiral segments. When drawing letters in the past one made use of French curves, straights, and circles, and scraped to get the tangential transitions.

The outlines of letters can be built up using spiral segments. Purdy and McIntosh developed hardware which is able to convert the Purdy format into raster images "on the fly".

Unfortunately however, the digitization – i.e. data input – is too time-consuming and has a resolution lower than $1/1000$ per em. On average one needs about 15 minutes interactive work on the screen to fit the spiral segments to the letter. In comparison, the average marking time per letter is only 2.6 minutes using the IKARUS format plus 2.6 minutes pure digitization time. We do not consider the Purdy format to be absolutely suited to data basing. It is difficult to edit and not very easily transformed or distorted.

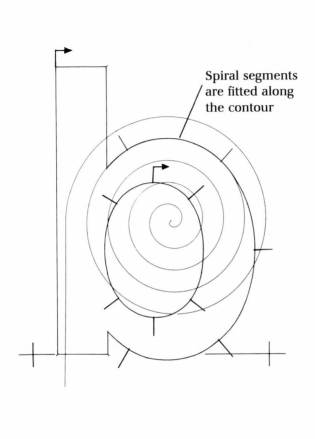

Spiral segments
are fitted along
the contour

Purdy format of lower case b at a raster of 4000 × 4000 for the em
(each coarser raster is calculable).

Splines

A spline function for the representation of letters is a very good attempt in the right direction. We have used this method since 1972, but have also dropped it to some extent. Put another way, of the spline interpolation for IKARUS points we only use the tangents of the digitized points. This is a fairly fast operation.

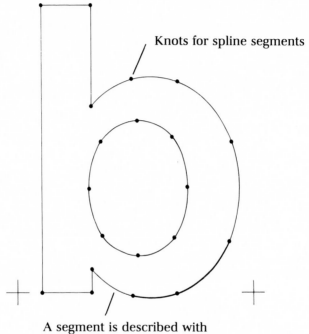

Knots for spline segments

A segment is described with
$$x(t) = a_x + b_x \cdot t + c_x \cdot t^2 + d_x \cdot t^3$$
$$y(t) = a_y + b_y \cdot t + c_y \cdot t^2 + d_y \cdot t^3$$
t = line distance
$\{a_x...d_y\}$ are constant for a segment

Spline format of lower case b at a raster of 15,000 × 15,000 for the em.
The scanned knots are at a raster of 1000 × 1000 for the em
(each coarser raster is calculable).

To show this in more detail the figure below is an example of the spline method for letters as used by XEROX (ref. Stone). It is apparent that an automatic digitization is a good starting point; it would be very difficult and also time-consuming if the knots were to be found manually, guided by eye. However, this format has disadvantages: it cannot be edited by displacement of knots and is therefore not transformable.

The automatic digitization of letterforms within this format cannot follow the original more precisely than the scanning accuracy (i.e. approximately 1/1000 per em width).

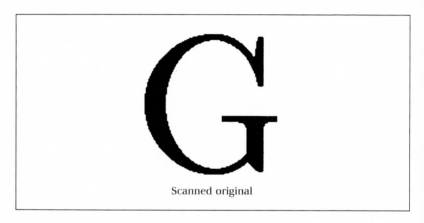

Scanned original

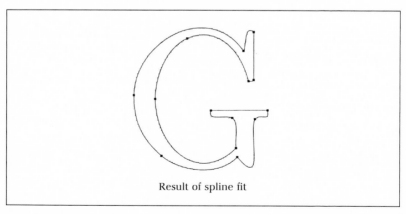

Result of spline fit

5.2 Other concepts

A short history of previous concepts for the preparation of digital types has been edited at the Stanford University (ref. Ruggles). A concept is assessed in this study according to its performance in the field of artificial generation of new letters, or rather, the degree of complexity thought up by the respective inventors.

Whilst not wishing to overlook the fact that such criteria are possibilities for assessment, we should not ignore the fact that the major criterion has been omitted.

There are very many typefaces available for all imaginable purposes. The main consideration is to place these faces into digital formats. Thus the most important criteria today are:
- speed of data acquisition
- quality of storage (accuracy, adaptability into machine formats).

The computer aided generation of new types should be considered as of secondary importance. We question whether a designer using a computer would be faster than using conventional methods.

At least two other concepts are of interest:

In contrast to previously considered formats, which do not consider individual letters as such, but use a more global digital description of a font as either pixels, run lengths or outlines, Philip Coueignoux and Donald Knuth have produced formats which require individual programs for individual letters.

Philip Coueignoux divided letters into elements and then designed appropriate software and hardware to generate letters out of these elements. The exact type reproduction – if one considers a larger cross section of types – does, however, leave something to be desired. The advantages of the Coueignoux format are in the low storage requirement.

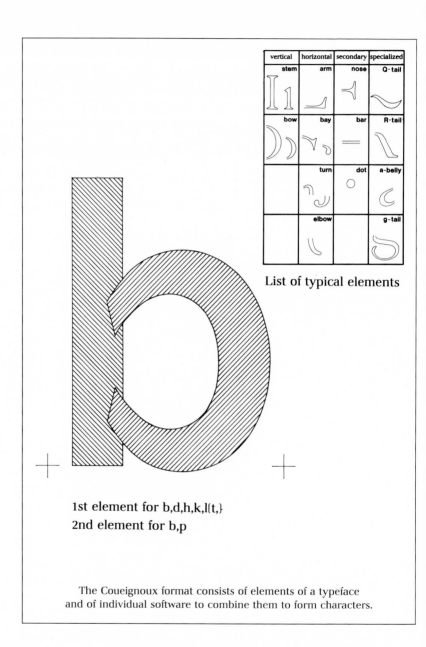

vertical	horizontal	secondary	specialized
stem	arm	nose	Q-tail
bow	bay	bar	R-tail
	turn	dot	a-belly
	elbow		g-tail

List of typical elements

1st element for b,d,h,k,l{t,}
2nd element for b,p

The Coueignoux format consists of elements of a typeface
and of individual software to combine them to form characters.

Donald Knuth created the Metafont concept. This is very well suited to varying a Metafont type. The modification possibilities are virtually infinite. On the other hand however, Metafont is not very well suited for exact and cost-effective reproduction of existing types. Furthermore, one has to write a rather long program for each individual character.

Steps have been made since 1983 to allow hand-digitized data to be also used as descriptive data.

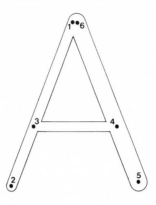

```
% The letter A
%
%
%------------------------------------------------------------------
% specify where output goes
drawdisplay;                            % draw letter on screen
proofmode;                              % print proof sheet
%------------------------------------------------------------------
charcode 'A;                            % this is a capital A
%------------------------------------------------------------------
% position the points
x1=98;   y1=250;                        % x and y coordinates for each of
x2=0;    y2=0;                          % 6 points
x3=40;   y3=90;
x4=170;  y4=y3;
x5-105;  y5=y1;
x6=203;  y6=5;
%------------------------------------------------------------------
% specify the pen
cpen;                                   % circular pen nib
%------------------------------------------------------------------
% draw the charcter                     % using a pen width of 15, draw a line
15 draw 1..2;                           % between points 1 and 2, and between
   draw 3..4;                           % points 3 and 4; then with a pen
25 draw 5..6;                           % of with 25, draw a line between
                                        % points 5 and 6.
end
```

The Metafont program for an upper case A.
All raster resolutions are programmable
(each coarser raster is calculable).

5.3 Special coding techniques

Over the last twelve years a lot of special coding techniques have been developed, some are described in the following section.

Bitmaps
Bitmaps could also be coded in "block encoding" (ref. Knudson). For example for 4 × 4 bits, it is not necessary to have 16 bit data, because many of the 256 combinations do not appear within the black and white image of a letter.We definitely have the elements:

and the element groups:

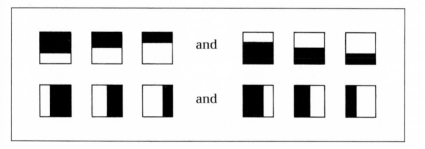

If one has enough information on stroke thickness one could perhaps exclude thin lines such as:

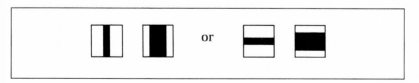

A similar argument applies to diagonals which perhaps only appear in the following forms:

One can almost sense that the reproduction of letters can very well be achieved with only $2^8 = 256$ possibilities, i.e. a reduction of the storage capacity necessitated by a factor of 2. In appendix P we describe our own internal bitmap format (BI format).

Bytemaps
In the case of halftone pictures it is relatively rare – as opposed to in a text – to have extreme black/white transitions. The very compact storage of halftone pictures as used in telecommunication makes use of this fact and uses an average of 2 bits per grey pixel (normally 8 bits), in order to code the relative colour tone change of one image point to that of its predecessor.
In appendix Q we have described our own internal halftone format (grey scale format = GS format). It is created from a bitmap which has to be previously generated.

Run lengths
We have considered various different run length codes. As a rule, one achieves a compression of approximately 30% by using the "line repeat" technique.An "I" e.g.:

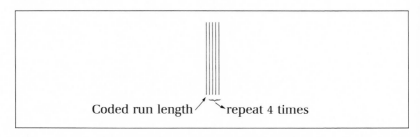

Coded run length ⟋ ⟍ repeat 4 times

Other methods of reducing memory requirements are to search for the largest occurring run length in letters or in the type for a pre-scribed raster. This allows the n-bit-byte to be calculated, allowing the largest run length to be coded, and also all smaller run lengths to be coded, incrementally. Incremental means having data not of the absolute position of the transition, but rather of the respective lengths of the black or white line segments. In appendix N we describe our own internal run length format (scanline format = SC format).

Vector formats

Open vector formats are available which run in small steps from edge point to edge point. This coding is known as nibble coding. As far as we are concerned there are two possibilities which are econ-omical:

a) 1-bit-nibbles 0 straight in X direction →
              1 straight and vertical skip. ↗

This requires super-imposed coding of the appropriate quadrant, e.g. when describing a circle. For certain quadrants "1" can only mean "upwards", for others it can mean "downwards".

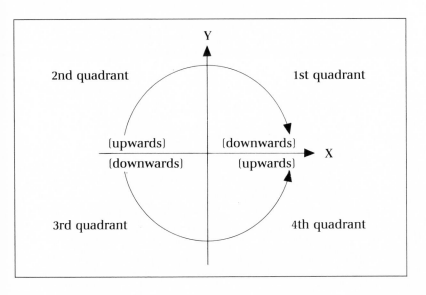

b) 2-bit-nibbles 0 ≙ north
1 ≙ west
2 ≙ south
3 ≙ east

Using this code one can, for instance, completely describe circles or spirals. This coding is very compact, and allows segments to be accessed by addressing (with pointers from/to).
See appendix M for a description of our internal vector format (VE format).

Complex outlines and run lengths

We expect future developments to produce a large number of machines which can directly handle and process complex outlines. Some are already in existence. In a technique corresponding to the vector format one can code straights as before, and circles incrementally. For segments of circles one states the end point with a vector plus the chord length. This has the advantage that one avoids the problem of coding large radii, and 3 bytes per circle segment are sufficient. However, the output of the chord height requires greater computer capacity for the regeneration of the circle data in the display. See appendix K for a description of our VC format.

To our knowledge there is currently no typesetting machine in which run lengths and outlines are so interrelated that run lengths lead to coarse, but rapid filling out of the black surfaces, and where one or two fine exact outlines can be used to smooth the surface outlines.

However, this method will be utilized in the future for engraving machines and laser engraving machines.

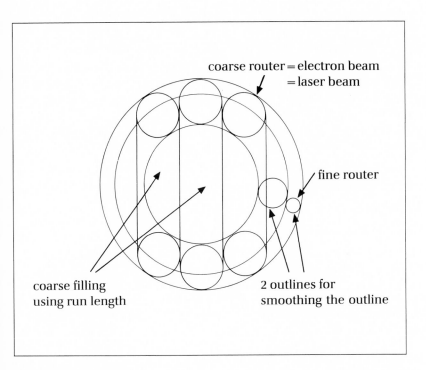

coarse router = electron beam
= laser beam

fine router

coarse filling
using run length

2 outlines for
smoothing the outline

General comments

The cost of data storage and of the electronic equipment itself will also fall in the future. To our way of thinking this will have the following positive consequences for the production of digital type formats:

- It will no longer be necessary to concentrate all efforts on the coding and compression of data.
- It will be possible to use digital storage of fine rasters instead of coarse rasters.
- The storage of complex curves will be easier and faster, and will therefore take place.
- It will be possible to store and process additional data for typesetting, e.g. kerning and touching tables.
- There will be more typefaces available per system.
- More characters will be available per typeface.

5.4 Listing of a selection of type manufacturers

In the following table we have used the designation "vector format" for machines from different manufacturers. This does not mean, however, that such machines use the same coding for the same digital type, because vectors, as we have seen, may be coded in "nibbles", open, closed, incremental, absolute, in normal or in rotated, or maybe in mirror image coordinate systems. Many different and varied compression techniques may also be applied (vector repeat, sign change etc). The field of coding allows so many possibilities that, to our knowledge, regrettably no two manufacturers use the same coding method.

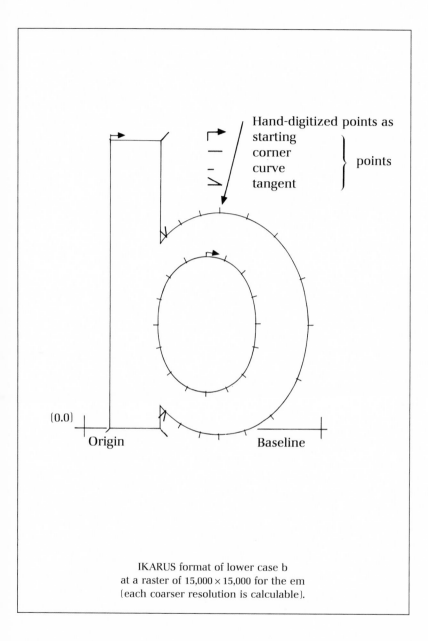

Hand-digitized points as
starting
corner
curve
tangent

} points

(0.0)

Origin

Baseline

IKARUS format of lower case b
at a raster of 15,000 × 15,000 for the em
(each coarser resolution is calculable).

103

These digitizations specify the run of letter outlines. This is why these digitizations represent the most important, non-transient digital data, because they form the data basis (for description of the related IK format see appendix I). One only has to be sure that this hand-digitized information allows all other digital formats to be derived. This has been no problem to date, we have been able to calculate everything from the hand-digitizations.

Bitstream has also taken over this concept. Here, hand-digitization is also storage in the same way as at URW. The Bitstream format is a combination of hand-digitization and complex outline descriptions with straights and circles.

6.2 Format hierarchy at URW

URW has internal formats which have a certain hierarchical relationship to one another. These formats have two-letter abbreviations and are arranged in the following hierarchical order:

IG format   (IKARUS graphic, structured hand-digitizations, appendix H);
IK format   (IKARUS, hand-digitizations, appendix I);
DI format   (display, circles/straights, appendix J);
VC format   (vector/circle, appendix K);
VS format   (vector/scaling, appendix L);
VE format   (vectors, appendix M);
SC format   (scanlines, run lengths, appendix N);
SN format   (scanline nibbles, appendix O);
BI format   (bitmap, appendix P);
GS format   (grayscale, bytemap, appendix Q).

In the appendices we have detailed formats which are in part written in a non-compressed form. We have done this in order to allow the respective data users to prepare their own compression and safety encryption to match their own electronics from the transferred data.

On the other hand, we have so far been able to use our own non-compressed formats to calculate all existing digital machine formats, e.g. the special vector format for the client from the internal VE format. As a rule this conversion (programming the post processor) takes between one day and six weeks work (on average: two weeks).

It is undoubtedly possible to reach a deeper hierarchy step using programmed versions. At URW such programs exist for the conversion of:

IK → DI   program DI
IK → VC   program VC
IK → VS   program VS
IK → VE   program VE
DI → SC   program SC
DI → SN   program SN
SC → BI   program BI
BI → GS   program GS

Moving the other way is however, not as clear. In principle it is also not necessary, when one is always able to refer back to hand-digitizations. Even so some companies have invested more than 100 man-years of work in the preparation of a library of digital types on the basis of scanline data. They now face the problem of using this to create a data base in outline form to cover the demands of future machines. We would suggest solving this problem as follows:

LINUS

LINUS is a machine for reading or scanning black and white pictures. Basically LINUS consists of hardware for image scanning, image storage and processing as well as software for the conversion of scan data to digitized data, which should be of the same kind as hand-digitization and of almost the same quality. The figure below shows an example of hand and automatic outline digitization.

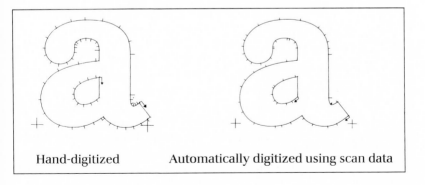

Hand-digitized   Automatically digitized using scan data

At URW this reverse conversion (VE→IK) took a great deal of effort (from 1979 to 1984). Other reverse conversions have, however, been appreciably easier to program:

DI → IK   no problem
SC → VE   no problem
BI → SC   no problem
GS → BI   is not possible, but then again not required.

Inherent in the hierarchy, and fundamental in the URW philosophy, is that the IK format has a digital precision which is greater than that required by the typesetting machine. Letters in IK format are stored in a raster of 15,000 × 15,000 per em. This has the advantage that when preparing coarser rasters there is no interference between the stored raster and the target raster.

The finest raster required by typesetting machines is 2500 × 2500 per em, for good typesetting machines an average of 400 × 400, and for all other machines still coarser. The resolution of our storage raster is thus usually by a factor of 10 finer, which means that for example, both a 400 × 400 raster as well as a 401 × 401 raster can be calculated to the same quality.

The 400 lines may be precisely placed on the IKARUS raster with approximately a 1/40 line separation, in the same way the 401 with a slightly lower separation, namely:

at 400 with 15,000/400 = 37.5
at 401 with 15,000/401 = 37.4

The line separation resulting is:
37, 38, 37, 38, 37, 38, 37, 38, ...
and 37, 38, 37, 38, 37, 37, 38, 37, 38, ...,

as counted in IKARUS fine raster points.

This is what we mean when we say: "There is no interference between storage raster and target raster". The picture would be different if the storage raster were only 800 × 800 per em. The 400 × 400 raster would present no problem by accessing every second line. The line separation would be 2 everywhere, counted in points of the storage raster. The 401 × 401 raster would not be so simple, however; we would have 398 times a line separation of 2 and twice a line separation of 1, counted in storage raster points. One either has to take two sequential lines out of the 800 once, or one would have to continuously interpolate a new line between two lines in correlation to their real position between these lines. Both methods produce mistakes! The very fine resolution of the IKARUS data avoids this and is a good solution to the problem – and no mistakes!

In addition to the degree of fineness of the digitized data according to the "digitized once and for all" mode, it is extremely important that the hand-digitizations themselves are stored. Only in this way can one carry out subsequent manipulations upon the data easily, like moving a single point (corrections) or calculating a sphere projection (typesetting on a globe).

We have summarized the manner and method of digitization in appendix X. These manipulations are always followed by the calculation of a closed curve through the given hand-digitizations, to be regarded as knot points.

In the selection of this procedure we spent a great deal of time determining the cleanest and most elegant technical route. We consider it to be of primary importance to carry out the curve calculations in such a way that each hand-digitized point is also hit by the calculated line.

It is for this reason that we find Bézier functions, for example, to be a little off course. They do not hit the original points. For the same reasons we have also not included a curve fit calculation, only the curve interpolation is taken into consideration.

6.3. The IK interpolation

The spline interpolation appears to us to be the best solution for the calculation of the tangent directions of the digitized points. We also carried out calculations of the tangents using circle fitting, polynom fits and other methods, we compared them with the spline interpolation – and rejected them.

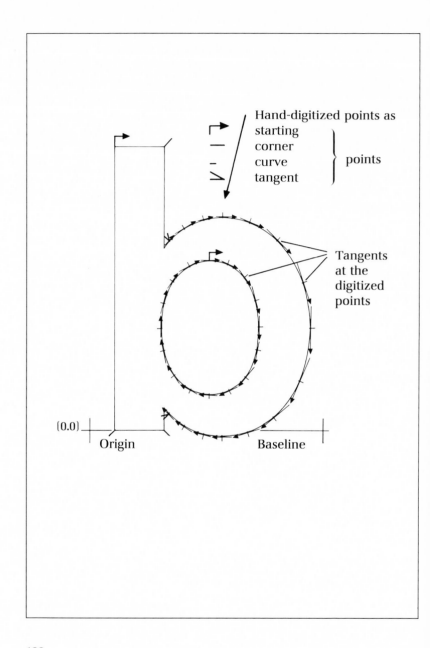

The step after the tangent calculation might initially appear unexpected. We do not take the spline function to display the closed curve but rather, between any two digitized points, we determine two segments of circles. The first segment starts at the first point with the first tangent determined, and stops at a mid-point having a specific direction. The second segment starts at this mid-point, with that same direction, and stops at the second digitized point with the second tangent determined. Thus, the curve is generated by linking together a chain of arc segments which tangentially merge into one another. Graphically, this has the advantage that the curve path is smoothed out in steps, and appeased locally because of the same curvature. Furthermore, straights and circles allow very fast calculation of whether any arbitrary point is on the line or not, which is a very useful feature for a whole series of control calculations, e.g. margin justification, clipping, letter touching or covering.

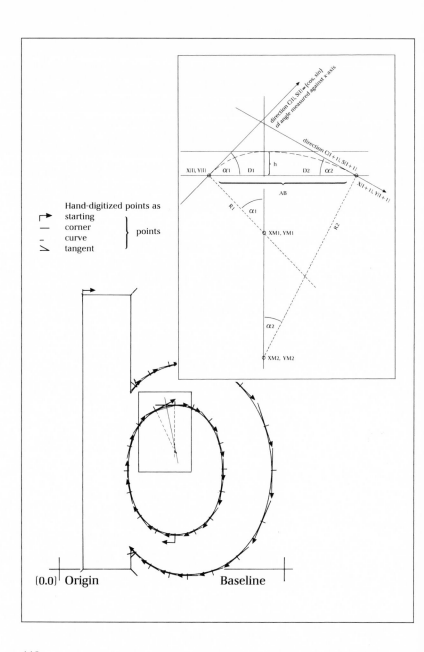

Hand-digitized points as
starting
corner
curve
tangent

} points

[0,0] Origin

Baseline

Furthermore, this method does not produce undesirable changes of curvature which have to be excluded by the inclusion of damping terms when using spline functions. When using damping terms, however, it is not necessarily easy to convert the outline description during the typesetting on the fly into control signals for the letter output. Straights and circles on the other hand present no problems in this case. Electronic modules are available which, aided by a DDA (Digital Differential Analyzer), are capable of a rapid conversion of straights and circles into pixels.

The circle parameters can be more quickly calculated than the 8 coefficients of the spline functions between two digitizations. We have included the appropriate programs in appendix W, written in FORTRAN.

The result of these curve calculations is known as the DI format (display format). It can be used directly in graphic displays, in some typesetting machines and on all NC machines.

The DI format is the basis for the SC format (scanline format). A raster is placed under that closed representation and a program then searches for intersection points of the raster lines with the DI format (see sketch).

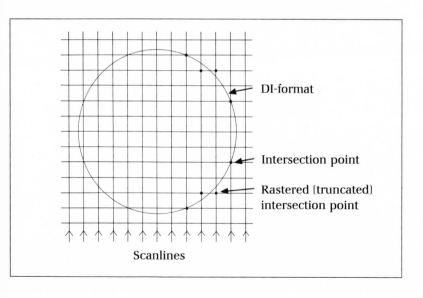

DI-format

Intersection point

Rastered (truncated) intersection point

Scanlines

This method is known as soft-scanning as opposed to hard-scanning with scanners.

Soft-scanning has enormous advantages compared with hard-scanning:

- It runs on the computer without any manual work.
- It doesn't scan dirt marks or other original inadequacies like ragged edges.
- The pattern (here the IK format) is adjusted automatically to be rectangular to the scan direction.
- Errors at black and white edges caused by electronic noise can always be avoided.

So much time can be saved using the automatic method of soft-scanning for the preparation of good rastered types that the time requirement for the hand-digitizing is more than compensated for.

7. The preparation of rasters

We have already pointed out that open vector formats, run length codes or bitmaps are only special descriptions for what which is normally understood as digital type, i.e. a letter presented in certain raster form.

This statement also applies ultimately to all formats which use curved lines to describe digitization. Except that in this case the resolution is so fine (in the case of our DI format: $15,000 \times 15,000$ per em), it is no longer the raster itself, but only general details, e.g. cap height, thickness or accuracy of analog reproduction (machine cutting) which need to be discussed (see point 3.3).

At URW the generation of such scanline rasters is known as the preparation of SC formats. The raster size per em can be selected arbitrarily. However, we have already seen that a 10×8 raster really is the lower limit, and a 1600×1600 raster per em presents a very fine resolution. Video display units or matrix printers work with 2 or 3 lines/mm, the better typesetting machines with 100 lines/mm. In this case, a raster with 1600×1600 per em would mean a body size of 16 mm $=42.7$pt$=$"display of headlines in text". One can of course, create rasters with different separations between X scanlines and Y scanlines.

At URW the SC format is prepared in two steps. Firstly automatic soft-scanning and secondly any possible residual work required by interactive corrections on a graphic display. We deliberately say "possible residual work" because most soft-scanned letters do not require any correction.

There are many applications in which such corrections are not needed anyway. There have indeed been cases where rastered types have been introduced on the market which were the direct result of hard-scanning with all marks, contaminations and flaws caused by the electronic noise and using "normal" artwork.

7.1 Soft-scanning

At URW soft-scanning is a fairly established procedure which has developed over the years and has shown itself to be correct.

We first of all had to recognize that the fine DI format may be regarded as thin lines lying across a usually coarser raster. This hardly affects the overall rastering, provided that small adjustments are made to define DI lines. We have programmed the corrections and achieved the following effects – automatically:

Channel processing

The "channelling" program sets almost vertical and almost horizontal straight lines exactly vertical or exactly horizontal. The effect is that these lines are reproduced in the rastered form without raster skips. The program also takes the following matters into account:

– All curves with slight curvature, e.g. the flutes of a serif, are not treated by the channelling.
– Diagonals or slightly sloped straights are not affected.

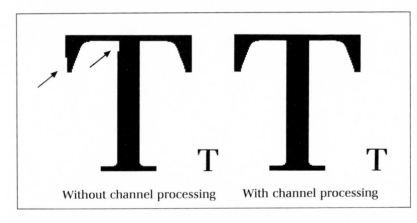

Without channel processing   With channel processing

Grid fitting of straight stems and crossbars

The program "PA" for "grid fitting" takes stems of approximately the same thickness, but which through the rastering would come out with slightly non-uniform thicknesses, and fits the same number of

114

raster lines. The fitting should not, as far as possible, change the appearance of the original, and a modification or change of weight should not occur.

The program takes the following matters into account:
- Straight stems with ductus changes e.g. "Optima" type, are not affected.
- The fitting is carried out for raster sizes of up to approx. 400 × 400 per em. Finer rastering no longer requires such a detailed treatment.

Diagonals are not treated.

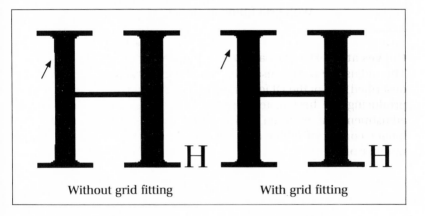

Without grid fitting   With grid fitting

Thickness of horizontal and vertical curve strokes
Curved strokes with uniform thickness in a typeface, which rastering has altered to be non-uniform, can be specifically refitted to the same number of raster lines in their horizontal and vertical segments.

The path of curves can also be automatically adjusted to a prescribed raster. Particularly in the case of light type in small type sizes, a large number of inconsistencies would otherwise crop up in the uniform parallel path of curved strokes.

115

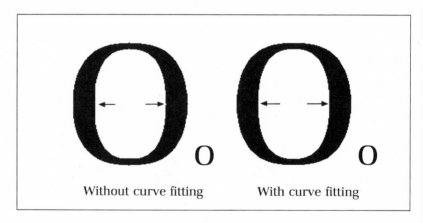

With grid-fitting of straights and curves

Curves at 0°, 90°, 180°, and 270° (degrees)

This adjustment also uses the following procedure: it places the described line of the DI format exactly between two "soft-scan lines", producing the best raster representation of curves. After such an adjustment, the extrema of the curves at 0°, 90°, 180° and 270° no longer consist of either only a few raster points or of too large a number of them.

Without curve fitting   With curve fitting

In the following sketches we have attempted to show this effect as clearly as possible:

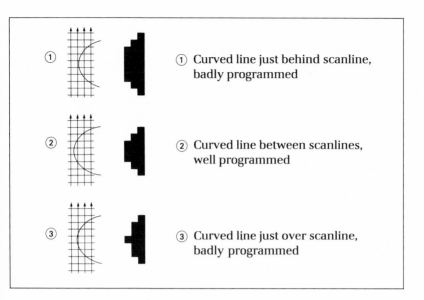

① Curved line just behind scanline, badly programmed

② Curved line between scanlines, well programmed

③ Curved line just over scanline, badly programmed

Curves at 45°, 135°, 225° and 315°

The curved segments at 45°, 135°, 225° and 315° are treated similarly, where an obvious step structure may form that can lead to good or bad reproduction.

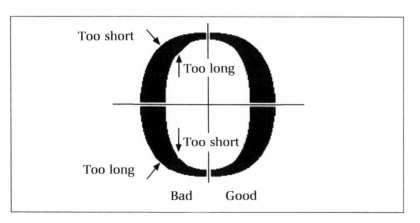

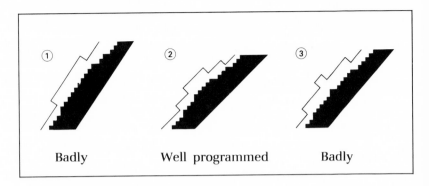

| Badly | Well programmed | Badly |

Treatment of serifs

– The joins of the curves of horizontal serifs to vertical stems of a face are made uniform and the lengths and heights of serifs are equalized, where required.

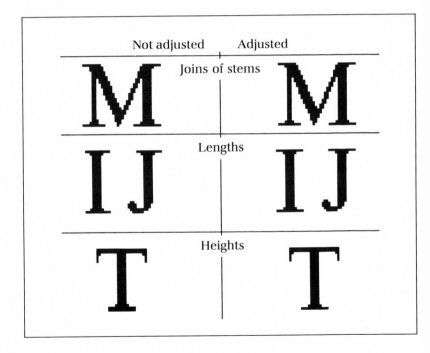

Not adjusted   Adjusted

Joins of stems

Lengths

Heights

The following situations must always be taken into consideration:

- Vertical serifs such as those to be found on the E cannot automatically be adjusted.
- Serifs, whose upper or lower edges are not parallel to the base line cannot be adjusted.
- The same considerations apply of course to those serifs found on diagonal stems.

Treatment of individual raster points
Raster dots which are entirely isolated or only have a diagonal connection to a neighbouring dot may be automatically deleted.
However, points both black or white, which have either a vertical or horizontal connection with another point are not automatically deleted.

Height adjustment of the characters of a font
The standard characters of a font (lower case, upper case, numerals) are adjusted in raster steps to match prescribed auxiliary lines. These lines lie on a calculated raster line of the respective scanline step. The determining factors are, naturally enough, descender, baseline, x-height, cap height, lower case ascender height and the respective overhangs of curves.

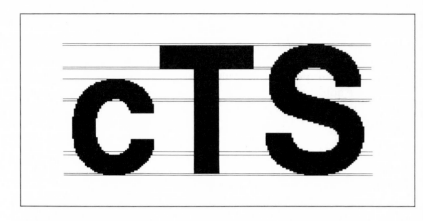

One should realize that:
- The more exotic the face the less it should be adjusted.
- Special characters or punctuation marks sometimes have heights which well exceed the normal, and should not be adjusted for that reason.

Identity of various point sizes
Various point sizes of a face may not be reproduced identically if the raster size proves to be different, because there are only whole but no half pixels. The table below lists guideline parameters for cap height (H), vertical stems (X) and crossbars (Y) measured in scanlines, for the rastering in 32pt, 16pt and 8pt as examples:

	32pt	16pt	8pt
H	84	42	21
X	11	6	3
Y	10	5	3

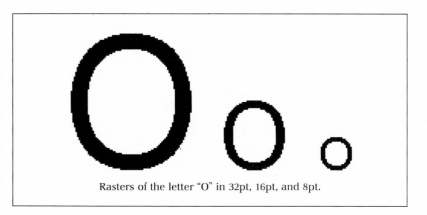

Rasters of the letter "O" in 32pt, 16pt, and 8pt.

Since in the case of letters in 32pt not all sizes are even, the 16pt size is not produced by simple halving. The 8pt version has also to be changed because when halving uneven numbers of scanlines either up or down it will not exactly match the 32pt version or the 16pt version. In fact, in the case in question it will turn out to be bolder.

On the other hand, point sizes can be matched when working " from bottom to top". One calculates the parameter for the smallest point size and increases by multiplication. In our example the parameter lists for this would be as follows:

	32pt	16pt	8pt
H	84	42	21
X	12	6	3
Y	12	6	3

The result now shows greater deviations from the original. The heights, stem thicknesses etc. are, however, consistent in all three point sizes.

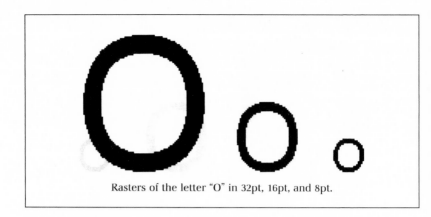

Rasters of the letter "O" in 32pt, 16pt, and 8pt.

Disputable cases

The following example demonstrates how a non-adjusted letter with 1.5 pixel stroke width can be adjusted to two different stem thicknesses. In the first case one scanline was used, in the second case, two scanlines to give the corresponding stem parameters to the grid fitting procedure.

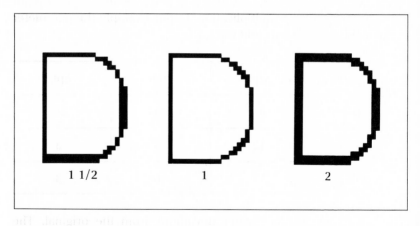

1 1/2   1   2

1 1/2 = without fitting
1   = with grid fitting of stroke width to one pixel
2   = with grid fitting of stroke width to two pixels.

122

All three results are unsatisfactory, soft-scanning alone is no help. One has to use the outline program beforehand to either carry out a thinning to one line (inner outline), or thicken up to two lines (outer outline).

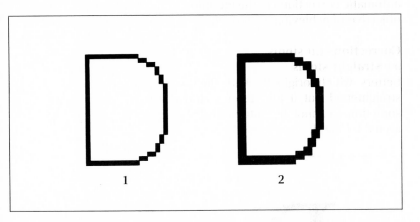

1   2

1 = with grid fitting of stroke width to one pixel and thinning of curves by automatic inlining.
2 = with grid fitting of stroke width to two pixels and thickening of curves by automatic outlining.

URW produces the VS format (vector scaling), see also appendix L. This format is generated by giving specific parameters for a typeface and using the VS program. It takes about 8 up to 16 hours to prepare a VS format which can be used in a RIP (raster image processor) to perform "sizing with stem control". This yields round about a performance as described in this chapter, leaving some arbitrary rastering which can only be avoided by manual raster corrections.

7.2 Manual corrections

In the following examples we mainly wish to bring the problems of automatic corrections to the attention of the reader and to stress the objective of achieving as perfect a type reproduction as possible.

Corrections on stems
a) Straight stems
Letters which originally had slightly curved stems can become straightened out if the raster is too coarse. These straight stems sometimes cannot be automatically adjusted and have to be corrected by hand.

Corrected

b) Stroke thicknesses
Rasters which are too coarse can lead to the loss of fine differences in stroke thicknesses. The lighter or heavier a typeface – compared with the standard version – and the coarser the display, the more difficult it is to decide for or against a scanline. This applies to horizontal, vertical, diagonal and curved strokes.

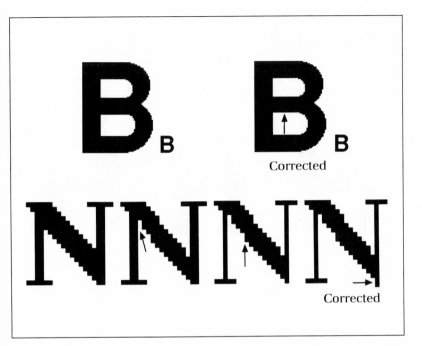

Corrected

Corrected

c) Flat curves become straight

When the raster is very coarse, very flat curves can be turned into straights. In the example below only one point is left of the original curvature and has to be deleted interactively.

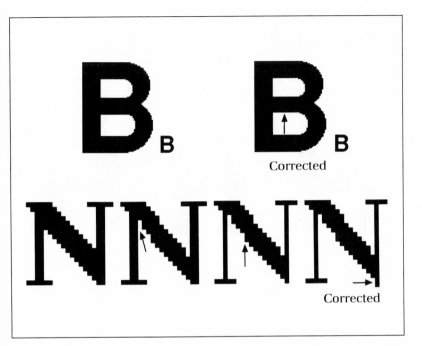

d) Stems with changes in ductus

Stems which have slight curves can be neither straightened nor adjusted. In order to keep them uniform, they have to be adjusted manually point for point.

e) Scanline skips

Scanline skips appearing in curves, which are detrimental or detracting in their visual effect, have to be corrected manually.

Corrected

f) Discontinuous curves

At the points where curved strokes and other segments of letters intersect, there is no possibility of automatic adjustment. In such case a manual operation is necessary.

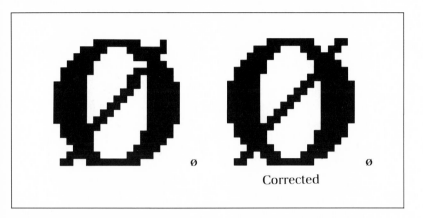

Corrected

Corrections of serifs
a) Serifs of italic types

When the raster is coarse, the ends of serifs can be very problematic. In the example shown, the serif ends have an inclination of 0°. If one were to delete only one point, one would create a 45° slope.

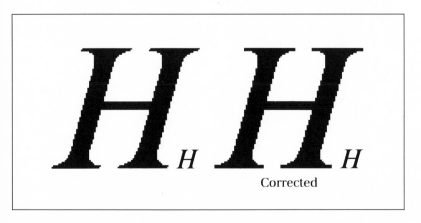

Corrected

b) Serifs on diagonal stems

Serifs on diagonal stems cannot be adjusted automatically. In order to achieve a good transition from the stem into the serif, corrections are necessary when the raster is coarse.

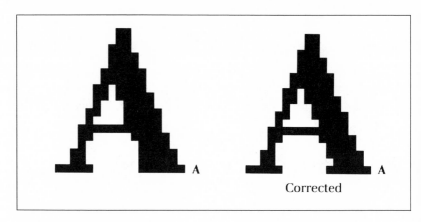

A   A
Corrected

c) Flutes on serifs

Flutes on serifs cannot be treated automatically either. With a coarse raster one must decide how many scanlines need to be left out. Uniform flutes often have to be generated by hand.

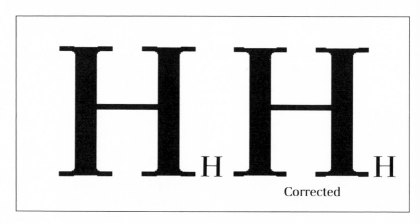

H   H
Corrected

d) Serif lengths

With a coarse raster, serifs on letters m, n, w, v, y etc. can easily "intergrow". Whereas in some cases it is possible to deal with straight stems (m) automatically, diagonals always have to be corrected by hand.

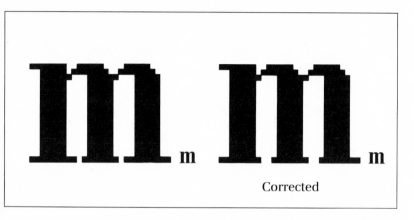

Corrected

Corrections on segments of letters

Certain segments of letters (apart from horizontal serifs) can only be made to keep their uniform appearance through the use of interactive corrections.

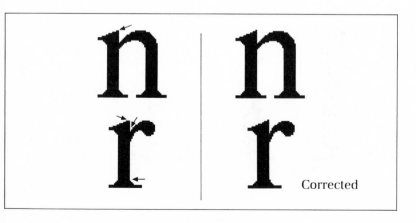

Corrected

Intersection of diagonals

Rastering of intersections of diagonals often causes the form to appear random in shape. Such points have to be checked and possibly corrected manually.

Stems with slight slopes

Slightly sloping stems produce problems when the raster is too coarse. The coarser the raster the fewer are the number of steps available to describe the inclination. The numeral 5 in a coarse raster causes the right slope of the vertical stem to disappear.

In the case of a special character such as the asterisk, the horizontal stroke can become simply rectangular as a result of coarse rastering.

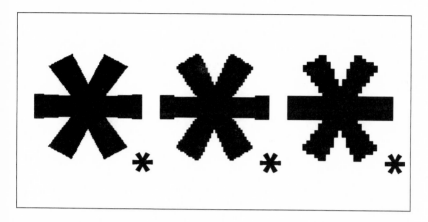

Ink traps
a) The optimum ink trap
Joints of letters having acute angles are often cut relatively deep for printing or repro reasons. This is achieved on raster letters by removing points. A result as in "M" is only possible using manual correction.

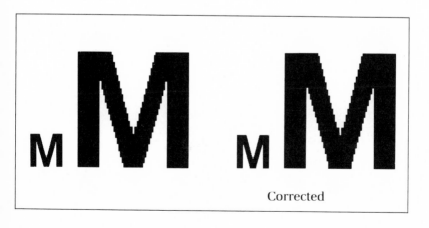

Corrected

b) Changing ink traps

Coarse rastering can sometimes create exaggerations or distortions in the joints. The slope in the original then disappears, e.g. in the letters "r" and "b".

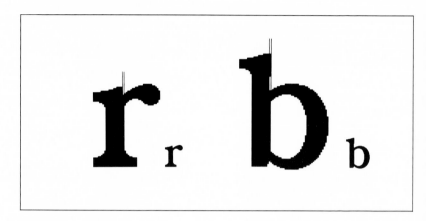

Tails

Rastering can sometimes cause the fineness of detail in the tails to disappear completely. When this is the case nothing but professional manual correction can hope to bring this fineness (of detail) back in a character.

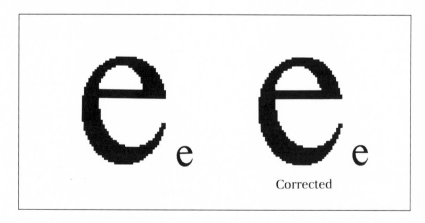

Corrected

7.3 SC formats for laser printers

It is already clear today that laser printers, LED printers and electro-erosion printers will continue to spread in the graphics industry in the future. They have long ago left their role as "fast printers for computers" in commercial usage. We are certain that the use of these devices as in-house printers and proof printers is going to expand. It is also apparent that they will be increasingly used in connection with PCs as "typewriters" in offices. It is only a question of price. The word from the industry is that by the year 1990 such printers will be available for $1000.

These printers are classified as low resolution printers, they write with 12 lines/mm, sometimes with 16 lines/mm or with 24 lines/mm (300 lines/inch, 400 lines/inch and 600 lines/inch).

The people developing type are aware that typefaces for this area of use need to be specially designed (ref. Bigelow).

Parallel to the development of new typefaces, the typefaces already in existence will have to be adapted for these printers. Provided one sticks to the use of proof printing for high resolution typesetting machines, one can accept certain quality losses. In this area it is mainly necessary to have a similar reproduction in order to gain an idea of the typography e.g., of a whole newspaper page. In general, the set width, point size and weight (boldness) have to be approximately the same. Laser printers are quite capable of meeting this objective from 12 lines/mm upwards.

We predict however, that such laser printers will also find uses in offices. In offices they are used to create the final product, i.e. text and typography for reading. To this end typefaces have to be redesigned to some extent. The following must be taken into account when doing so:

The most common size for text is 9p. Body size is then 39 pixels and cap height 26 pixels at 12 lines/mm (300 lines/inch). In chapter 2 we described the overhang of round shapes. This overhang is usually around 1.5% of cap height. When capital letters have a height of 26 pixels (39 for the em), then round forms are given either 26 as well, or 28 pixels. This means that the cap overhang or base overhang is either 0% or 3.8%.

133

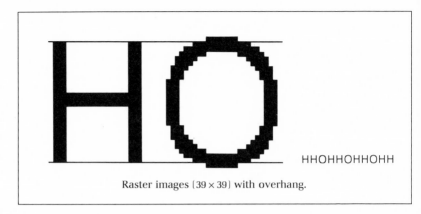

HHOHHOHHOHH

Raster images (39 × 39) with overhang.

Such a large overhang shows up and makes the "O" appear greater than an "H". On the other hand an "O" appears too small if it has no overhang.

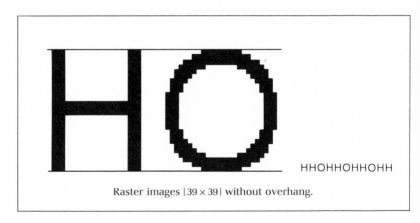

HHOHHOHHOHH

Raster images (39 × 39) without overhang.

Half dots are, naturally enough, not available, but half lines can be created with very little effort, if next to a fully filled line one produces a new line consisting of alternating black and white pixels (half-bitting).

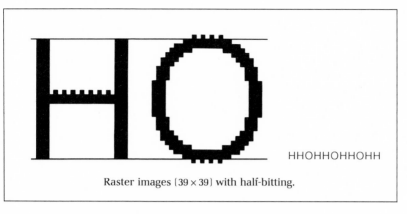

HHOHHOHHOHH

Raster images (39 × 39) with half-bitting.

As one can see on the "H", it has a crossbar of 2.5 point thickness, as does the "O". The overhang of the "O" is now approx. 1.5%, as it should be. It is interesting to note that with most laser printers one does not see a very distinct zigzagging along lines where the half bitting method has been used to produce stroke thicknesses with half point sizes. The manufacturers of such machines are lucky in that the physical effects (equalization of charge distribution, transfer of toner) produce a blending of the optical density.

On the other hand however, the above examples do show that only machines with writing densities of more than 24 lines/mm (600 lines/inch) are capable of producing the correct and important overhang. We would thus recommend all manufacturers of such machines to heed our experience, and try to aim for a writing density of 24 lines/mm (600 lines/inch) for their machines.

Even if individual points cannot be copied with the machine at a resolution corresponding to 24 lines/mm, the overall appearance of the individual letters will be finer and more pleasing to the eye. The type representations would have a higher quality.

8. Conclusions

We have been dealing with digital formats for 13 years. Eight years went by after the invention of the CRT machine by Dr. Hell before we started. We consider ourselves lucky that we had to begin with the control of drawing machines in order to cut original letters for photosetting, i.e. that right from the start we had to concentrate on the quality of digital type reproduction because of the size and accuracy of output required. In most typesetting machines the maximum letter height is approximately 3.1 cm, in drawing machines 10 cm is a standard height, and large starts at 100 cm.

This led us to discover the best data base. We held our peace for a long time before proclaiming that the IKARUS format is the only correct one for this purpose; at first we could not really believe that the most sensible procedure was the one of storing hand-digitized data. For a long time this appeared to us to be just too simple: after all, the basic concept did not require a great deal of thought.

It is probable that anyone who has to deal with graphics eventually ends up differentiating between three types of points (corners, tangents and curves). This is also a very natural process when analysing letter outlines. Starting points as a fourth type of point are only of importance to us in enabling the differentiation of individual closed outlines (for example the letter "O" has two outlines).

The coding of IKARUS points is thus extremely simple. The X and Y coordinates are coded with one word each and the point type is put into the sign bits of these two words, i.e. 4 bytes per point (see appendix I).

In discussing these matters with critical users, a further argument in the IKARUS format's favour made itself apparent: hand-digitizing almost automatically leads to a minimum of points being considered, because people tend to like saving work. It is thus almost natural that the IKARUS method is the method which requires the least number of contour points for the reproduction of an original letter, no matter how it was drawn. In this respect, it is of no consequence which method is used to produce smooth and rounded connections of the hand-digitized points. We are still of the opinion that in addition to our method (IK interpolation), the spline interpolations and Bézier method are also of use. We described the IK interpolation method in chapter 6.3 and have also explained why we stuck to our method.

These considerations led to a more detailed investigation of the properties of other formats.

8.1 Properties of formats

The following summary lists format properties in the sequence in which, during their short history, technicians have become interested in them.

E0: Electronics (speed)
Cost of electronics for the generation of control signals.

E1: Storage capacity (high res)
Storage capacity for high resolutions.

E2: Storage capacity (low res)
Storage capacity for low resolutions.

E3: Sizing
Possibilities for creating different type sizes from one original.

E4: Transformations
Possibility of displacing, rotating, italicizing and deforming type faces.

To these already well known and accepted properties we have added a few of our own:

E5: Input
Keeping input as simple as possible.

E6: User friendliness
Simple data structure for easy corrections.

E7: Presentation
Accurate output on flat bed drawing machines to allow comparisons with the original, and the output of lettering on self-adhesive material.

E8: Soft-scanning
Accurate, closed mathematical curve description in order to be able to use calculation methods to arrive at other digital formats, e.g. bitmaps, vector formats and run length codes.

E9: Programmer friendliness
Cost-effective programming of modifications; easy programming for new machine formats.

In the following table we have evaluated the properties of the individual formats as follows: 15 = very good ... 8 = satisfactory ... 0 = unsatisfactory.
The groups of properties have been divided into subtotals for
- machine format   (E0...E2)
- typesetting machine format   (E0...E4)
- data base   (E5...E9).
In the past particular attention has been paid to properties E0 and E1. So we shall also pay particular attention to these, in sections 8.1.1 and 8.1.2.

	Machine format			Type-setter format		Data base format					Sums				
	Electronics (speed)	Storage capacity (high res)	Storage capacity (low res)	Sizing	Transformations	Input	User friendliness	Output	Soft-scanning	Programmer friendliness	E0+E1	E0+E2	E0-E4	E5-E9	E0-E9
	E0	E1	E2	E3	E4	E5	E6	E7	E8	E9					
IKARUS format	1	13	13	15	15	10	15	15	15	12	14	14	57	67	124
DI format	5	8	8	15	12	15[3]	12	15	8	10	13	13	48	60	108
VE format	7	15[1]	12	12	15	15[3]	10	12	7	8	22	19	61	52	113
SC format	9	15[1]	4	3	5	15[3]	7	8	6	2	24	13	36	38	74
BI format	9	15[1]	0	3	5	15[3]	6	6	5	2	24	9	32	34	66
GS format	9	13	0	3	5	15[3]	3	4	2	2	22	9	30	26	56
Adobe format	5	13	13	15	10	7	9	13	8	10	18	18	56	47	103
Bitstream format	5	8	8	12[2]	12[2]	10	15	15	15	12	13	13	45	67	112
Coueignoux format	9	15	15	10[2]	10[2]	10	10	6	8	8	24	24	59	42	101
Metafont format	0	3	3	12[2]	10[2]	3	12	10	8	15	3	3	28	48	76
Purdy format	10	13	13	12[2]	10[2]	4	10	8	8	8	23	23	58	38	96
XEROX spline format	5	10	10	12[2]	10[2]	12	9	9	8	8	15	15	47	46	93
Open vector format	13	15[1]	8	3	5	12	8	10	6	2	28	21	44	38	82
Closed vector format	7	15[1]	8	7	10	12	10	12	7	8	22	15	47	49	96
Run length format	14	15[1]	4	3	5	12	7	8	6	2	29	18	41	35	76
Bitmap format	15	15[1]	0	3	5	12	6	6	5	2	30	15	38	31	67

[1] Look also table and histograms for storage needs for different rasters

[2] These formats have a primary resolution of less than 4000 × 4000 pixel per em

[3] These formats could be calculated by computer

Comparison of formats.

8.1.1 Electronic requirements for the generation of control signals

It is clear that the electronic effort required increases correspondingly, as the digital reproduction of the formats used becomes more complex or compressed. We shall now attempt to make assessments for the manufacturing costs of the appropriate electronics – not for the development costs – and summarize these in the table below. The table contains details in the form of "number of IC boards" required for the generation of control signals from the particular digital form of data storage.

	Electronic 1	Electronic 2	Electronic 3	Electronic 4
IKARUS format	–	–	–	15
DI format	–	–	8	10
Open vector format	3	3	–	–
Closed vector format	4	4	7	10
Running length format	2	2	–	–
Bitmap format	1	1	–	–
Adobe format	3	6	10	10
Bitstream format	–	–	–	10
Coueignoux format	6	6	6	6
Metafont format	–	–	–	–
Purdy format	3	5	5	5
XEROX spline format	–	–	10	10

Electronic 1 up to 4 perform all about 500 characters per second in 10 pt size

Electronic 1: low resolution (VDT's, laser printer)

Electronic 2: high resolution (laser recorder, CRT-machines)

Electronic 3: high resolution with performances E2 and E3
(high resolution and sizing)

Electronic 4: high resolution with performances E2, E3 and E4
(high resolution, sizing, transformation)

Cost of electronics on basis
of number of IC boards in double Europe format.

The number of IC boards for the more complex formats could be reduced if one were to use the following method to generate the control signals:

- One stores the type as basic data format, which is in itself complex.
- Prior to setting the text, the typeface commands are searched for (font change commands).
- A preparatory process is started on a standard IC board (e.g. a CPU with 512 KByte RAM memory), in which for the required type the complex format is converted relatively slowly into a simple machine format using a program (approximately 40 char./sec.).
- The simple machine format is then stored in a buffer prior to the actual typesetting.

8.1.2 Storage requirements

In the framework of the IKARUS concept it is relatively easy to simulate special encodings, and thus to find the storage requirements for corresponding formats. In the following we show a table and two graphic presentations. The table contains an estimate of the storage required for complex formats. The diagrams show curves of the storage required as a function of the raster per em for complex, but also for simple formats. The storage requirement for complex formats is virtually independent of the resolution.

	Bytes per digitized point or element	Points per character	Bytes per character	General information and data for a typeface	KBytes per 100 latin characters	KBytes per 5000 Kanji characters
IKARUS-format	4	50	200	2	22	4950
DI-format	8	75	600	2	62	13950
VC-format	3	75	225	2	24.5	5513
Adobe-format	10	20	200	2	22	4950
Bitstream-format	7	75	525	4	56.5	12713
Coueignoux-format			25	10	12.5	2813
Metafont-format			400	20	60	13500
Purdy-format	5	40	200	5	25	5625
XEROX-spline-format	20	20	400	2	42	9450

Storage requirement for different formats.

141

The numbers show net values. Optionally, one can add storage for
- width tables,
- kerning/kissing tables,
- keyboard layouts,
- special typeface parameters and indicators.

The storage needs of Kanji can be estimated on the basis of IKARUS digitizations. Kanji characters have an average of 225 digitizations instead of 50, and thus require 4.5 times more storage space.

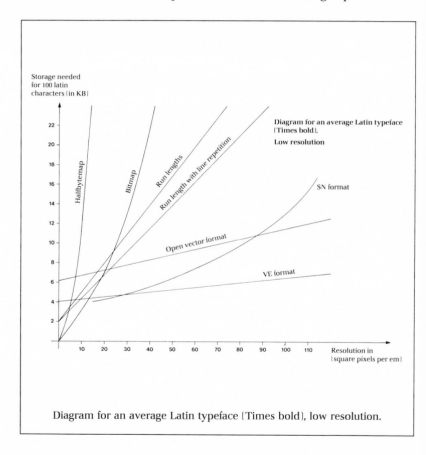

Diagram for an average Latin typeface [Times bold], low resolution.

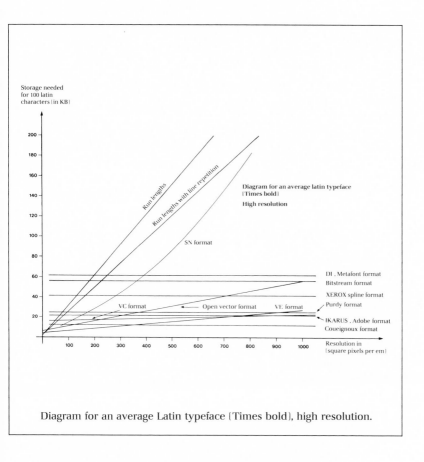

Storage needed
for 100 latin
characters (in KB)

Run lengths

Run lengths with line repetition

Diagram for an average latin typeface
(Times bold)

High resolution

SN format

DI , Metafont format
Bitstream format

XEROX spline format
Purdy format

VC format — Open vector format — VF format

IKARUS , Adobe format
Coueignoux format

Resolution in
(square pixels per em)

Diagram for an average Latin typeface (Times bold), high resolution.

8.2 Requirements to be met by formats

What follows is a summary of our findings as requirements to be met
by formats.
- The raster resolution should be square.
- A data bank should be set up for future machines.
- Using this data bank, one should be able to calculate current and
  future machine formats (soft-scanning).
- The format of the data bank should be based on hand-digitization.

143

- The machine formats should be unified.
- It should be possible to exchange digital formats amongst different manufacturers.
- The right format for the data bank will allow manufacturers to change or expand the data more easily.
- The following em square division would appear in our opinion the most sensible:

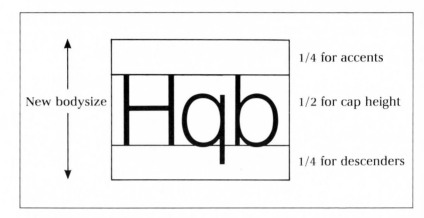

This produces the following:
new body size = old body size × 1.33 = 2.0 × cap height.
Several firms have already introduced this and results have been satisfactory so far. The new body size is for storage purposes and does not determine the line spacing (leading) when typesetting. It would be even better to replace the term em by exposing window, selecting this window with dimensions equal to or slightly greater than the new em.

8.3 Recommendations for manufacturers

- Should the raster pattern be smaller than 50 × 50 pixels, the representation of overhangs necessary to the correct display of round forms within an alphabet will have a detrimental effect, causing the curves to appear flatter than they should.

144

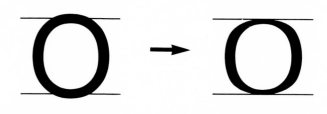

- Laser printers should write with 600 lines/inch.
- Technicians should always remember one thing: the development of a new typesetting machine requires approximately 5 to 10 persons for the duration of 2 years. If one already has a good data base, then during this time 2 persons can work concurrently on the preparation of types and machine formats.

To our knowledge it has been the case to date that the type is only developed when the machine is finished, and then as fast as possible. This has got to change!

- The descenders should have the same length as the ascenders in order to achieve better proportions.
- We would argue for fixed accents in the type library (data base).
- We also argue for complete and comprehensive kerning and touching tables in the data base.
- One should make efforts to allow variable type and/or keyboard setups. Every data base should be flexible in this area.
- Type should be loadable from a host computer and not be a fixed part of the typesetting machine.

8.4 Time required for producing type

In our type studio we have digitized approximately 1400 type versions to date (end of 1986) and can speak from experience.

On average we require 100 man-hours to digitize a font of 186 Latin characters (normal URW layout of a typeface) by hand in the IK format. For 186 Latin characters the work involved is divided as follows:

145

– Administration	10 h
– Marking	8 h
– Digitizing	8 h
– Correction/operating	24 h
– Spacing	20 h
– Design of missing characters	30 h
	100 h

The last item is due to the fact that on average original documentation usually contains about 120 characters. The missing 66 characters are then drawn, partly by hand and partly calculated using programs, or with the aid of graphic editors on a visual display terminal. For the hand-digitization of Kanji type characters in Hamburg and Tokyo, we have come to the following values by experience (this also applies to a 186 Kanji character font):

– Administration	10 h
– Marking	24 h
– Digitizing	24 h
– Correction/operating	35 h
– Spacing	–
– Design of missing characters	?? h
	93 h

With regard to marking and digitizing, Kanji characters have on average 4.5 times the number of points contained in the average Latin letter. Despite this, the data preparation and digitizing takes only three times longer, approximately 15 minutes per Kanji character.

With regard to corrections, it should be noted that Kanji characters are drawn in the middle of the em square and appear more individual than Latin letters. The vertical strokes of Latin type are usually uniform within all the caps or lower case letters of a particular typeface. This can only be achieved by a relatively large amount

146

of corrective work. The originals are drawn by hand and therefore naturally have the inaccuracies of hand work, e.g. with respect to stroke widths. Fortunately, the same rigidity of rule does not apply to the individual Kanji characters, i.e. the amount of editorial work for Kanji is fairly limited.

We would, however, indicate the very large extent of a Kanji font, i.e. around 10,000 characters for "mincho" (roman) and approximately 6000 characters for "gothic" (sans serif).

The Japanese have – just as the Europeans or Americans – developed a large number of different type fonts and versions. We estimate that for all existing Kanji type one would require approximately 30 times the digitization work needed for all the Latin type in the western world.

In addition to the amount of effort involved in the preparation of IK formats, we also have an appreciable amount of manual work with the preparation of SC formats. The demands made by different firms and therefore the corresponding amount of work are very different. The effort involved with soft-scanning is fixed:

First point size parameterization	10 hours
Other point size parameterizations	4 hours

The next working steps take place on the graphic display. At this point we should perhaps say that some manufacturers of type offer digitizations which are of a quality lower than that of the results produced by automatic soft-scanning.

In our opinion corrections are always to be expected. There are just too many possibilities for graphic variations at joints, serifs and stroke intersections. No programmed procedure can be expected to deal with all these eventualities. On the other hand there are already high resolution machines available (60 lines/mm up to 100 lines/mm) which no longer require the correction of rasters made with soft-scanning.

The average amount of time required by us for the correction of 186 Latin type characters for each point size in a range of 50×50 up to

147

400×400 is about 15 hours, while the first point size of all point sizes of a particular version usually takes between 30 to 45 hours.

The production of digital type is therefore expensive. It is for this very reason that when preparing a data base, the digitization of the typeface should only be required **once in the life of that typeface.** Once it is stored one only needs a relatively small amount of rastering work for each machine, whether available now or yet to be developed.

Appendices

Appendix A
Type classification

There are several competing classifications. We follow the DIN-classification based on proposals made by the ATYPI (Association Typographic Internationale).

The American and English standards use 9 groups of typefaces, we have added group 10 for the black letters and group 11 for eccentric typefaces. We like to use group 11 to gather all those typefaces, which are hard to read, and are therefore only of limited use, except maybe in advertizing.

A few years ago, an ISO group has been established to work on international font standards (ISO/TC97/SC18). Unfortunately, their work has not been finished to date, but it shows promising results (ref. ISO).

Group 1
Venetian Serif
Characteristic to this group are the sloped cross stem of the lower case e and the sloped (45 degree) up-stroke of the stems of lower case characters. The axis of bowls is slightly slanted to the left.

Centaur
Schneidler
Trump Mediaeval

Group 2
Old Face/Old Style
The cross stem of the lower case e is horizontal. The terminals of the upper case and the vertical stems of the lower case curve smoothly into the serifs.

Bembo

Palatino

SABON-ANTIQUA

Group 3
Transitional
The differences between thickness of hairlines and stems are greater. The axis of the bowls is nearly vertical.

Baskerville

Caslon

Concorde

Times

Group 4
Modern Face/Modern Roman
The serifs are smooth and horizontal. The stems do not curve smoothly into the serifs. The axis of bowls is vertical. Differences in thickness between hairlines and stems are more extreme here.

Bodoni

Fenice

Madison

Walbaum Buch

Group 5
Egyptian Slab/Serif Antique
Characteristic to this group are the slab serifs. Hairlines and strokes are mostly as thick as the terminals.

Beton

Clarendon

Egyptienne

Rockwell

Group 6
Sans Serif/Gothic
This group of typefaces has no serifs, and is also recognized by the name "Grotesque". Crossbars and stems are optically of the same thickness.

Akzidenz-Grotesk
Futura
Helvetica
Optima

Group 7
Display Roman
These roman versions are not classifiable within the first six groups, due to their widely differing ductus.

Group 8
Scripts
These typefaces have been developed from writing at schools and chancelleries. The roman italics are however not to be mistaken for members of this group.

Brush Script
Commercial Script
Murray Hill
Palace Script

Group 9
Graphic
These typefaces have been developed from the hand-written forms of the roman typefaces.

Time-Script
Post-Antiqua
Pracht-Antiqua

Group 10
Black Letter

These typefaces mostly have a condensed and irregular lower case. The upper case is decorated with hairlines and has forms full of verve. This group usually does not exist in English classifications.

Group 11
Eccentrics

This group does not exist, but the author wants to show typefaces that are almost illegible.

Appendix B
Characters of a typeface

Upper case

101 A	113 M	125 Y
102 B	114 N	126 Z
103 C	115 O	127 Æ
104 D	116 P	128 Œ
105 E	117 Q	129 Ø
106 F	118 R	201 Ä
107 G	119 S	208 Å
108 H	120 T	210 Ç
109 I	121 U	215 Đ
110 J	122 V	261 Þ
111 K	123 W	237 Ö
112 L	124 X	251 Ü

Lower case

301 a	314 n	327 æ
302 b	315 o	328 œ
303 c	316 p	329 ø
304 d	317 q	330 ß
305 e	318 r	331 ı
306 f	319 s	332 ȷ
307 g	320 t	401 ä
308 h	321 u	408 å
309 i	322 v	413 ç
310 j	323 w	436 ö
311 k	324 x	449 ü
312 l	325 y	459 ð
313 m	326 z	460 þ

Numerals

501 1	546 4	581 7
502 2	547 5	582 8
503 3	548 6	583 9
504 4	549 7	584 0
505 5	550 8	665 ¼
506 6	551 9	662 ½
507 7	552 0	666 ¾
508 8	575 1	663 ⅓
509 9	576 2	664 ⅔
510 0	577 3	511 £
543 1	578 4	512 $
544 2	579 5	513 ¢
545 3	580 6	516 ¥

Punctuation marks, special characters

601	.	614	!	627	)
602	:	615	¡	628	[
603	•	616	?	629	]
604	•	617	¿	630	**&**
605	.	618	»	631	**§**
606	...	619	«	632	†
607	‚	620	›	633	‡
608	;	621	‹	634	*
609	'	622	/	646	A⁄S
610	'	623	-	698	%
611	"	624	–	699	‰
612	"	625	—	637	@
613	„	626	(	638	#

Special characters and floating accents

648	©	701	••	751	••
649	®	702	•	752	⌄ •
650	TM	703	o	753	o
651	¶	704	′	754	′
652	Ⓠ	705	‵	755	‵
639	o	706	∧	756	∧
635	′	707	ˇ	757	ˇ
636	″	708	˘	758	˘
640	+	709	~	759	~
641	—	710	″	760	″
642	×	711	ς	761	ς
643	÷	713	ϲ	763	ϲ
644	=	714	═	764	▬

Special character designations

We assume that we rarely need to give the names for upper and lower case, or for numerals, whereas we give the names of punctuations and other special characters and accents completely. The character numbers are listed sequentially.

127	–	Upper case AE dipthong
128	–	Upper case OE dipthong
129	–	Upper case O with sloped stem
201	–	Upper case A with umlaut
208	–	Upper case A with angstroem
210	–	Upper case C with cedilla
215	–	Upper case D with horizontal stroke
237	–	Upper case O with umlaut
251	–	Upper case U with umlaut
261	–	Upper case Thorn (Icelandic)
327	–	Lower case ae dipthong
328	–	Lower case oe dipthong
329	–	Lower case o with sloped stem
330	–	German eszett (double s)
331	–	Lower case i without dot
332	–	Lower case j without dot
401	–	Lower case a with umlaut
408	–	Lower case a with angstroem
413	–	Lower case c with cedilla
436	–	Lower case o with umlaut
449	–	Lower case u with umlaut
459	–	Sound notation for th
460	–	Lower case thorn (Icelandic)
501-510	–	Tabular figures
512	–	Pound Sterling
543-552	–	Mediaevals (old style figures)
601	–	Period
602	–	Colon
603	–	Bullet

604	–	Dot (Catalonian)
605	–	Leader dot
606	–	Ellipsis
607	–	Comma
608	–	Semicolon
609	–	Apostrophe
610	–	Single upper quotation mark
611	–	Double upper quotation mark (end 99)
612	–	Double upper quotation mark (start 66)
613	–	Double lower quotation mark
614	–	Exclamation mark
615	–	Inverted exclamation mark (Spanish)
616	–	Question mark
617	–	Inverted question mark (Spanish)
618	–	French citation mark (start), guillemet
619	–	French citation mark (end), guillemet
620	–	Single French citation mark (start), guillemet
621	–	Single French citation mark (end), guillemet
622	–	Slash
623	–	Hyphen
624	–	En-dash
625	–	Em-dash
626	–	Open parenthesis
627	–	Close parenthesis
628	–	Open bracket
629	–	Close bracket
630	–	Ampersand
631	–	Section mark
632	–	Single dagger
633	–	Double dagger
634	–	Asterisk
635	–	Single vertical quote
636	–	Double vertical quote
637	–	Commercial at
638	–	Number sign
639	–	Degree sign
640	–	Plus
641	–	Minus

642	–	Multiplication
643	–	Division
644	–	Equal
646	–	A/S from 60% upper case
648	–	Copyright
649	–	Registered
650	–	Trademark
651	–	Paragraph mark
652	–	General currency symbol
661-676	–	60% fractions
698	–	Percent
699	–	Per mille
701	–	Upper case accent umlaut
702	–	Single dot of upper case accent umlaut
703	–	Upper case accent angstroem
704	–	Upper case accent acute
705	–	Upper case accent grave
706	–	Upper case accent circumflex
707	–	Upper case accent caron
708	–	Upper case accent breve
709	–	Upper case accent tilde
710	–	Upper case accent double acute (Hungarian)
711	–	Upper case accent cedilla
713	–	Upper case accent hook (Polish/Lithuanian)
714	–	Upper case accent macron
751	–	Lower case accent umlaut
752	–	Single dot of lower case accent umlaut
753	–	Lower case accent angstroem
754	–	Lower case accent acute
755	–	Lower case accent grave
756	–	Lower case accent circumflex
757	–	Lower case accent caron
758	–	Lower case accent breve
759	–	Lower case accent tilde
760	–	Lower case accent double acute (Hungarian)
761	–	Lower case accent cedilla
763	–	Lower case accent hook (Polish/Lithuanian)
764	–	Lower case accent macron

Appendix C
Accents for latin type

Albanian	Albanian 3,5	ABCDEFGHIJKLMNOPQRSTUVWXYZ abcdefghijklmnopqrstuvwxyz ÇçËë «H» "H„
Finnish-Ugrish	Estonian 1	ABCDEFGHIJKLMNOPQRSTUVWXYZ abcdefghijklmnopqrstuvwxyz ÄäÕõÖöÜü (ČčŠšŽž) «H» „H"
	Finnish 4,5	ABCDEFGHIJKLMNOPQRSTUVWXYZ abcdefghijklmnopqrstuvwxyz ÄäÖö "H" »H» 'H'
	Lappish 0,038	ABCDEFGHIJKLMNOPQRSTUVWXYZ abcdefghijklmnopqrstuvwxyz
	Hungarian 13	ABCDEFGHIJKLMNOPQRSTUVWXYZ abcdefghijklmnopqrstuvwxyz ÁáÉéÍíÓóÖöŐőÚúÜüŰű „H" »H«
Celtic	Breton 1	ABCDEFGHIJKLMNOPQRSTUVWXYZ abcdefghijklmnopqrstuvwxyz ÉéÈèÊêÏïÑñÜü
	Gaelic 0,08	ABCDEFGHIJKLMNOPQRSTUVWXYZ abcdefghijklmnopqrstuvwxyz ÀàÉéÍíÒóÓòÙù
	Irish 0,4	ABCDEFGHIJKLMNOPQRSTUVWXYZ abcdefghijklmnopqrstuvwxyz ÁáÉéÍíÓóÚú "H" 'H' H-H
	Welsh h 0,5	ABCDEFGHIJKLMNOPQRSTUVWXYZ abcdefghijklmnopqrstuvwxyz ÂâÀàÄäÊéÉêÊëÎîÏïÔôÖöÙúÛûÜüŴŵŴŵŶŷŸÿ
Germanic	Africaans 4	ABCDEFGHIJKLMNOPQRSTUVWXYZ abcdefghijklmnopqrstuvwxyz „H" 'H' H-H ÁáÀàÄäÉéÈèÊêËëÍíÌìÎîÏïÓóÒòÔôÖöÚúÙùÛûÜü
	Danish 5	ABCDEFGHIJKLMNOPQRSTUVWXYZ abcdefghijklmnopqrstuvwxyz ÅåÉéØøÆæ »H« „H"
	German 100-120	ABCDEFGHIJKLMNOPQRSTUVWXYZ abcdefghijklmnopqrstuvwxyz ÄäÖöÜüß „H" »H« H - H

Taken from Berthold Fototypes EDITION 2.

English 350-370	ABCDEFGHIJKLMNOPQRSTUVWXYZ abcdefghijklmnopqrstuvwxyz "H" 'H' H–H
Faroen 0,036	ABCDEFGHIJKLMNOPQRSTUVWXYZ abcdefghijklmnopqrstuvwxyz ÁáÐðÍíÓóØøÚúÝýÆæ
Frisian 0,3	ABCDEFGHIJKLMNOPQRSTUVWXYZ abcdefghijklmnopqrstuvwxyz ÅåÉéëïÊêÔôöÚúÛû
Dutch 19	ABCDEFGHIJKLMNOPQRSTUVWXYZ abcdefghijklmnopqrstuvwxyz „H" "H" ÁáÀàÂâÄäÉéÈèÊêËëÎîÍïÓóÒòÔôÖöÛûÜü
Icelandic 0,2	ABCDEFGHIJKLMNOPQRSTUVWXYZ abcdefghijklmnopqrstuvwxyz ÁáÐðÉéÍíÓóÖö ÞþÚúÝýÆæ „H" 'H'
Norwegian 4	ABCDEFGHIJKLMNOPQRSTUVWXYZ abcdefghijklmnopqrstuvwxyz ÀàÅåÉéÈèÒòØøÓôÆæ «H»
Swedish 8,5	ABCDEFGHIJKLMNOPQRSTUVWXYZ abcdefghijklmnopqrstuvwxyz ÅåÄäÉéÖö "H"»H» 'H'
Romanic	French 80-90	ABCDEFGHIJKLMNOPQRSTUVWXYZ abcdefghijklmnopqrstuvwxyz ÀàÂâÇçÉéÈèÊêËëÎîÏïÔôÙùÛûÜüÆæŒœ «H»

	Italian n 60-65	ABCDEFGHIJKLMNOPQRSTUVWXYZ abcdefghijklmnopqrstuvwxyz ÀàÈèÉéÌìÎîÒòÓóÙù «H» "H„
	Catalonian 5	ABCDEFGHIJKLMNOPQRSTUVWXYZ abcdefghijklmnopqrstuvwxyz ÀàÇçÉéÈèÍíÏïÓóÒòÚúÜü
	Latin t	ABCDEFGHIJKLMNOPQRSTUVWXYZ abcdefghijklmnopqrstuvwxyz „H"
	Portugese 125-135	ABCDEFGHIJKLMNOPQRSTUVWXYZ abcdefghijklmnopqrstuvwxyz «H» "H" 'H' ÁáÀàÂâÃãÇçÉéÈèÊêÍíÏïÓóÒòÔôÕõÚúÙù

Taken from Berthold Fototypes EDITION 2.

Romanic	Ratoromanian 0,6	ABCDEFGHIJKLMNOPQRSTUVWXYZ abcdefghijklmnopqrstuvwxyz ÀáÂâÉéÊêÈèÊêÎîÏïÒòÔôÖöÙùÜü
	Rumanian 22	ABCDEFGHIJKLMNOPQRSTUVWXYZ abcdefghijklmnopqrstuvwxyz ÂâĂăÎîŞşŢţ „H" «H» ‚H'
	Spanish 220–225	ABCDEFGHIJKLMNOPQRSTUVWXYZ abcdefghijklmnopqrstuvwxyz ÁáÉéÍíÑñÓóÚúÜü ¿H? ¡H! «H» "H" 'H' H-H
Baltic	Lithuanian 2,5	ABCDEFGHIJKLMNOPQRSTUVWXYZ abcdefghijklmnopqrstuvwxyz ĄąČčĖėĘęĮįŠšŲųŪūŽž „H" «H»
	Lettish 1,5	ABCDEFGHIJKLMNOPQRSTUVWXYZ abcdefghijklmnopqrstuvwxyz ĀāČčĒēĢģĪīĶķĻļŅņŖŗŠšŪūŽž «H» „H"
Slawian	Croatic 5	ABCDEFGHIJKLMNOPQRSTUVWXYZ abcdefghijklmnopqrstuvwxyz ĆćČčĐđŠšŽž »H«
	Lower sorbic 0,025	ABCDEFGHIJKLMNOPQRSTUVWXYZ abcdefghijklmnopqrstuvwxyz ČčĚěŁłNńŔŕŚśŠšŹźŻž „H"
	Upper sorbic 0,025	ABCDEFGHIJKLMNOPQRSTUVWXYZ abcdefghijklmnopqrstuvwxyz ĆćČčĚěŁłNńÓóŔŕŠšŹźŻž „H"·
	Polish 34	ABCDEFGHIJKLMNOPQRSTUVWXYZ abcdefghijklmnopqrstuvwxyz ĄąĆćĘęŁłNńÓóŚśŹźŻż „H" »H« ‚H'
	Slovak 4,5	ABCDEFGHIJKLMNOPQRSTUVWXYZ abcdefghijklmnopqrstuvwxyz ÁáÄäČčĎďÉéÍíĽĺĹÍŇňÓóÔôŔŕŠšŤťÚúÝýŽž „H" »H«
	Slowenian 2	ABCDEFGHIJKLMNOPQRSTUVWXYZ abcdefghijklmnopqrstuvwxyz ČčŠšŽž »H« ‚H'
	Czech 9,5	ABCDEFGHIJKLMNOPQRSTUVWXYZ abcdefghijklmnopqrstuvwxyz ÁáČčĎďÉéĚěÍíŇňÓóŘŕŠšŤťÚúŮůÝýŽž „H" »H«

Taken from Berthold Fototypes EDITION 2.

Others	Basque 0,7	ABCDEFGHIJKLMNOPQRSTUVWXYZ abcdefghijklmnopqrstuvwxyz ÇçD̄dĿl Ñ ñ Ñ ñ Ŕ ŕ Ŕ ŕ Ṫ ṫ Ü ü
	Esperanto (3–5)	ABCDEFGHIJKLMNOPQRSTUVWXYZ abcdefghijklmnopqrstuvwxyz Ĉ ĉ Ĝ ĝ Ĥ ĥ Ĵ ĵ Ŝ ŝ Ŭ ŭ
	Haussa 15	ABCDEFGHIJKLMNOPQRSTUVWXYZ abcdefghijklmnopqrstuvwxyz
	Indonesian 80	ABCDEFGHIJKLMNOPQRSTUVWXYZ abcdefghijklmnopqrstuvwxyz É é 'H' 'H'
	Malagassi 4	ABCDEFGHIJKLMNOPQRSTUVWXYZ abcdefghijklmnopqrstuvwxyz 'H'
	Maltese 0,3	ABCDEFGHIJKLMNOPQRSTUVWXYZ abcdefghijklmnopqrstuvwxyz À Ċ ċ Ġ ġ Ħ ħ Ż ż
	Samoan 0,2	ABCDEFGHIJKLMNOPQRSTUVWXYZ abcdefghijklmnopqrstuvwxyz Ō ō
	Suaheli 15	ABCDEFGHIJKLMNOPQRSTUVWXYZ abcdefghijklmnopqrstuvwxyz
	Tagalog 8	ABCDEFGHIJKLMNOPQRSTUVWXYZ abcdefghijklmnopqrstuvwxyz Á á À à Â â É é È è Ê ê Ĝ ĝ Í í Ì ì Î î Ñ ñ Ó ó Ò ò Ô ô Ú ú Ù ù Û û
	Turkish 34	ABCDEFGHIJKLMNOPQRSTUVWXYZ abcdefghijklmnopqrstuvwxyz Â â Ç ç Ĝ ĝ I ı İ i Ö ö Ş ş Ü ü Û û «H» "H" "H„ 'H'
	Vietnamese 50	Á À Â Ã Ä Å Ấ Ầ Ẩ Ẫ Ậ Ǎ Ǎ Ǒ Ǒ Ǒ Ǒ Ǎ Ð É Ế Ề Ể Ễ Ệ É É È Ê Ẻ Ì Ỉ Ĩ Ị Ó Ò Ổ Õ Ọ Ố Ồ Ổ Ỗ Ộ Ớ Ờ Ở Ỡ Ợ Ù Ú Ù Ủ Ũ Ụ Ứ Ừ Ử Ữ Ự Ý
		á à â ã ä å ấ ầ ẩ ẫ ậ ǎ đ é è ê ẻ ẽ ệ é è ê ê ệ i ì ỉ ĩ ị ó ò ổ õ ọ ố ồ ổ ỗ ộ ơ ớ ờ ở ỡ ợ ù ú ù ủ ũ ụ ứ ừ ử ữ ự ý

Taken from Berthold Fototypes EDITION 2.

Appendix D
Dingbats

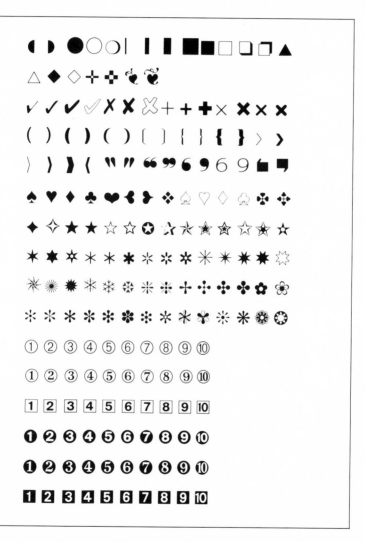

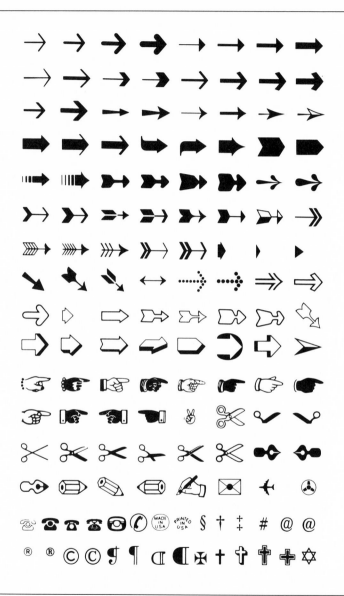

Appendix E
Explanation of optical effects

We confronted approximately 130 people with questions 1 to 5 at URW in Hamburg, and obtained the following statistical answers:

Result 1 (squares):	Field b9 ± 2 fields
Result 2 (circles):	Field b9 ± 2 fields
Result 3 (overhangs):	Field b3 ± 1 field
Result 4 (diagonals):	Field a4 ± 2 fields
Result 5 (apices):	Field b2 ± 2 fields

We conclude the following:

- A square appears optically correct when it is 1% ± 1% taller than it is wide.
- A circle appears to be optically correct when it is 1% ± 1% taller than it is wide.
- A circle appears optically as tall as a rectangle when it has an cap and base overhang of 1.5% ± 0.5% respectively.
- A triangle appears optically as wide as a rectangle when it is 5% ± 1% wider.
- A sharp apex (A,V,W) appears to be as high as a straight only when it is 3% ± 1% longer than the square side.

It is of course possible that the people tested at URW have a certain bias, which we did not recognize. We would therefore ask our readers to try out the test and send the results on a postcard as follows:

> "optical appearance"
> a7, b9, c4, b3, b2 (example)

to the following address:

> URW Unternehmensberatung
> c/o Dr. Peter Karow
> Harksheider Straße 102
> D–2000 Hamburg 65
> West Germany

We guarantee that the data and results sent in by readers will be used only for the improvement of the statistical base.

Appendix F
Short dictionary of type terminology

English	French	German
accent	accent	Akzent
accented character	lettre accentuée	Akzentbuchstabe
adjustment	ajustement, adaptation	Anpassung
aesthetic box	programme esthétique	Ästhetik-Tabelle
angle of italicization	angle d'italisation, inclinaison	Kursivwinkel
to antique	antiquer	antiquieren
artwork	original	Schriftoriginal
ascender	longue du haut	Oberlänge
automatic channelling	canalisation automatique	Kanalautomatik
bar	bras	Schwengel
baseline	ligne d'écriture, ligne de base	Grundlinie, Schriftlinie
bearing value	approche	Fleisch
black	extra gras	schwarz, extrafett
blackletter	caractère gothique	Fraktur
blending	fusionée	verschmelzend
body	corps de lettre	Kegel
body size	hauteur du corps	Kegelhöhe
bold	gras	dick, fett
border	cadre, bordure	Rahmen
bounding box	rectangle d'encombrement	umschreibendes Rechteck
bow	arc	Bogen
bowl	rond	Rundung
broken	fracturée	gebrochen

English	French	German
calligraphy	calligraphie	Kalligraphie
cap height	hauteur des capitales	Versalhöhe
cathode ray	rayon cathodique	Kathodenstrahl
character	lettre	Buchstabe
	caractère	
character style	forme de la lettre,	Buchstabenform
	style	
composition	composition	Satz
to condense	condenser	kondensieren
condensed	étroite	schmal
contour	contour	Kontur
to contour	dessiner le contour	konturieren
corner point	point d'angle	Eckpunkt
counter	contre poinçon	Innenraum, Punze
cross stem	trait horizontal	Querstrich
curve	courbe	Kurve
curve adjustment	compensation des	Kurvenausgleich
	courbes	
curve point	point de courbe	Kurvenpunkt
data base	base des données	Datenbasis
dancing	valsante	tanzend
decorative typeface	alphabet gracile	Zierschrift
demi (bold)	demi-gras	halbfett
descender	jambage inférieur	Unterlänge
diagonal	diagonale	Diagonale
digital	digital, numérisé	digital
digitalization	digitalisation	Digitalisierung
digital representation	représentation	digitale Darstellung
	digitale	
display typeface	caractéres de titre,	Auszeichnungsschrift,
	caractéres de titrage	Displayschrift
dot	pixel,	Rasterpunkt
	point de trame	
down-stroke	plein	Abstrich
ductus	ductus	Duktus, Strichführung

173

English	French	German
ear	oreille	Ohr
em square	cadratin	Geviert
to enlarge	agrandir	vergrößern
to expand	élargir	expandieren
expanded	élargi, large	breit
exponent	exposant	Exponent
extension	sortie gracile, paraphe	Auszug
extra bold	extra gras	extra fett
extra light	extra maigre	extra leicht
fixed accent	accent fix	Festakzent
floating accent	accent flottant	fliegender Akzent
foot note	note en base (de page courant)	Fußnote
form setting	composition formée	Formsatz
formula setting	composition de formules	Formelsatz
foundry	fonderie	Gießerei
fraction	fraction	Bruchziffer
grid	grille	Gitter, Raster
grid size	grille	Raster
grotesque	style grotesque, (sans patin)	grotesk
hairline	délié	Haarlinie
headline	titre	Headline, Überschrift
high resolution	haute résolution	feine Auflösung
hot metal	composition au plomb	Bleisatz
index	index	Index
indentation	renfoncement	Einzug im Text
initial	lettre initiale	Initial

English	French	German
ink trap	renfoncement du caractère	Einzug im Buchstaben
interpolation	interpolation	Interpolation
italic	italique	kursiv
to italicize	pencher, italiser	kursivieren
job printing	travaux de ville	Akzidenzdruck
join	entrée	Einlauf
kerning	à crénage	unterschneidend
kerning table	tableau de crénage	Unterschneidungs-tabelle
laser beam	rayon laser	Laserstrahl
laser printer	copieuse laser	Laserdrucker
leading	interlignage	Durchschuß
left side bearing (value)	approche gauche	Vorbreite
letter space	espace des caractères	Buchstaben-Zwischenraum
letter spacing	interlettrage	Spationierung
ligature	ligature	Ligatur
light	maigre	dünn, leicht, mager
line	ligne	Linie, Zeile
line element	filet	Linienelement
line graphic	reproduction au trait	Strichgraphik
line resolution	résolution par ligne	Linienauflösung
line spacing	interlignage	Durchschuß
link	liaison	Steg, Verbindung
logo(type)	logo(type)	Logo(type)
loop	boucle	Schleife
lower case (characters)	bas de casse, minuscules	Gemeine, Minuskeln
low resolution	basse résolution	grobe Auflösung
mean line	hauteur des minuscules	Minuskelhöhe

English	French	German
medium	normal	normal
mirroring	effet miroir	spiegelnd
modification	modification	Modifikation
monospaced	chasse de fixe	dicktengleich
numeral	chiffre	Ziffer
original	original	Schriftoriginal
outline	contour	Kontur
overhang	avance	Überhang
overlapping	superposée	überdeckend
overlapping table	table pour superposer	Überdeckungstabelle
performance specification	cahier des charges	Pflichtenheft
photo type setting	photocomposition	Fotosatz
pixel	pixel, point de trame	Pixel, Rasterpunkt
point	point	Punkt
point size	corps	Punktgröße, Schriftgrad
punctuation	ponctuation	Interpunktion
punctuation mark	signe de ponctuation	Interpunktionszeichen
rectangular alignment	alignement automatique	Kanalverarbeitung
to reduce	réduire	verkleinern
resolution	résolution	Auflösung
resolution mark	pointe	Spitze
right side bearing (value)	approche de droite	Nachbreite
roman typeface	romain, elzévir	Antiqua (Schrift)
to rotate	faire une rotation	rotieren
to round	arrondir	runden, verrunden
run length code	codage des parcours	Lauflängenkodierung
running width	approche de chasse	Laufweite

English	French	German
sans serif	style grotesque (sans patin)	grotesk
scan data	données de scanning	Rasterdaten
scanner	scanner	Scanner
scanning	scanning (analyse)	Aufrasterung
serif	patin, empattement	Serife
serif type	style romain	Antiqua (Schrift)
setting	composition	Satz
sexy spacing	sexy spacing	sexy spacing
to shadow	ombrer	schattieren
shaping	déformée	verformend
shoulder	épaule	Schulter
to size	mettre à la cote	umgrößern
spacing (letter ~)	chasse de caractères (de l'alphabet)	Zurichtung
small caps	petites capitales	Kapitälchen
sparkling (bouncing)	valsante	tanzend
special setting	chasse spéciale	Spezialsatz
spline	spline	S-Kurve
spur	compensation extérieur, éperon	Sporn
starting point	point de début	Anfangspunkt, Startpunkt
stem	trait, jambage	Balken, Grundstrich
stem edge	bornée	Balkenrand
stem width	épaisseur de trait	Balkenstärke, Strichstärke
stress	épaissement	Verdickung
stretching	extensible	streckend
stroke	trait	Strich
stroke thickness	épaisseur de trait	Strichdicke
swash	sortie gracile, paraphe	Auszug, Zierstrich

English	French	German
swash character	lettre ornée	Zierbuchstabe, Schwungbuchstabe
symbol	symbole	Signet
tabular setting	composition de tableau	Tabellensatz
tail	queue	Abschwung, Schwanz
tangent point	point de tangente	Tangentenpunkt
terminal	sortie	Endung
text setting	composition de texte	Textsatz
text type, text typeface	caractères de textes	Brotschrift, Textschrift, Werkschrift
total width	chasse	Dickte
touching	d'acollage	berührend
touching table	table de chasse reduites	Berührungstabelle
traditional	traditionelle	traditionell
type	style, caractère	Schrift
typeface	oeil de caractère	Schriftbild
typeface family	famille des caractères	Schriftfamilie
type height	hauteur des caractères	Schrifthöhe
type size	corps	Schriftgrad
type style	style de caractère	Schriftstil
upright	droite	gerade(stehend)
up-stroke	delié	Aufstrich
version	graisse, version	Schriftschnitt, Version
vignette	vignette	Vignette
weight	graisse, ensemble	Fettegrad, Schriftschnitt
white space	espace blanc	Zwischenraum

178

English	French	German
width	chasse	Weite
width table	table de chasse	Dicktentabelle
word space	espace entre des mots	Wortzwischenraum
x-height	hauteur des minuscules	Minuskelhöhe

Appendix G
Data structure for typefaces

Fonts can be stored digitally by a vast number of different methods, as we have seen. These often very different sorts of data lead to different formats. Each format presents the image information of a letter in a different manner. Despite this it is possible to find a uniform structure for the data on a data carrier. In the following, we describe the structure as used by URW. This description goes for all fonts supplied irrespective of format. The formats themselves are described individually in the appropriate appendices I to Q.

1. Data carrying media for font data
1.1 Magnetic tape, 9 track, 800 or 1600 bpi writing density. This is the data carrier recommended by URW as standard because of its many advantages (price, large capacity, mechanical tolerance, wide availability of reading equipment, reliability).
1.2 Diskette (floppy disk), soft sectored, single or double density, written on an IBM PC or a MacIntosh.
1.3 Standard disk cartridges compatible with the DEC computer systems (RL01, RL02, Phoenix, CDC etc.) can be supplied.
1.4 Other data carriers, e.g. TU58 cassettes or paper tapes can also be supplied.
All data carriers are written sequentially, independent of the operating system. The client therefore has direct access to the data to allow further processing using a simple reading program. Several fonts can be supplied on either one or more data carriers. A font usually consists of less than 256 characters, it may however consist of a maximum of 32,000 characters. On the other hand a font may consist of a maximum of 32,000 records of 2048 words in length, i.e. 128 megabytes.

2. The label on data carriers
Every single data carrier belonging to a font has a label of 40 words length. This label is written completely in ASCII and provides an individual identification of the data carrier, also within each font

delivery. It currently includes information as to the origin of the data carrier, the time of its generation, an index number for the data carriers within one font delivery, and details as to the record length of all subsequent data records.

A label has the following form:

Word	Meaning
1	Length of label: **40**
2–20	Origin of data media e.g. **URW_IKARUS_V3.1_VAX_11/750_VMS**
21–30	Start of generation of this data carrier e.g. **17_JAN_85_17:31**
31–35	Data carrier index e.g. **VOL_0**
36–40	Length of physical record in words e.g. **_BLK_2048** If record length is given as 0 then the data records of this data carrier have variable lengths.

3. Record structure

The remaining records of a data carrier contain the data proper of a font delivery in a uniform, format independent form.

A font delivery (volume) is divided into two levels, fonts and characters, i.e. a delivery can consist of one or more fonts of which each may consist of one or more characters. In a similar manner one can distinguish between two sorts of logical data records, i.e. those with information concerning a font as a whole (font header), and those with information concerning an individual character of a font (character records).

Every logical data record consists of sections of variable length: The font header consists of
- name section
- font information
- character index;

the character record consists of   – name section
                                   – setting information
                                   – contour index
                                   – image information.
Every logical data record and every part thereof starts with a data word which contains the length of the record or the section in words. **We quantify and describe the data in words (16 bit)!**
The data is recorded in so-called physical records. At URW we use a record length of 2048 words for disk storage and magnetic tape storage. A font always starts with a new physical data record. A font delivery has the following structure:

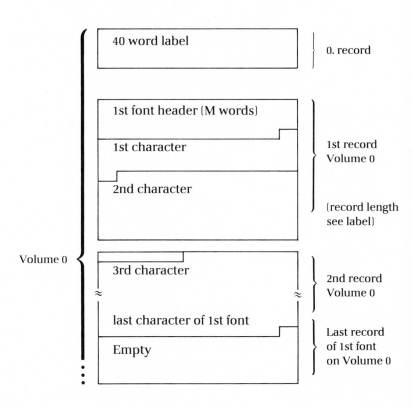

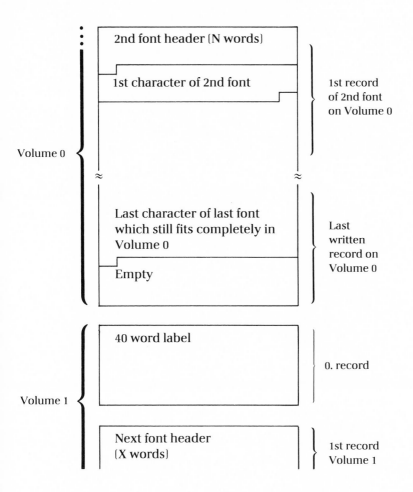

The capacity of the data carrier is known, as is the memory require-ment of a font. When the first data carrier of a delivery has no more space for another font then the next data carrier (next volume) is started.

When the storage requirements of a font exceed the capacity of the data carrier we divide the font into sensible character groups (part fonts). An automatic division as such has not yet been programmed, it would however be possible.

In the following, the font header is detailed and the character record comprehensively described. Within the terms of the character record the contour index is only applicable to IK, DI, VC, VS and VE formats. The SC, SN, BI and GS formats have no contour index.

The image information is only described generally here, and then detailed in the appendices of the individual formats. The unit for coordinates is normally 1/100 mm or 1 pixel, in which the ident for the measurement unit is set to 1 (see below). A font always starts on a new physical data record. The corresponding information (font header, character records) is recorded sequentially and without spaces. In this, the limits of the physical data records only lead to an incrementation of the record counter but not to its logical division.

Character numbers run from 1 to 32,000. At URW the numbers 1 to 999 are used for latin fonts. Kanji fonts generally require the use of all of the numbers.

If a letter has more than 10,000 digitizations it is divided into the fol-lowing parts. In such a case the character is separated for practical reasons at, for example, the end of a contour (IK, DI, VC, VS and VE formats). In the SC format we have chosen a description which allows approx. $32,000 \times 2048$ digitizations (transitions).

If the following part number is set to 0 then there are no following parts. The numbers of the following parts are selected automatically from unused character numbers above 999.

4. Font header

Word	Meaning	Comment
1	Length of font header in words	$= 1 + I + J + L + M$
2	**Name section** Length of name section in words	(I)
3	Number on URW list	
4–9	**File name**	6 words
10–49	Font name in ASCII	40 words
50	Format ident of data	e.g. IK, DI, G1...G4, VC, ...
51–53	Production date	3 words
54–56	Date of last change	e.g. 16, 6, 85 for 16th of June 1985. Currently (1985) I has the value 55 at URW.
I+2	**Font information** Length of font data in words	(J)
I+3	Ident of font	$= 1$ for typeface $\neq 1$ for IG structure
I+4	**Number of characters**	
I+5	Cap height	
I+6	Body size	
I+7	x-height	given in units,
I+8	Distance of base line from lower body line	usually 1/100 mm, or in pixels
I+9	Line distance for composition	
I+10	Stroke thickness	
I+11	Italic angle	in 1/10 degrees

Word	Meaning	Comment
I + 12	Optimum size for composition in Didot points	e.g. 12 p
I + 13	Average character width (based on international character frequency)	in 1/100 mm
		At URW (1985) J currently has the value 12.
Hierarchy section		
I + J + 2	**Hierarchy section** Length of hierarchy section in words	(L) = 1 for fonts ≠ 1 for IG graphics (see appendix H)
Character index		
I + J + L + 2	**Character index** Length of character index in words	(M)
I + J + L + 3	**Pointer to last written physical record (= length of font in physical records)**	
I + J + L + 4	Pointer to last written word of last record	
I + J + L + 5	Number of first character	
I + J + L + 6	Pointer to record in this font which contains the start of the first character	
I + J + L + 7	Pointer in this record to the word which is the first word of the corresponding character record	3 words for one character

Word	Meaning	Comment
$I+J+L+8$	Number of second character etc.	
$\cdot$	$\cdot$	
$\approx$	$\approx$	$\approx$
$\cdot$	$\cdot$	
$I+J+L+M+1$	Pointer to the word of the character record where the last character starts	

5. Character record

Word	Meaning	Comment
1 2	Length of first character in records (length = 2048 words) in words	2 + N1 + N2 + N3 + M
3 4 5	**Name section** Length of name section in words Character number Character number of following part	N1 (currently = 3) 1,2...999 At URW currently character numbers are 1,2...999. Character names (in ASCII) are predefined by separate character layouts (e.g. keyboard layouts). Following parts have numbers of 1000...32,000. 0 means there is no following part.
N1 + 3 N1 + 4 N1 + 5 N1 + 6	**Setting information** Length of setting information Character sort **Number of digitizations** **Total width (T)**	N2 (currently = 12) 1 = letter 2 = logo/signet 3 = line graphic 4 = frame given in units

Word	Meaning	Comment
N1+7 N1+8 N1+9 N1+10 N1+11 N1+12 N1+13	Left side bearing (L) Width (W) Right side bearing (R) X minimum ⎤ X maximum ⎜ bounding Y minimum ⎜ box Y maximum ⎦	given in units $T = L + W + R$ given in units
N1+N2+2	Unit size (definition of the unit)	$=1 \triangleq$ unit is $1/100$ mm or $\triangleq 1$ pixel **(normal)** $=2 \triangleq$ unit is $2/100$ mm $=3$ etc. When the unit is set to 2, for example, one must multiply the coordinates prior to the use of the character by a factor of 2.
N1+N2+3 N1+N2+4 N1+N2+5 N1+N2+6	**Contour index** Length of contour index in records (N4) in words (N5) Record pointer, Word pointer of first contour relative to start of image information. The start of the image information relative to character data record is **3 + N1 + N2 + N3.**	$N3 = N4 \times 2048 + N5$

Word	Meaning	Comment
N1 + N2 + 7	Sense of rotation of first contour	−1 = clockwise 0 = open contour +1 = anti-clockwise
N1 + N2 + 8	Identifier for nesting hierarchy	0 = outer contour 1st order 1 = inner contour 1st order 2 = outer contour 2nd order 3 = inner contour 2nd order 4 = etc.
N1 + N2 + 9	Color inside contour	0 = transparent 1 = black, etc.
N1 + N2 + 10	Number of digitizations of 1st contour	
N1 + N2 + 11	Record pointer to 2nd contour	
N1 + N2 + 12	Word pointer	
N1 + N2 + 13	Sense of rotation	
N1 + N2 + 14	Nesting identification	6 words per contour
N1 + N2 + 15	Color	
N1 + N2 + 16	Number of digitizations	
N1 + N2 + 17	Record pointer to 3rd contour	
.	.	
≈ .	≈ .	≈
.	.	
N1 + N2 + N3 + 2	Number of digitizations of last contour of first character	

Word	Meaning	Comment
$N1 + N2 + N3$ $+3$ $+4$ $+5$ $+6$ $+7$	**Image information** Length of data in records (N6) in words (N7) Storage of image information of first character of this font (in 16 bit words) This can be followed by either IK, DI, VC, VS, VE, SC, SN, BI or GS formats, see appendices I to Q.	$M = N6 \times 2048 + N7$
≈ . . .	≈ . . .	≈
$N1 + N2 + N3$ $+M+2$	Final word of image information of first character of this font	
...$+3$	Length of 2nd character in records	
≈ . . .	≈ . . .	≈
xyz	Last word of image information of last character of this font	See font header

Appendix H
Data structure for graphics: IG format

Graphics are created doing design jobs at computer aided graphic work stations. They can take the form of an IK job in a display lettering system, of an advertisement in a page make-up or of a design system for layouts of magazine pages. The storage of graphics is the same as for fonts, i.e. the data is physically divided into records of fixed length which cause no other logical division of the data.

Graphics can also be generated by the LINUS system for the automatic recording of black and white images and the output of their IK digitizations.

Any graphic can be converted by programs into a character of a font and vice versa. When storing a graphic as a character the hierarchy information is lost, when storing a character as a graphic only a basic hierarchy is automatically generated.

1. Data carrying media for graphic data
1.1 Magnetic tape, 9 track, 800 or 1600 bpi density. This is the data carrier recommended by URW as standard because of its many advantages (price, large capacity, mechanical tolerance, wide availability of reading equipment, reliability).

1.2 Diskette (floppy disk), soft sectored, single or double density, written on an IBM PC or a MacIntosh.

1.3 Standard disk cartridges compatible with the DEC computer systems (RL01, RL02, Phoenix, CDC etc.) can be supplied.

1.4 Other data carriers, e.g. TU58 cassettes or paper tapes can also be supplied.

All data carriers are written sequentially, independent of the operating system. The client therefore has direct access to the data to allow further processing using a simple reading program. Several graphics can be supplied on either one or more data carriers. A graphic usually consists of less than 256 characters, it may however consist of a maximum of 32,000 characters. On the other hand a graphic may consist of a maximum of 32,000 records of 2048 words in length, i.e. 128 megabytes.

2. The label on data carriers

Every single data carrier belonging to a graphic has a label of 40 words length. This label is written completely in ASCII and provides an individual identification of the data carrier, also within each graphic delivery. It currently includes information as to the origin of the data carrier, the time of its generation, an index number for the data carriers within one graphic delivery, and details as to the record length of all subsequent data records.
A label has the following form:

Word	Meaning
1	Length of label: **40**
2–20	Origin of data media e.g. **URW_IKARUS_V3.1_VAX_11/750_VMS**
21–30	Start of generation of this data carrier e.g. **17_JAN_85_17:31**
31–35	Data carrier index e.g. **VOL_0**
36–40	Length of physical record in words e.g. **_BLK_2048** If record length is given as 0 then the data records of this data carrier have variable lengths.

3. Record structure

The remaining records of a data carrier contain the data proper of a graphic delivery in a uniform, format independent form.
A graphic delivery (volume) is divided into two levels, graphics and characters, i.e. a delivery can consist of one or more graphics of which each may consist of one or more characters. In a similar manner one can distinguish between two sorts of logical data records, i.e. those with information concerning a graphic as a whole (graphic header) and those with information concerning an individual character of a graphic (character records).

193

Every logical data record consists of sections of variable length:
The graphic header consists of   – name section
                                     – hierarchy section;
The character data record consists of – name section
                                     – setting information
                                     – contour index
                                     – image information.
Every logical data record and every part thereof starts with a data word which contains the length of the record or the section in words. **We quantify and describe the data in words (16 bit)!**
The data is recorded in so-called physical records. At URW we use a record length of 2048 words for disk storage and magnetic tape storage. A graphic always starts with a new physical data record. A graphic delivery has the following structure:

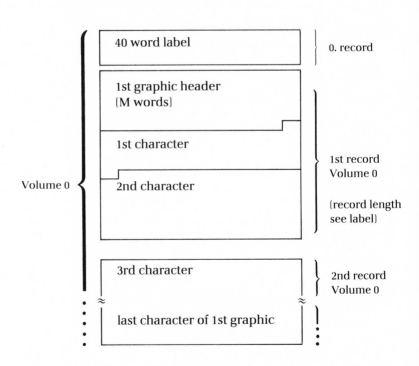

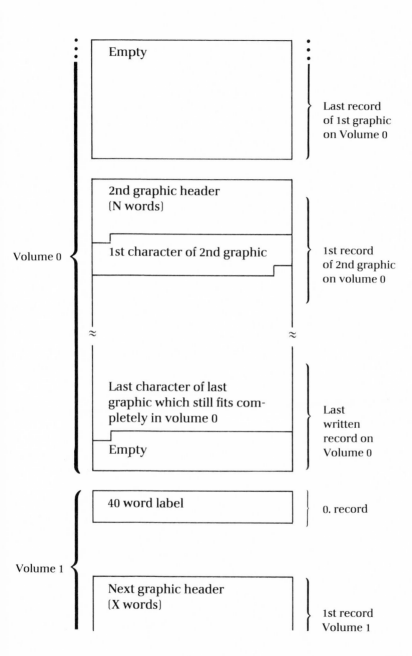

The capacity of the data carrier is known, as is the memory requirement of a graphic. When the first data carrier of a delivery has no more space for another graphic then the next data carrier (next volume) is started.

When the storage capacity requirement of one graphic exceeds the capacity of the data carrier we divide the graphic into sensible character groups (part graphics). An automatic division as such has not yet been programmed, it would however be possible.

In the following, the graphic header is detailed and the character record clearly described. Within the terms of the character record the contour index is only applicable to IK, DI, VC, VS and VE formats. The SC, SN, BI and GS formats have no contour index.

The image information is only described generally here, and then detailed in the appendices of the individual formats. The unit for coordinates is normally 1/100 mm or 1 pixel, in which the ident for the measurement unit is set to 1 (see below). A graphic always starts at the beginning of a physical data record. The corresponding information (graphic header, character records) is recorded sequentially and without spaces. In this, the limits of the physical data records only lead to an incrementation of the record counter but not to its logical division.

If a character has more than 10,000 digitizations it is divided into the following parts. In such a case the character is separated for practical reasons at, for example, the end of a contour (IK, DI, VC, VS and VE formats). In the SC format we have chosen a description which allows approx. $32,000 \times 2048$ digitizations (transitions).

If the following part number is set to 0 then there are no following parts. The numbers of the following parts are selected automatically from unused character numbers above 999.

The IG format has been designed conceptually in such a way that with the right preconditions it can also be read from disk and correctly interpreted by programs which can process the IK format. In this sense the IG format is only an expanded version of the IK format.

A part of the utility data of the knots is ignored then, i.e.:
- The coordinate system of all knots must have the same origin and may not be rotated respective to each other.
- The color of the knots is ignored.

4. Graphic header

The graphic header has the same structure as a font header. However, the hierarchy section is now fully defined. It includes data on the characters respective to superimposed levels, e.g. lines, blocks or layers. The character index is dropped.

4.1 Description of the hierarchy

The image information is divided into the following hierarchy (see figure 1):
- Graphic (advert., article, job)
- Layer
- Block (column)
- Line
- Character

- Contour (in the contour index of the character)

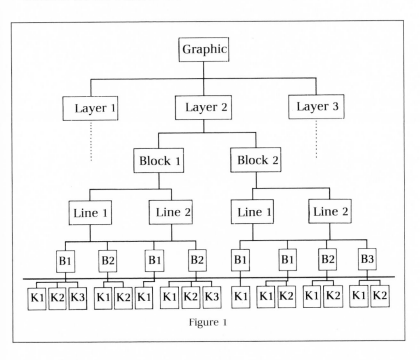

Figure 1

Bn identifies characters and **Kn** the contours. The image information proper is contained in the IK, DI, VC, VS, VE or SC format of the digitized points of the contours or scanlines respectively.

Knots are located at those points where the hierarchy tree divides. There are therefore graphic, layer, block, line and character knots. Those knots related to another knot but lying one step higher are known as **fathers**. Those knots at the same hierarchy level related to one father are known as **brothers**. A succession is then defined. This is created during the work session in which a graphic is prepared. The chronological succession is also the **order succession**. In a hierarchy tree, left is defined as earlier and right defined as later.

Every knot can therefore have left and right brothers. Those knots related to a knot but lying one step lower are known as **sons**. There are first and last sons.

In figure 1 lines 1 and 2 are brothers and they have block 1 as their father whereas line 1 from block 2 is not their brother since they only have the grandfather (level 2) in common with 1 and 2.

In the IG format every knot contains information concerning the element as a whole, which the knot represents, over the whole line.

The following information is stored on each knot:
- pointer information
- utility data.

4.2 Describing the knots

Knots are allocated to graphics, layers, blocks, lines and characters. They contain the following pointers to other knots:

	e.g. for line 2 block 2 (figure 1)
pointer – to itself (sequential number)	line 2
– to the father	block 2
– to the left brother	line 1
– to the right brother	missing
– to the first son	B(character) 1
– to the last son	B(character) 2

In this manner one may move both from one hierarchy step to another as well as within one hierarchy level. Some movements require detours, in full one can only reach the "cousins" by passing through the grandfather, i.e. via an "ancestor", and the "penultimate son" can only be arrived at via a detour over the first son. In many cases pointers do not point to a knot, and the "first" of course does not have a left brother. In general one may say that each knot (except for the graphic) has a father and at least one son. **Utility data** of a constant length is allocated to every knot.

Utility data
- **Factor**
  One may state a factor for sizing (enlarging/reducing). 1000 is a factor 1.000, 500 the factor 0.5. It first comes into operation in the output of the complete part tree of the hierarchy to which the knot belongs, and on the knot itself. The sizing can only take place as seen from the father.
- **Position of coordinate system relative to father (X and Y coordinates)**
  The coordinate origin can be moved relatively to the father. The values are given in double words and respective to the coordinate system of the father.
- **Angle of rotation relative to father**
  Details of the angle of rotation are given in positive mathematical figures. The rotation axis is the coordinate origin of the knot. The angular details are given in 1/100 degree (e.g. 9000 = 90 degrees). The rotation can only be realized respective to the coordinate system of the father.
- **Size of bounding box (XMIN, XMAX, YMIN, YMAX)**
  relative to the coordinate origin of the knot.
  The data is given in double words.
  In order to be able to find characters, lines etc. via, for example, the geometrical position of one of their IK points, it is useful to know the boundaries of an element via the data of the bounding box. It is quite possible that rectangles of this sort within the various elements of the same hierarchy level can overlap (see figure 3).

- **Color**

The color is an additional characteristic, which can be important when cutting foils or exposing films. Since each knot can be allocated a color there is the possibility that one and the same element can have more than one color, for example, a "red" line in a "black" block. This line then has red as well as black color. This however leads to no conflict since either the color is ignored or only one color at a time is cut in the foil or exposed.

By changing the utility data and not tampering with the image data, the following may be carried on with whole lines, blocks etc.:

- sizing
- shifting
- rotating or coloring.

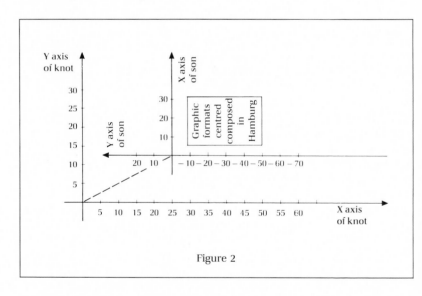

Figure 2

In this example the utility data of the son has the following values:

- factor is 0.5 (see axis designation)
- position of coordinate system is (25, + 13)
- angle of rotation 9000 (= 90.00 degrees)
- size of bounding box XMIN = 5   XMAX = 32
                                      YMIN = − 50   YMAX = − 8.

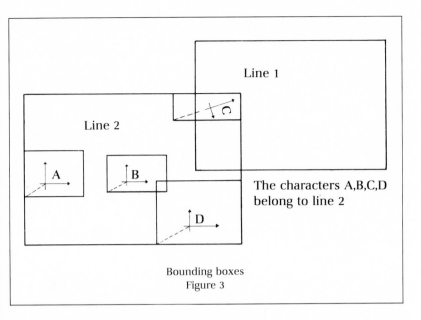

Line 1

Line 2

C

A

B

The characters A,B,C,D
belong to line 2

D

Bounding boxes
Figure 3

4.3 Guidelines for programming

When the data is stored in the working area, only the pointers and
utility data at the knots are continuously updated.

New additional data, e.g. knots or new image information, is stored
at the end of the corresponding data section, and old obsolete data is
initially left, and later deleted during reorganization.

The reorganization of the data, i.e. the deletion of obsolete information and the reordering of the pointers, is something which should
take place automatically:

– as required (when the overflow of data buffers is possible), but at
  least
– prior to archiving to disk.

The data at the knots is of a fixed length (21 words).

The knots within the same hierarchy levels should be ordered in
ascending succession. This **does not** however necessarily mean that
knots with sequentially ascending numbers are logically related. The
relationships (e.g. to the same father) are uniquely specified by the
pointers.

4.4 Summary of knot information

Word		Meaning	Comment
1		Sequential number	Within the level, the sons of each father are counted
2		Pointer to father	
3		Pointer to left brother	
4		Pointer to right brother	
5	Pointer	Pointer to first son	
6		Pointer to last son	
		On the character level in the words 5 and 6 instead:	Utility data
		5 Pointer to physical record which contains the start of the character	Pointer
		6 Pointer to the word in the record where the character record starts.	Utility data
7		Factor	Operates as multiplier on sons, grandsons etc.
8–9		X position	Measured in units, relative to father coordinate system
10–11		Y position	
12	Utility data	Angle of rotation	Around the origin of father
13–14		X minimum	See comment on (X,Y) position
15–16		X maximum	
17–18		Y minimum	See comment on (X,Y) position
19–20		Y maximum	
21		Color	e.g. 0 = transparent 1 = black

4.5 Example of pointer information in hierarchy section

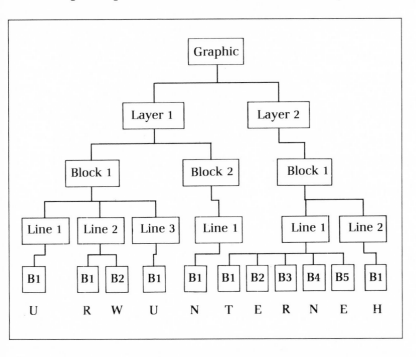

A total of 23 knots results. The first knot stored in the data is the graphic knot.
We abbreviate as follows:

LN = Sequential number
ZF = Pointer to father
ZL = Pointer to left brother
ZR = Pointer to right brother
ZA = Pointer to first son
ZZ = Pointer to last son

Word	Meaning						Comment	
1	484						Length of hierarchy section	
	LN	ZF	ZL	ZR	ZA	ZZ		
2– 22	1	0	0	0	23	275	Graphic	
23– 43	1	2	0	275	44	212	Layer 1	
44– 64	1	23	0	212	65	170	Block 1	
65– 85	1	44	0	107	86	86	Line 1	
86–106	1	65	0	0	...	...	Character 1	U
107–127	2	44	65	170	128	149	Line 2	
128–148	1	107	0	149	...	...	Character 1	R
149–169	2	107	128	0	...	...	Character 2	W
170–190	3	44	107	0	191	191	Line 3	
191–211	1	170	0	0	...	...	Character 1	U
212–232	2	23	44	0	233	233	Block 2	
233–253	1	212	0	0	254	254	Line 1	
254–274	1	233	0	0	...	...	Character 1	N
275–295	2	2	23	0	296	296	Layer 2	
296–316	1	275	0	0	317	443	Block 1	
317–337	1	296	0	443	338	422	Line 1	
338–358	1	317	0	359	...	...	Character 1	T
359–379	2	317	338	380	...	...	Character 2	E
380–400	3	317	359	401	...	...	Character 3	R
401–421	4	317	380	422	...	...	Character 4	N
422–442	5	317	401	0	...	...	Character 5	E
443–463	2	296	317	0	464	464	Line 2	
464–484	1	443	0	0	...	...	Character 1	H

5. Graphic header

Word	Meaning	Comment
1	Length of graphic header in words	$= 1 + I + J + K + L$
2	**Name section** Length of name section in words	(I)
3	Number on URW list	
4–9	**File name**	6 words
10–49	Graphic name in ASCII	40 words
50	Format ident of data	e.g. IK, DI, G1, VC, ...
51–53	Production date	3 words
54–56	Date of last change	e.g. 16, 6, 85 for 16th of June 1985. Currently (1985) I has the value 55 at URW.
I + 2	**Graphic information** Length of graphic data in words	(J = 2)
I + 3	Ident of structure	2 for IG structure
I + J + 2	**Hierarchy section** Length of hierarchy section in words	(K)
I + J + 3 . . . . I + J + 23	Knot for the graphic	(21 words)

Word	Meaning	Comment
I + J + 24 . . . . I + J + 44	} Knots of 1st layer	(21 words)
I + J + 45 . . . I + J + 65 . ≈ .	Knots	if present
I + J + K + 1	Last knot	(21 words)
I + J + K + 2	**Character index** Length of character index in words	(L) = 1, because contained in knot data

6. Character record

Word	Meaning	Comment
1 2	Length of first character in records (length = 2048 words) in words	2 + N1 + N2 + N3 + M
3 4	**Name section** Length of name section in words Character number	N1 (currently = 9) 1,2...999 At URW currently character numbers are 1,2...999. Character names (in ASCII) are predefined by separate character layouts (e.g. keyboard layouts).
5 6–11	Character number of following part File name	Following parts have numbers of 1000...32,000. 0 means there is no following part. 6 words (as font name)
N1 + 3 N1 + 4	**Setting information** Length of setting information Character type	N2 (currently = 8) 1 = letter 2 = logo/signet 3 = line 4 = frame

Word	Meaning	Comment
N1 + 5	**Number of digitizations**	
N1 + 6	**Total width (T)**	
N1 + 7	Left side bearing (L)	given in units
N1 + 8	Width (W)	$T = L + W + R$
N1 + 9	Right side bearing (R)	
N1 + N2 + 2	Unit size (definition of the unit)	$= 1 \cong$ unit is 1/100 mm or $\cong 1$ pixel **(normal)** $= 2 \cong$ unit is 2/100 mm $= 3$ etc. When the unit size is set to 2 for example, one must multiply the coordinates prior to use of character by a factor of 2.
	Contour index Length of contour index	$N3 = N4 \times 2048 + N5$
N1 + N2 + 3	in records (N4)	
N1 + N2 + 4	in words (N5)	
N1 + N2 + 5	Record pointer,	
N1 + N2 + 6	Word pointer of first contour relative to start of image information. The start of image information relative to character data record is **3 + N1 + N2 + N3.**	
N1 + N2 + 7	Sense of rotation of first contour	$-1 =$ clockwise $0 =$ open contour $+1 =$ anti-clockwise

Word	Meaning	Comment
N1 + N2 + 8	Identifier for nesting hierarchy	0 = outer contour 1st order 1 = inner contour 1st order 2 = outer contour 2nd order 3 = inner contour 2nd order 4 = etc.
N1 + N2 + 9	Color inside contour	0 = transparent 1 = black etc.
N1 + N2 + 10	Number of digitizations of 1st contour	
N1 + N2 + 11	Record pointer to 2nd contour	
N1 + N2 + 12	Word pointer	
N1 + N2 + 13	Sense of rotation	
N1 + N2 + 14	Nesting identification	6 words per contour
N1 + N2 + 15	Color	
N1 + N2 + 16	Number of digitizations	
N1 + N2 + 17	Record pointer to 3rd contour	
≈ .	≈ .	≈
N1 + N2 + N3 + 2	Number of digitizations of last contour of first character	

209

Word	Meaning	Comment
	Image information	
N1 + N2 + N3	Length of data	$M = N6 \times 2048 + N7$
+3	in records (N6)	
+4	in words (N7)	
+5	Storage of image information of first character of this graphic (16 bit words).	
+6	This can be done by using	
+7	either IK, DI, VC, VS, VE, SC, SN, BI or GS formats, see appendices I to Q.	
.	.	
≈ .	≈ .	≈
.	.	
N1 + N2 + N3 + M + 2	Final word of image information of first character of this graphic	
N1 + N2 + N3 + M + 3	Length of 2nd character in records	
.	.	
≈ .	≈ .	≈
.	.	
XYZ	Last word of image information of last character of this graphic	

Appendix I
Description of the IK format

1. Structure of an IK font
For the structure of an IK typeface font see the structure as described in appendix G.

2. Description of the IK format
The **IKARUS format** (IK format) is a digital description of contours of any arbitrary two dimensional plane figure (surface). Such figures are for example letters (type characters), company symbols, logos or line graphics.

Contours of such figures are known in mathematics as simple closed curves, which are continuous everywhere and differentiable almost everywhere. This can also be expressed by saying:

Closed: Start and end point of a contour are identical.

Simple: A contour does not cross itself (and in addition, as can easily be imagined, various contours of a figure do not cross each other either).

Continuous overall: A contour has no "gaps".

Differentiable almost overall: An edge has only a finite number of "corners", it is thus "smooth" almost everywhere.

Every character has its own coordinate system, whose X origin is on the X minimum of the character and whose Y origin is on the base line.

The IK format is able to describe such general curved lines with remarkably little effort, i.e. in a space saving manner. A contour is described by a sequence of selected points along the contour, each of which has an (X,Y) coordinate pair referring to a right-angled (Cartesian) coordinate system, plus one of three designations. Such a triple, i.e. designation, X and Y coordinate, is referred to in the following as a "digitization".

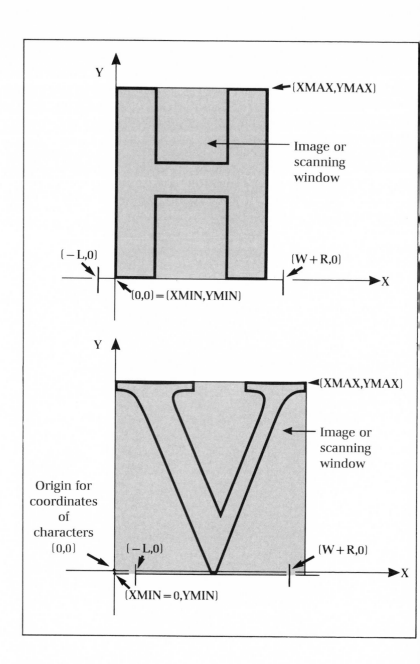

The importance of the three different designations will be discussed in the following. It will become obvious why not only the three different sorts of digitization are necessary, but also why they are sufficient to comprehensively describe the above named contours.

A contour may be pictured as a succession of straight and curved contour segments or, in brief, as a sequence of straights and curves. Two neighbouring straights or two neighbouring curves always, by definition, form a "corner" where they meet. Where they meet is also where we find the first kind of digitization; the corner point. If they were to form a smooth transition into one another then one could describe them as a single straight or a single curve.

Digitization points of the second kind are found on curves; curve points. They have the function of "aid points" and are set whenever the direction of the curve has changed by approximately 30 degrees. In addition, all local X and Y values at the extrema of contours are digitized with curve points. Thus, for example, in a circle these extrema would be the outermost left, right, upper and lower points.

The third sort of digitization is known as the "tangent point". Tangent points are used wherever a straight runs "tangentially" into a curve or vice versa. At a tangent point the straights or curves running in from the left or right thus have the same direction.

In order to be able to identify the beginnings of contours within a figure the IK format has a fourth sort of digitization, the start point. In order to "properly" identify a start point, the start point to is digitized again at the end of a contour with its normal identification.

The values of X and Y coordinates are limited to an upper value 32,767. The various identifications in the IK format are derived as follows:

Point type	Internal ident.	Change of X coordinate	Change of Y coordinate
Start	12	$-(X+1)$	$Y-YMIN+1$
Corner	13	$-(X+1)$	$-(Y-YMIN+1)$
Curve	14	$X+1$	$Y-YMIN+1$
Tangent	15	$X+1$	$-(Y-YMIN+1)$

The X and Y coordinates are stored in the smallest possible units. As a rule this is 1/100 mm (see also measurement unit in appendix G, character record).

In the URW archive all type fonts are stored with a standard cap height of 100 mm. This is achieved by either adjusting the original artwork to this value using repro prior to the digitization or, in so far as it appears to be sensible, with the help of software after digitization. All size details in IK format headers are taken to be measured in the said units.

One IK point is counted as one digitization.

3. Example of an IK format

First of all we represent the lower case letters a, b, c of the typeface "URW Antiqua 2015 normal", with marks. Subsequently the complete font format is reproduced as a data list.

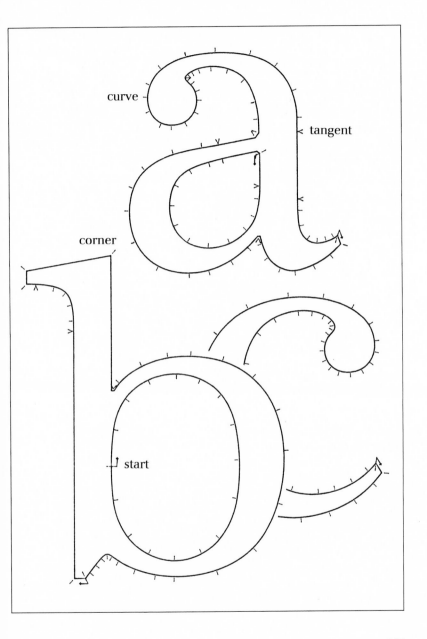

curve

tangent

corner

start

```
--------- ------------------ ------------------------------------------------
WORDNO.  |    CONTENT        |
         |                   |                    COMMENT
--------- ------------------ ------------------------------------------------
   1     |            477    | Length of font header
--------- ------------------ ------------------------------------------------
         | NAME SECTION
         | ------------
   2     |             55    | Length of name section
   3     |            825    | Number on URW list
 4 - 10  | AN201512.IK       | File name (ASCII)

11 - 49  |     URW-Antiqua 2000              | Font name (ASCII)
         |         normal

  50     |             IK    | Data format (ASCII)
51 - 53  |        4 12 85    | Production date:     4-Dec-85
54 - 56  |       15 12 86    | Date of last change: 15-Dec-86
--------- ------------------ ------------------------------------------------
         | FONT INFORMATION
         | ----------------
  57     |             12    | Length of font information
  58     |              1    | Indicator for font
  59     |            135    | Number of characters
  60     |          10000    | Cap height (in 1/100mm)
  61     |          15000    | Body size (in 1/100mm)
  62     |           7000    | x-height (in 1/100mm)
  63     |           3750    | Distance base line - lower body line(in 1/100mm)
  64     |          15000    | Text line distance for setting (in 1/100mm)
  65     |           1500    | Stem thickness (in 1/100mm)
  66     |              0    | Angle of italisation (in 1/10 degree)
  67     |             12    | Optimum point size for setting (in p)
  68     |           6521    | Average character width (in 1/100mm)
--------- ------------------ ------------------------------------------------
         | HIERARCHY SECTION
         | -----------------
  69     |              1    | No hierarchy section in this format
--------- ------------------ ------------------------------------------------
         | CHARACTER INDEX
         | ---------------
  70     |            408    | Length of character index
  71     |              9    | LENGTH OF FONT IN PHYSICAL RECORDS
  72     |            770    | Last word of last record

  73     |            101    | Character number:  1
  74     |              1    | Pointer to record containing start of character
  75     |            478    | Word pointer to start of character

  76     |            102    | Ch. no.: 2
  77     |              1    | Record pointer
  78     |            603    | Word pointer

79- 81   | 103   1  780  | No., record pointer, word pointer of ch.:     3
82- 84   | 104   1  889  | No., record pointer, word pointer of ch.:     4
85- 87   | 105   1 1010  | No., record pointer, word pointer of ch.:     5
88- 90   | 106   1 1149  | No., record pointer, word pointer of ch.:     6
91- 93   | 107   1 1282  | No., record pointer, word pointer of ch.:     7
94- 96   | 108   1 1427  | No., record pointer, word pointer of ch.:     8
97- 99   | 109   1 1600  | No., record pointer, word pointer of ch.:     9
100- 102 | 110   1 1693  | No., record pointer, word pointer of ch.:    10
103- 105 | 111   1 1784  | No., record pointer, word pointer of ch.:    11
106- 108 | 112   1 1947  | No., record pointer, word pointer of ch.:    12
--------- ------------------ ------------------------------------------------
```

WORDNO.	CONTENT		COMMENT
109- 111	113	1 2046	No., record pointer, word pointer of ch.: 13
112- 114	114	2 143	No., record pointer, word pointer of ch.: 14
115- 117	115	2 266	No., record pointer, word pointer of ch.: 15
118- 120	116	2 367	No., record pointer, word pointer of ch.: 16
121- 123	117	2 506	No., record pointer, word pointer of ch.: 17
124- 126	118	2 647	No., record pointer, word pointer of ch.: 18
127- 129	119	2 840	No., record pointer, word pointer of ch.: 19
130- 132	120	2 983	No., record pointer, word pointer of ch.: 20
133- 135	121	2 1084	No., record pointer, word pointer of ch.: 21
136- 138	122	2 1221	No., record pointer, word pointer of ch.: 22
139- 141	123	2 1316	No., record pointer, word pointer of ch.: 23
142- 144	124	2 1439	No., record pointer, word pointer of ch.: 24
145- 147	125	2 1612	No., record pointer, word pointer of ch.: 25
148- 150	126	2 1741	No., record pointer, word pointer of ch.: 26

WORDNO.	CONTENT		COMMENT
286- 288	502	6 659	No., record pointer, word pointer of ch.: 72
289- 291	503	6 794	No., record pointer, word pointer of ch.: 73
292- 294	504	6 927	No., record pointer, word pointer of ch.: 74
295- 297	505	6 1004	No., record pointer, word pointer of ch.: 75
298- 300	506	6 1155	No., record pointer, word pointer of ch.: 76
301- 303	507	6 1308	No., record pointer, word pointer of ch.: 77
304- 306	508	6 1397	No., record pointer, word pointer of ch.: 78
307- 309	509	6 1574	No., record pointer, word pointer of ch.: 79
310- 312	510	6 1729	No., record pointer, word pointer of ch.: 80
313- 315	511	6 1830	No., record pointer, word pointer of ch.: 81
316- 318	512	7 27	No., record pointer, word pointer of ch.: 82
319- 321	513	7 266	No., record pointer, word pointer of ch.: 83
322- 324	601	7 425	No., record pointer, word pointer of ch.: 84
325- 327	602	7 462	No., record pointer, word pointer of ch.: 85
328- 330	603	7 515	No., record pointer, word pointer of ch.: 86
331- 333	604	7 552	No., record pointer, word pointer of ch.: 87
334- 336	605	7 589	No., record pointer, word pointer of ch.: 88
337- 339	606	7 626	No., record pointer, word pointer of ch.: 89
340- 342	607	7 695	No., record pointer, word pointer of ch.: 90
343- 345	608	7 770	No., record pointer, word pointer of ch.: 91
346- 348	609	7 861	No., record pointer, word pointer of ch.: 92
349- 351	610	7 936	No., record pointer, word pointer of ch.: 93
352- 354	611	7 1011	No., record pointer, word pointer of ch.: 94
355- 357	612	7 1140	No., record pointer, word pointer of ch.: 95
358- 360	613	7 1269	No., record pointer, word pointer of ch.: 96

WORDNO.	CONTENT		COMMENT
463- 465	754	9 462	No., record pointer, word pointer of ch.: 131
466- 468	755	9 511	No., record pointer, word pointer of ch.: 132
469- 471	756	9 560	No., record pointer, word pointer of ch.: 133
472- 474	759	9 601	No., record pointer, word pointer of ch.: 134
475- 477	761	9 692	No., record pointer, word pointer of ch.: 135

WORDNO.	CONTENT	COMMENT
1	0	Records length of character
2	185	Words

NAME SECTION

3	3	Length of name section
4	301	Character number
5	0	Number of following part

SETTING INFORMATION

6	12	Length of setting information
7	1	Character type = letter
8	76	Number of digitizations
9	7710	Total set width (T=L+W+R)
10	550	Left side bearing (L)
11	7280	Width (W)
12	-120	Right side bearing (R)
13	0	X-minimum
14	7280	X-maximum
15	-150	Y-minimum
16	7150	Y-maximum
17	1	Unit is 1/100mm

CONTOUR INDEX

18	0	Records length of contour index
19	14	Words
20	0	Record pointer for 1. contour: 0
21	3	Word pointer : 34
22	-1	Sense of rotation of contour = clockwise
23	0	Nesting: outer 1. order
24	0	Colour inside: transparent
25	60	Number of digitizations
26	0	Record pointer for 2. contour: 0
27	123	Word pointer : 154
28	-1	Sense of rotation of contour = clockwise
29	1	Nesting: inner 1. order
30	0	Colour inside: transparent
31	16	Number of digitizations

IMAGE INFORMATION

32	0	Records		length of image information		
33	154	Words				
34- 35	-7184 1204	12	7183	1053	(K,X,Y)	1.DIG; typ: STRP
36- 37	-7281 -921	13	7280	770	(K,X,Y)	2.DIG; typ: -EP-
38- 39	6915 575	14	6914	424	(K,X,Y)	3.DIG; typ: .C..
40- 41	6343 234	14	6342	83	(K,X,Y)	4.DIG; typ: .C..
42- 43	5714 51	14	5713	-100	(K,X,Y)	5.DIG; typ: .C..
44- 45	5215 147	14	5214	-4	(K,X,Y)	6.DIG; typ: .C..
46- 47	4795 493	14	4794	342	(K,X,Y)	7.DIG; typ: .C..
48- 49	4583 952	14	4582	801	(K,X,Y)	8.DIG; typ: .C..
50- 51	-4513 -1204	13	4512	1053	(K,X,Y)	9.DIG; typ: -EP-

WORDNO.	CONTENT				COMMENT	
52- 53	-4428	-1204	13	4427	1053 (K,X,Y)	10.DIG; typ: -EP-
54- 55	4075	842	14	4074	691 (K,X,Y)	11.DIG; typ: .C..
56- 57	3491	406	14	3490	255 (K,X,Y)	12.DIG; typ: .C..
58- 59	2724	88	14	2723	-63 (K,X,Y)	13.DIG; typ: .C..
60- 61	2055	1	14	2054	-150 (K,X,Y)	14.DIG; typ: .C..
62- 63	99I	239	14	990	88 (K,X,Y)	15.DIG; typ: .C..
64- 65	196	1068	14	195	917 (K,X,Y)	16.DIG; typ: .C..
66- 67	1	2075	14	0	1924 (K,X,Y)	17.DIG; typ: .C..
68- 69	138	2820	14	137	2669 (K,X,Y)	18.DIG; typ: .C..
70- 71	542	3417	14	541	3266 (K,X,Y)	19.DIG; typ: .C..
72- 73	1530	3940	14	1529	3789 (K,X,Y)	20.DIG; typ: .C..
74- 75	2523	4150	14	2522	3999 (K,X,Y)	21.DIG; typ: .C..
76- 77	3094	-4240	15	3093	4089 (K,X,Y)	22.DIG; typ: >TP<
78- 79	-4370	-4469	13	4369	4318 (K,X,Y)	23.DIG; typ: -EP-
80- 81	-4491	-4635	13	4490	4484 (K,X,Y)	24.DIG; typ: -EP-
82- 83	4479	5086	14	4478	4935 (K,X,Y)	25.DIG; typ: .C..
84- 85	4385	5665	14	4384	5514 (K,X,Y)	26.DIG; typ: .C..
86- 87	4019	6424	14	4018	6273 (K,X,Y)	27.DIG; typ: .C..
88- 89	3442	6770	14	3441	6619 (K,X,Y)	28.DIG; typ: .C..
90- 91	2851	6849	14	2850	6698 (K,X,Y)	29.DIG; typ: .C..
92- 93	2421	6780	14	2420	6629 (K,X,Y)	30.DIG; typ: .C..
94- 95	2185	6685	14	2184	6534 (K,X,Y)	31.DIG; typ: .C..
96- 97	2050	6595	14	2049	6444 (K,X,Y)	32.DIG; typ: .C..
98- 99	1962	6476	14	1961	6325 (K,X,Y)	33.DIG; typ: .C..
100- 101	2025	6364	14	2024	6213 (K,X,Y)	34.DIG; typ: .C..
102- 103	2155	6237	14	2154	6086 (K,X,Y)	35.DIG; typ: .C..
104- 105	2302	6011	14	2301	5860 (K,X,Y)	36.DIG; typ: .C..
106- 107	2353	5734	14	2352	5583 (K,X,Y)	37.DIG; typ: .C..
108- 109	2256	5343	14	2255	5192 (K,X,Y)	38.DIG; typ: .C..
110- 111	1931	5010	14	1930	4859 (K,X,Y)	39.DIG; typ: .C..
112- 113	1469	4908	14	1468	4757 (K,X,Y)	40.DIG; typ: .C..
114- 115	1123	4979	14	1122	4828 (K,X,Y)	41.DIG; typ: .C..
116- 117	735	5384	14	734	5233 (K,X,Y)	42.DIG; typ: .C..
118- 119	654	5843	14	653	5692 (K,X,Y)	43.DIG; typ: .C..
120- 121	748	6240	14	747	6089 (K,X,Y)	44.DIG; typ: .C..
122- 123	1142	6761	14	1141	6610 (K,X,Y)	45.DIG; typ: .C..
124- 125	2001	7168	14	2000	7017 (K,X,Y)	46.DIG; typ: .C..
126- 127	3009	7301	14	3008	7150 (K,X,Y)	47.DIG; typ: .C..
128- 129	4198	7203	14	4197	7052 (K,X,Y)	48.DIG; typ: .C..
130- 131	5057	6815	14	5056	6664 (K,X,Y)	49.DIG; typ: .C..
132- 133	5641	6012	14	5640	5861 (K,X,Y)	50.DIG; typ: .C..
134- 135	5813	5130	14	5812	4979 (K,X,Y)	51.DIG; typ: .C..
136- 137	5813	-4657	15	5812	4506 (K,X,Y)	52.DIG; typ: >TP<
138- 139	5813	-2422	15	5812	2271 (K,X,Y)	53.DIG; typ: >TP<
140- 141	5820	2043	14	5819	1892 (K,X,Y)	54.DIG; typ: .C..
142- 143	5869	1528	14	5868	1377 (K,X,Y)	55.DIG; typ: .C..
144- 145	6135	1070	14	6134	919 (K,X,Y)	56.DIG; typ: .C..
146- 147	6482	959	14	6481	808 (K,X,Y)	57.DIG; typ: .C..
148- 149	6799	1011	14	6798	860 (K,X,Y)	58.DIG; typ: .C..
150- 151	7061	1121	14	7060	970 (K,X,Y)	59.DIG; typ: .C..
152- 153	-7184	-1204	13	7183	1053 (K,X,Y)	60.DIG; typ: -EP-
154- 155	-4513	3950	12	4512	3799 (K,X,Y)	61.DIG; typ: STRP
156- 157	4513	-2866	15	4512	2715 (K,X,Y)	62.DIG; typ: >TP<
158- 159	4488	2434	14	4487	2283 (K,X,Y)	63.DIG; typ: .C..
160- 161	4351	1832	14	4350	1681 (K,X,Y)	64.DIG; typ: .C..
162- 163	4056	1388	14	4055	1237 (K,X,Y)	65.DIG; typ: .C..
164- 165	3462	974	14	3461	823 (K,X,Y)	66.DIG; typ: .C..
166- 167	2718	822	14	2717	671 (K,X,Y)	67.DIG; typ: .C..
168- 169	1990	1023	14	1989	872 (K,X,Y)	68.DIG; typ: .C..

WORDNO.	CONTENT	COMMENT
170- 171	1521 1552	14 1520 1401 (K,X,Y) 69.DIG; typ: .C..
172- 173	1390 2238	14 1389 2087 (K,X,Y) 70.DIG; typ: .C..
174- 175	1555 2933	14 1554 2782 (K,X,Y) 71.DIG; typ: .C..
176- 177	2076 3437	14 2075 3286 (K,X,Y) 72.DIG; typ: .C..
178- 179	2751 3675	14 2750 3524 (K,X,Y) 73.DIG; typ: .C..
180- 181	3226 3790	14 3225 3639 (K,X,Y) 74.DIG; typ: .C..
182- 183	-4420 -4019	13 4419 3868 (K,X,Y) 75.DIG; typ: -EP-
184- 185	-4513 -3950	13 4512 3799 (K,X,Y) 76.DIG; typ: -EP-

WORDNO.	CONTENT	COMMENT
1	0	Records length of character
2	135	Words

NAME SECTION

3	3	Length of name section
4	302	Character number
5	0	Number of following part

SETTING INFORMATION

6	12	Length of setting information
7	1	Character type = letter
8	51	Number of digitizations
9	9637	Total set width (T=L+W+R)
10	0	Left side bearing (L)
11	8887	Width (W)
12	750	Right side bearing (R)
13	0	X-minimum
14	8887	X-maximum
15	-200	Y-minimum
16	10500	Y-maximum
17	1	Unit is 1/100mm

CONTOUR INDEX

18	0	Records length of contour index
19	14	Words
20	0	Record pointer for 1. contour: 0
21	3	Word pointer : 34
22	-1	Sense of rotation of contour = clockwise
23	0	Nesting: outer 1. order
24	0	Colour inside: transparent
25	34	Number of digitizations
26	0	Record pointer for 2. contour: 0
27	71	Word pointer : 102
28	-1	Sense of rotation of contour = clockwise
29	1	Nesting: inner 1. order
30	0	Colour inside: transparent
31	17	Number of digitizations

```
        IMAGE INFORMATION
        ----------------
   32                    0  | Records     length of image information
   33                  104  | Words

   34- 35   -2005       1   | 12   2004   -200 (K,X,Y)     1.DIG; typ: STRP
   36- 37   -1629      -1   | 13   1628   -200 (K,X,Y)     2.DIG; typ: -EP-
   38- 39    1629   -8197   | 15   1628   7996 (K,X,Y)     3.DIG; typ: >TP<
   40- 41    1627    8536   | 14   1626   8335 (K,X,Y)     4.DIG; typ: .C..
   42- 43    1571    9067   | 14   1570   8866 (K,X,Y)     5.DIG; typ: .C..
   44- 45    1363    9479   | 14   1362   9278 (K,X,Y)     6.DIG; typ: .C..
   46- 47     954    9679   | 14    953   9478 (K,X,Y)     7.DIG; typ: .C..
   48- 49     326   -9762   | 15    325   9561 (K,X,Y)     8.DIG; typ: >TP<
   50- 51      -1   -9771   | 13      0   9570 (K,X,Y)     9.DIG; typ: -EP-
```

AN201512.IK   20-MAR-87   PAGE   9

WORDNO.	CONTENT		COMMENT	
52- 53	-1 -10201	13 0 10000 (K,X,Y)	10.DIG; typ: -EP-	
54- 55	-2929 -10701	13 2928 10500 (K,X,Y)	11.DIG; typ: -EP-	
56- 57	-2929 -6217	13 2928 6016 (K,X,Y)	12.DIG; typ: -EP-	
58- 59	-3023 -6217	13 3022 6016 (K,X,Y)	13.DIG; typ: -EP-	
60- 61	3211 6467	14 3210 6266 (K,X,Y)	14.DIG; typ: .C..	
62- 63	3975 7021	14 3974 6820 (K,X,Y)	15.DIG; typ: .C..	
64- 65	4883 7304	14 4882 7103 (K,X,Y)	16.DIG; typ: .C..	
66- 67	5680 7351	14 5679 7150 (K,X,Y)	17.DIG; typ: .C..	
68- 69	6775 7182	14 6774 6981 (K,X,Y)	18.DIG; typ: .C..	
70- 71	7811 6619	14 7810 6418 (K,X,Y)	19.DIG; typ: .C..	
72- 73	8609 5518	14 8608 5317 (K,X,Y)	20.DIG; typ: .C..	
74- 75	8888 4212	14 8887 4011 (K,X,Y)	21.DIG; typ: .C..	
76- 77	8673 2466	14 8672 2265 (K,X,Y)	22.DIG; typ: .C..	
78- 79	7809 987	14 7808 786 (K,X,Y)	23.DIG; typ: .C..	
80- 81	6539 257	14 6538 56 (K,X,Y)	24.DIG; typ: .C..	
82- 83	5068 51	14 5067 -150 (K,X,Y)	25.DIG; typ: .C..	
84- 85	4418 114	14 4417 -87 (K,X,Y)	26.DIG; typ: .C..	
86- 87	3719 299	14 3718 98 (K,X,Y)	27.DIG; typ: .C..	
88- 89	3161 573	14 3160 372 (K,X,Y)	28.DIG; typ: .C..	
90- 91	2930 728	14 2929 527 (K,X,Y)	29.DIG; typ: .C..	
92- 93	2754 800	14 2753 599 (K,X,Y)	30.DIG; typ: .C..	
94- 95	2545 664	14 2544 463 (K,X,Y)	31.DIG; typ: .C..	
96- 97	2354 444	14 2353 243 (K,X,Y)	32.DIG; typ: .C..	
98- 99	2153 192	14 2152 -9 (K,X,Y)	33.DIG; typ: .C..	
100- 101	-2005 -1	13 2004 -200 (K,X,Y)	34.DIG; typ: -EP-	
102- 103	-2909 3706	12 2908 3505 (K,X,Y)	35.DIG; typ: STRP	
104- 105	2995 4933	14 2994 4732 (K,X,Y)	36.DIG; typ: .C..	
106- 107	3404 5949	14 3403 5748 (K,X,Y)	37.DIG; typ: .C..	
108- 109	4197 6571	14 4196 6370 (K,X,Y)	38.DIG; typ: .C..	
110- 111	5182 6769	14 5181 6568 (K,X,Y)	39.DIG; typ: .C..	
112- 113	6000 6596	14 5999 6395 (K,X,Y)	40.DIG; typ: .C..	
114- 115	6732 6071	14 6731 5870 (K,X,Y)	41.DIG; typ: .C..	
116- 117	7202 5096	14 7201 4895 (K,X,Y)	42.DIG; typ: .C..	
118- 119	7347 3907	14 7346 3706 (K,X,Y)	43.DIG; typ: .C..	
120- 121	7263 2627	14 7262 2426 (K,X,Y)	44.DIG; typ: .C..	
122- 123	6656 1291	14 6655 1090 (K,X,Y)	45.DIG; typ: .C..	
124- 125	6026 803	14 6025 602 (K,X,Y)	46.DIG; typ: .C..	
126- 127	5076 574	14 5075 373 (K,X,Y)	47.DIG; typ: .C..	
128- 129	4179 795	14 4178 594 (K,X,Y)	48.DIG; typ: .C..	
130- 131	3468 1359	14 3467 1158 (K,X,Y)	49.DIG; typ: .C..	
132- 133	2973 2581	14 2972 2380 (K,X,Y)	50.DIG; typ: .C..	
134- 135	2909 3706	14 2908 3505 (K,X,Y)	51.DIG; typ: .C..	

WORDNO.	CONTENT		COMMENT
1 2	0 119		Records length of character Words
NAME SECTION			
3 4 5	3 303 0		Length of name section Character number Number of following part
SETTING INFORMATION			
6 7 8 9 10 11 12 13 14 15 16 17	12 1 46 7407 749 6249 409 0 6249 -150 7150 1		Length of setting information Character type = letter Number of digitizations Total set width (T=L+W+R) Left side bearing (L) Width (W) Right side bearing (R) X-minimum X-maximum Y-minimum Y-maximum Unit is 1/100mm
CONTOUR INDEX			
18 19	0 8		Records length of contour index Words
20 21 22 23 24 25	0 3 -1 0 0 46		Record pointer for 1. contour: 0 Word pointer : 28 Sense of rotation of contour = clockwise Nesting: outer 1. order Colour inside: transparent Number of digitizations
IMAGE INFORMATION			
26 27	0 94		Records length of image information Words

	CONTENT			COMMENT	
28- 29	-6003	1593	12	6002	1442 (K,X,Y) 1.DIG; typ: STRP
30- 31	-6173	-1263	13	6172	1112 (K,X,Y) 2.DIG; typ: -EP-
32- 33	5848	940	14	5847	789 (K,X,Y) 3.DIG; typ: .C..
34- 35	5145	455	14	5144	304 (K,X,Y) 4.DIG; typ: .C..
36- 37	4258	122	14	4257	-29 (K,X,Y) 5.DIG; typ: .C..
38- 39	3283	1	14	3282	-150 (K,X,Y) 6.DIG; typ: .C..
40- 41	2117	206	14	2116	55 (K,X,Y) 7.DIG; typ: .C..
42- 43	1081	854	14	1080	703 (K,X,Y) 8.DIG; typ: .C..
44- 45	281	2101	14	280	1950 (K,X,Y) 9.DIG; typ: .C..
46- 47	1	3691	14	0	3540 (K,X,Y) 10.DIG; typ: .C..
48- 49	245	5183	14	244	5032 (K,X,Y) 11.DIG; typ: .C..
50- 51	862	6244	14	861	6093 (K,X,Y) 12.DIG; typ: .C..
52- 53	1982	7030	14	1981	6879 (K,X,Y) 13.DIG; typ: .C..
54- 55	3397	7301	14	3396	7150 (K,X,Y) 14.DIG; typ: .C..
56- 57	4589	7172	14	4588	7021 (K,X,Y) 15.DIG; typ: .C..
58- 59	5541	6763	14	5540	6612 (K,X,Y) 16.DIG; typ: .C..

WORDNO.	CONTENT		COMMENT
60- 61	6097 6192	14 6096 6041 (K,X,Y)	17.DIG; typ: .C..
62- 63	6250 5644	14 6249 5493 (K,X,Y)	18.DIG; typ: .C..
64- 65	6209 5289	14 6208 5138 (K,X,Y)	19.DIG; typ: .C..
66- 67	6023 4964	14 6022 4813 (K,X,Y)	20.DIG; typ: .C..
68- 69	5724 4748	14 5723 4597 (K,X,Y)	21.DIG; typ: .C..
70- 71	5335 4674	14 5334 4523 (K,X,Y)	22.DIG; typ: .C..
72- 73	4962 4743	14 4961 4592 (K,X,Y)	23.DIG; typ: .C..
74- 75	4712 4913	14 4711 4762 (K,X,Y)	24.DIG; typ: .C..
76- 77	4561 5147	14 4560 4996 (K,X,Y)	25.DIG; typ: .C..
78- 79	4510 5449	14 4509 5298 (K,X,Y)	26.DIG; typ: .C..
80- 81	4565 5716	14 4564 5565 (K,X,Y)	27.DIG; typ: .C..
82- 83	4710 5936	14 4709 5785 (K,X,Y)	28.DIG; typ: .C..
84- 85	4858 6084	14 4857 5933 (K,X,Y)	29.DIG; typ: .C..
86- 87	4916 6254	14 4915 6103 (K,X,Y)	30.DIG; typ: .C..
88- 89	4830 6432	14 4829 6281 (K,X,Y)	31.DIG; typ: .C..
90- 91	4588 6637	14 4587 6486 (K,X,Y)	32.DIG; typ: .C..
92- 93	4192 6788	14 4191 6637 (K,X,Y)	33.DIG; typ: .C..
94- 95	3707 6840	14 3706 6689 (K,X,Y)	34.DIG; typ: .C..
96- 97	2844 6658	14 2843 6507 (K,X,Y)	35.DIG; typ: .C..
98- 99	2216 6226	14 2215 6075 (K,X,Y)	36.DIG; typ: .C..
100- 101	1703 5248	14 1702 5097 (K,X,Y)	37.DIG; typ: .C..

GRAND TOTAL

	WORDS	KBYTES
Length of font:	17154	34.308
Length of font header:	477	0.954
Length of all character headers:	3927	7.854
Length of total image information:	12750	25.500

DIGITIZATIONS	NUMBER
Start points:	227
Corner points:	1306
Curve points:	4232
Tangent points:	475
Total:	6240

Characters:	135
Records (a 2048 words):	9

Raster (grid):	15000 X 15000

Digitizations per character:	46
Image information per character:	188 bytes

Appendix J
Description of the DI format

1. Structure of a DI font
The structure of a DI font is as described in appendix G.

2. Description of the DI format
Because most graphic display terminals and NC machines (plotters) have hardware and software to decode and raster straight and circular line commands as given by the host computer, we have created a general, binary **display format.**

This is a closed contour format (as is the IK format) which describes the contours of any arbitrary flat surface as a sequence of straights and arcs.

With regard to typesetters using circular and straight line interpolation, and for drawing machines which can only address a certain grid resolution with line commands, this format may also be supplied with all positions of straights and arcs matching points within the corresponding equipment grid.

This display format describes a contour such that it contains the coordinates of the end points of all straights and arcs, and radii and direction of arc rotation in a binary form. Special command codes for the various codes of certain machine types (e.g. in ASCII) can be easily derived with the aid of a simple converter program (as a post processor). In a similar manner such a post processor needs to be programmed with only simple formulae from elementary geometry, in order to be able to generate other determinant arc parameters for these machine types from the data supplied (e.g. instead of end point and radius: angle interval, start angle and direction of tangent).

Each character has its own coordinate system with the X zero point at the X minimum of the character, and the Y zero point on the base line.

Straights are described using three words (K, X, Y) in which the identification $K = 100$ applies to non-visible straights (movement of writing head without writing) and where $K = 200$ applies to visible straights. Circles are described in 5 words (K, X, Y, R); where $K = 300$.

X and Y are the absolute X and Y positions of the circle segment end points in the character coordinate system. R is the radius of the circle, in a double word form (INTEGER × 4).
The sign of the R gives the direction (sense) of rotation of the circle: positive R means an anti-clockwise direction (mathematically right).
The DI format is calculated from the IK format. For the purposes of easy reconversion, the identification K of a point which was also an IK point is raised by the IK identification.
Thus, DI identifications are:
K = 112 for starting points,
K = 200, 213, 214, 215 for straight end points,
K = 300, 313, 314, 315 for arc segment end points.
The cap height is set to the standard value of 100 mm unless otherwise provided.
Each straight and each arc is counted as one digitization.

3. Example of a DI format

First of all we represent the lower case letters a, b, c of the typeface "URW Antiqua 2015 normal", with marks. Subsequently the complete font format is reproduced as a data list.

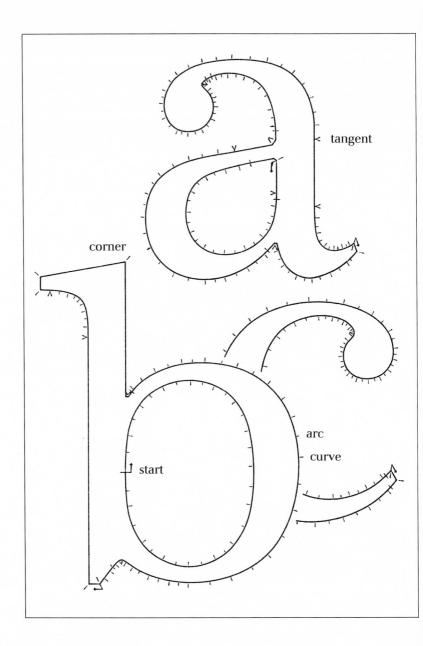

tangent

corner

arc

curve

start

WORDNO.	CONTENT	COMMENT
1	477	Length of font header

NAME SECTION

2	55	Length of name section
3	825	Number on URW list
4 - 10	AN201512.DI	File name (ASCII)
11 - 49	URW-Antiqua 2000 normal	Font name (ASCII)
50	DI	Data format (ASCII)
51 - 53	20 3 87	Production date: 20-Mar-87
54 - 56	20 3 87	Date of last change: 20-Mar-87

FONT INFORMATION

57	12	Length of font information
58	1	Indicator for font
59	135	Number of characters
60	10000	Cap height (in 1/100mm)
61	15000	Body size (in 1/100mm)
62	7000	x-height (in 1/100mm)
63	3750	Distance base line - lower body line(in 1/100mm)
64	15000	Text line distance for setting (in 1/100mm)
65	1500	Stem thickness (in 1/100mm)
66	0	Angle of italisation (in 1/10 degree)
67	12	Optimum point size for setting (in p)
68	6521	Average character width (in 1/100mm)

HIERARCHY SECTION

69	1	No hierarchy section in this format

CHARACTER INDEX

70	408	Length of character index
71	25	LENGTH OF FONT IN PHYSICAL RECORDS
72	1210	Last word of last record
73	101	Character number: 1
74	1	Pointer to record containing start of character
75	478	Word pointer to start of character
76	102	Ch. no.: 2
77	1	Record pointer
78	752	Word pointer
79- 81	103 1 1267	No., record pointer, word pointer of ch.: 3
82- 84	104 1 1639	No., record pointer, word pointer of ch.: 4
85- 87	105 1 1968	No., record pointer, word pointer of ch.: 5
88- 90	106 2 248	No., record pointer, word pointer of ch.: 6
91- 93	107 2 558	No., record pointer, word pointer of ch.: 7
94- 96	108 2 1053	No., record pointer, word pointer of ch.: 8
97- 99	109 2 1459	No., record pointer, word pointer of ch.: 9
100- 102	110 2 1665	No., record pointer, word pointer of ch.: 10
103- 105	111 2 1904	No., record pointer, word pointer of ch.: 11
106- 108	112 3 247	No., record pointer, word pointer of ch.: 12

WORDNO.	CONTENT		COMMENT	
109- 111	113	3 477	No., record pointer, word pointer of ch.:	13
112- 114	114	3 816	No., record pointer, word pointer of ch.:	14
115- 117	115	3 1111	No., record pointer, word pointer of ch.:	15
118- 120	116	3 1470	No., record pointer, word pointer of ch.:	16
121- 123	117	3 1843	No., record pointer, word pointer of ch.:	17
124- 126	118	4 313	No., record pointer, word pointer of ch.:	18
127- 129	119	4 905	No., record pointer, word pointer of ch.:	19
130- 132	120	4 1408	No., record pointer, word pointer of ch.:	20
133- 135	121	4 1641	No., record pointer, word pointer of ch.:	21
136- 138	122	5 6	No., record pointer, word pointer of ch.:	22
139- 141	123	5 230	No., record pointer, word pointer of ch.:	23
142- 144	124	5 520	No., record pointer, word pointer of ch.:	24
145- 147	125	5 967	No., record pointer, word pointer of ch.:	25
148- 150	126	5 1282	No., record pointer, word pointer of ch.:	26
151- 153	127	5 1446	No., record pointer, word pointer of ch.:	27
154- 156	128	5 1909	No., record pointer, word pointer of ch.:	28
157- 159	129	6 370	No., record pointer, word pointer of ch.:	29
160- 162	201	6 834	No., record pointer, word pointer of ch.:	30
163- 165	208	6 1207	No., record pointer, word pointer of ch.:	31
166- 168	210	6 1580	No., record pointer, word pointer of ch.:	32
169- 171	237	7 88	No., record pointer, word pointer of ch.:	33
172- 174	251	7 705	No., record pointer, word pointer of ch.:	34
175- 177	301	7 1376	No., record pointer, word pointer of ch.:	35
178- 180	302	7 2029	No., record pointer, word pointer of ch.:	36

WORDNO.	CONTENT		COMMENT	
286- 288	502	16 924	No., record pointer, word pointer of ch.:	72
289- 291	503	16 1412	No., record pointer, word pointer of ch.:	73
292- 294	504	16 1862	No., record pointer, word pointer of ch.:	74
295- 297	505	16 1961	No., record pointer, word pointer of ch.:	75
298- 300	506	17 453	No., record pointer, word pointer of ch.:	76
301- 303	507	17 1047	No., record pointer, word pointer of ch.:	77
304- 306	508	17 1275	No., record pointer, word pointer of ch.:	78
307- 309	509	17 1961	No., record pointer, word pointer of ch.:	79
310- 312	510	18 524	No., record pointer, word pointer of ch.:	80
313- 315	511	18 883	No., record pointer, word pointer of ch.:	81
316- 318	512	18 1770	No., record pointer, word pointer of ch.:	82
319- 321	513	19 501	No., record pointer, word pointer of ch.:	83
322- 324	601	19 979	No., record pointer, word pointer of ch.:	84
325- 327	602	19 1049	No., record pointer, word pointer of ch.:	85
328- 330	603	19 1168	No., record pointer, word pointer of ch.:	86
331- 333	604	19 1238	No., record pointer, word pointer of ch.:	87

WORDNO.	CONTENT		COMMENT	
463- 465	754	25 466	No., record pointer, word pointer of ch.:	131
466- 468	755	25 575	No., record pointer, word pointer of ch.:	132
469- 471	756	25 684	No., record pointer, word pointer of ch.:	133
472- 474	759	25 732	No., record pointer, word pointer of ch.:	134
475- 477	761	25 1003	No., record pointer, word pointer of ch.:	135

WORDNO.	CONTENT	COMMENT
1	0	Records length of character
2	653	Words

NAME SECTION

3	3	Length of name section
4	301	Character number
5	0	Number of following part

SETTING INFORMATION

6	12	Length of setting information
7	1	Character type = letter
8	136	Number of DI-points
9	7710	Total set width (T=L+W+R)
10	550	Left side bearing (L)
11	7280	Width (W)
12	-120	Right side bearing (R)
13	0	X-minimum
14	7280	X-maximum
15	-150	Y-minimum
16	7150	Y-maximum
17	1	Unit is 1/100mm

CONTOUR INDEX

18	0	Records length of contour index
19	14	Words
20	0	Record pointer for 1. contour: 0
21	3	Word pointer : 34
22	-1	Sense of rotation of contour = clockwise
23	0	Nesting: outer 1. order
24	0	Colour inside: transparent
25	108	Number of digitizations
26	0	Record pointer for 2. contour: 0
27	499	Word pointer : 530
28	-1	Sense of rotation of contour = clockwise
29	1	Nesting: inner 1. order
30	0	Colour inside: transparent
31	28	Number of digitizations

IMAGE INFORMATION

32			0	Records lenght of image information
33			622	Words
34 - 36	112	7183	1053	(K,X,Y); 1. DIG; typ: STRP
37 - 39	213	7280	770	(K,X,Y); 2. DIG; typ: vector
40 - 42	200	7040	533	(K,X,Y); 3. DIG; typ: vector
43 - 45	214	6914	424	(K,X,Y); 4. DIG; typ: vector
46 - 50	300	6650	241	-2362	(K,X,Y,R); 5. DIG; typ: circle
51 - 55	314	6342	83	-2737	(K,X,Y,R); 6. DIG; typ: circle
56 - 60	300	5979	-48	-3017	(K,X,Y,R); 7. DIG; typ: circle
61 - 65	314	5713	-100	-1490	(K,X,Y,R); 8. DIG; typ: circle
66 - 70	300	5481	-90	-800	(K,X,Y,R); 9. DIG; typ: circle

229

WORDNO.	CONTENT				COMMENT
71 - 75	314	5214	-4	-1170	(K,X,Y,R); 10. DIG; typ: circle
76 - 80	300	4970	149	-1118	(K,X,Y,R); 11. DIG; typ: circle
81 - 85	314	4794	342	-915	(K,X,Y,R); 12. DIG; typ: circle
86 - 90	300	4677	549	-1458	(K,X,Y,R); 13. DIG; typ: circle
91 - 95	314	4582	801	-1880	(K,X,Y,R); 14. DIG; typ: circle
96 - 98	213	4512	1053		(K,X,Y); 15. DIG; typ: vector
99 -101	213	4427	1053		(K,X,Y); 16. DIG; typ: vector
102 -104	200	4195	809		(K,X,Y); 17. DIG; typ: vector
105 -107	214	4074	691		(K,X,Y); 18. DIG; typ: vector
108 -112	300	3789	453	-3431	(K,X,Y,R); 19. DIG; typ: circle
113 -117	314	3490	255	-3212	(K,X,Y,R); 20. DIG; typ: circle
118 -122	300	3109	66	-3116	(K,X,Y,R); 21. DIG; typ: circle
123 -127	314	2723	-63	-2864	(K,X,Y,R); 22. DIG; typ: circle
128 -132	300	2391	-127	-2784	(K,X,Y,R); 23. DIG; typ: circle
133 -137	314	2054	-150	-2793	(K,X,Y,R); 24. DIG; typ: circle
138 -142	300	1484	-89	-2518	(K,X,Y,R); 25. DIG; typ: circle
143 -147	314	990	88	-2108	(K,X,Y,R); 26. DIG; typ: circle
148 -152	300	515	440	-1766	(K,X,Y,R); 27. DIG; typ: circle
153 -157	314	195	917	-1660	(K,X,Y,R); 28. DIG; typ: circle
158 -162	300	45	1393	-2216	(K,X,Y,R); 29. DIG; typ: circle
163 -167	314	0	1924	-2522	(K,X,Y,R); 30. DIG; typ: circle
168 -172	300	40	2322	-2477	(K,X,Y,R); 31. DIG; typ: circle
173 -177	314	137	2669	-2015	(K,X,Y,R); 32. DIG; typ: circle
178 -182	300	314	3010	-1646	(K,X,Y,R); 33. DIG; typ: circle
183 -187	314	541	3266	-1307	(K,X,Y,R); 34. DIG; typ: circle
188 -192	300	992	3575	-2420	(K,X,Y,R); 35. DIG; typ: circle
193 -197	314	1529	3789	-2708	(K,X,Y,R); 36. DIG; typ: circle
198 -202	300	1985	3901	-7283	(K,X,Y,R); 37. DIG; typ: circle
203 -207	314	2522	3999	-9806	(K,X,Y,R); 38. DIG; typ: circle
208 -210	215	3093	4089		(K,X,Y); 39. DIG; typ: vector
211 -213	213	4369	4318		(K,X,Y); 40. DIG; typ: vector
214 -216	213	4490	4484		(K,X,Y); 41. DIG; typ: vector
217 -219	200	4485	4785		(K,X,Y); 42. DIG; typ: vector
220 -222	214	4478	4935		(K,X,Y); 43. DIG; typ: vector
223 -227	300	4444	5225	3297	(K,X,Y,R); 44. DIG; typ: circle
228 -232	314	4384	5514	3362	(K,X,Y,R); 45. DIG; typ: circle
233 -237	300	4216	5975	2451	(K,X,Y,R); 46. DIG; typ: circle
238 -242	314	4018	6273	1300	(K,X,Y,R); 47. DIG; typ: circle
243 -247	300	3789	6463	978	(K,X,Y,R); 48. DIG; typ: circle
248 -252	314	3441	6619	1608	(K,X,Y,R); 49. DIG; typ: circle
253 -257	300	3151	6683	1757	(K,X,Y,R); 50. DIG; typ: circle
258 -262	314	2850	6698	1799	(K,X,Y,R); 51. DIG; typ: circle
263 -267	300	2628	6676	1796	(K,X,Y,R); 52. DIG; typ: circle
268 -272	314	2420	6629	1629	(K,X,Y,R); 53. DIG; typ: circle
273 -275	200	2289	6583		(K,X,Y); 54. DIG; typ: vector
276 -278	214	2184	6534		(K,X,Y); 55. DIG; typ: vector
279 -281	200	2115	6492		(K,X,Y); 56. DIG; typ: vector
282 -284	214	2049	6444		(K,X,Y); 57. DIG; typ: vector
285 -289	300	1976	6368	415	(K,X,Y,R); 58. DIG; typ: circle
290 -294	314	1961	6325	79	(K,X,Y,R); 59. DIG; typ: circle
295 -299	300	1971	6282	80	(K,X,Y,R); 60. DIG; typ: circle
300 -304	314	2024	6213	306	(K,X,Y,R); 61. DIG; typ: circle
305 -307	214	2154	6086		(K,X,Y); 62. DIG; typ: vector
308 -312	300	2237	5985	-593	(K,X,Y,R); 63. DIG; typ: circle
313 -317	314	2301	5860	-691	(K,X,Y,R); 64. DIG; typ: circle
318 -322	300	2339	5726	-732	(K,X,Y,R); 65. DIG; typ: circle
323 -327	314	2352	5583	-777	(K,X,Y,R); 66. DIG; typ: circle
328 -332	300	2327	5380	-851	(K,X,Y,R); 67. DIG; typ: circle
333 -337	314	2255	5192	-832	(K,X,Y,R); 68. DIG; typ: circle

WORDNO.	CONTENT			COMMENT
338 -342	300	2110	4993	-862	(K,X,Y,R); 69. DIG; typ: circle
343 -347	314	1930	4859	-713	(K,X,Y,R); 70. DIG; typ: circle
348 -352	300	1720	4782	-849	(K,X,Y,R); 71. DIG; typ: circle
353 -357	314	1468	4757	-1083	(K,X,Y,R); 72. DIG; typ: circle
358 -362	300	1273	4778	-1058	(K,X,Y,R); 73. DIG; typ: circle
363 -367	314	1122	4828	-693	(K,X,Y,R); 74. DIG; typ: circle
368 -372	300	897	4988	-741	(K,X,Y,R); 75. DIG; typ: circle
373 -377	314	734	5233	-839	(K,X,Y,R); 76. DIG; typ: circle
378 -382	300	667	5454	-977	(K,X,Y,R); 77. DIG; typ: circle
383 -387	314	653	5692	-1036	(K,X,Y,R); 78. DIG; typ: circle
388 -392	300	682	5891	-1139	(K,X,Y,R); 79. DIG; typ: circle
393 -397	314	747	6089	-1220	(K,X,Y,R); 80. DIG; typ: circle
398 -402	300	919	6386	-1408	(K,X,Y,R); 81. DIG; typ: circle
403 -407	314	1141	6610	-1193	(K,X,Y,R); 82. DIG; typ: circle
408 -412	300	1541	6855	-2182	(K,X,Y,R); 83. DIG; typ: circle
413 -417	314	2000	7017	-2345	(K,X,Y,R); 84. DIG; typ: circle
418 -422	300	2482	7106	-4739	(K,X,Y,R); 85. DIG; typ: circle
423 -427	314	3008	7150	-5505	(K,X,Y,R); 86. DIG; typ: circle
428 -432	300	3631	7135	-5309	(K,X,Y,R); 87. DIG; typ: circle
433 -437	314	4197	7052	-4472	(K,X,Y,R); 88. DIG; typ: circle
438 -442	300	4675	6895	-2353	(K,X,Y,R); 89. DIG; typ: circle
443 -447	314	5056	6664	-1852	(K,X,Y,R); 90. DIG; typ: circle
448 -452	300	5399	6308	-1796	(K,X,Y,R); 91. DIG; typ: circle
453 -457	314	5640	5861	-1888	(K,X,Y,R); 92. DIG; typ: circle
458 -462	300	5772	5396	-2904	(K,X,Y,R); 93. DIG; typ: circle
463 -467	314	5812	4979	-2177	(K,X,Y,R); 94. DIG; typ: circle
468 -470	215	5812	4506		(K,X,Y); 95. DIG; typ: vector
471 -473	215	5812	2271		(K,X,Y); 96. DIG; typ: vector
474 -476	214	5819	1892		(K,X,Y); 97. DIG; typ: vector
477 -481	300	5838	1592	4908	(K,X,Y,R); 98. DIG; typ: circle
482 -486	314	5868	1377	2548	(K,X,Y,R); 99. DIG; typ: circle
487 -491	300	5969	1102	851	(K,X,Y,R); 100. DIG; typ: circle
492 -496	314	6134	919	599	(K,X,Y,R); 101. DIG; typ: circle
497 -501	300	6299	835	577	(K,X,Y,R); 102. DIG; typ: circle
502 -506	314	6481	808	574	(K,X,Y,R); 103. DIG; typ: circle
507 -511	300	6632	821	1012	(K,X,Y,R); 104. DIG; typ: circle
512 -516	314	6798	860	1285	(K,X,Y,R); 105. DIG; typ: circle
517 -521	300	6951	915	1597	(K,X,Y,R); 106. DIG; typ: circle
522 -526	314	7060	970	891	(K,X,Y,R); 107. DIG; typ: circle
527 -529	213	7183	1053		(K,X,Y); 108. DIG; typ: vector
530 -532	112	4512	3799		(K,X,Y); 109. DIG; typ: STRP
533 -535	215	4512	2715		(K,X,Y); 110. DIG; typ: vector
536 -538	200	4506	2503		(K,X,Y); 111. DIG; typ: vector
539 -541	214	4487	2283		(K,X,Y); 112. DIG; typ: vector
542 -546	300	4427	1930	-3242	(K,X,Y,R); 113. DIG; typ: circle
547 -551	314	4350	1681	-1713	(K,X,Y,R); 114. DIG; typ: circle
552 -556	300	4237	1465	-1159	(K,X,Y,R); 115. DIG; typ: circle
557 -561	314	4055	1237	-1667	(K,X,Y,R); 116. DIG; typ: circle
562 -566	300	3780	1002	-1809	(K,X,Y,R); 117. DIG; typ: circle
567 -571	314	3461	823	-1853	(K,X,Y,R); 118. DIG; typ: circle
572 -576	300	3095	707	-1840	(K,X,Y,R); 119. DIG; typ: circle
577 -581	314	2717	671	-1791	(K,X,Y,R); 120. DIG; typ: circle
582 -586	300	2320	727	-1553	(K,X,Y,R); 121. DIG; typ: circle
587 -591	314	1989	872	-1263	(K,X,Y,R); 122. DIG; typ: circle
592 -596	300	1707	1110	-1283	(K,X,Y,R); 123. DIG; typ: circle
597 -601	314	1520	1401	-1122	(K,X,Y,R); 124. DIG; typ: circle
602 -606	300	1417	1731	-1524	(K,X,Y,R); 125. DIG; typ: circle
607 -611	314	1389	2087	-1623	(K,X,Y,R); 126. DIG; typ: circle
612 -616	300	1442	2485	-1997	(K,X,Y,R); 127. DIG; typ: circle

WORDNO.	CONTENT				COMMENT
617 -621	314	1554	2782	-1248	(K,X,Y,R); 128. DIG; typ: circle
622 -626	300	1775	3076	-1178	(K,X,Y,R); 129. DIG; typ: circle
627 -631	314	2075	3286	-1161	(K,X,Y,R); 130. DIG; typ: circle
632 -636	300	2367	3408	-2787	(K,X,Y,R); 131. DIG; typ: circle
637 -641	314	2750	3524	-4469	(K,X,Y,R); 132. DIG; typ: circle
642 -644	214	3225	3639		(K,X,Y); 133. DIG; typ: vector
645 -647	200	3621	3722		(K,X,Y); 134. DIG; typ: vector
648 -650	213	4419	3868		(K,X,Y); 135. DIG; typ: vector
651 -653	213	4512	3799		(K,X,Y); 136. DIG; typ: vector

WORDNO.	CONTENT	COMMENT
1	0	Records length of character
2	444	Words

NAME SECTION

3	3	Length of name section
4	302	Character number
5	0	Number of following part

SETTING INFORMATION

6	12	Length of setting information
7	1	Character type = letter
8	89	Number of DI-points
9	9637	Total set width (T=L+W+R)
10	0	Left side bearing (L)
11	8887	Width (W)
12	750	Right side bearing (R)
13	0	X-minimum
14	8887	X-maximum
15	-200	Y-minimum
16	10500	Y-maximum
17	1	Unit is 1/100mm

CONTOUR INDEX

18	0	Records length of contour index
19	14	Words
20	0	Record pointer for 1. contour: 0
21	3	Word pointer : 34
22	-1	Sense of rotation of contour = clockwise
23	0	Nesting: outer 1. order
24	0	Colour inside: transparent
25	56	Number of digitizations
26	0	Record pointer for 2. contour: 0
27	251	Word pointer : 282
28	-1	Sense of rotation of contour = clockwise
29	1	Nesting: inner 1. order
30	0	Colour inside: transparent
31	33	Number of digitizations

IMAGE INFORMATION

32			0	Records lenght of image information
33			413	Words
34 - 36	112	2004	-200		(K,X,Y); 1. DIG; typ: STRP
37 - 39	213	1628	-200		(K,X,Y); 2. DIG; typ: vector
40 - 42	215	1628	7996		(K,X,Y); 3. DIG; typ: vector
43 - 45	214	1626	8335		(K,X,Y); 4. DIG; typ: vector
46 - 50	300	1609	8620	3135	(K,X,Y,R); 5. DIG; typ: circle
51 - 55	314	1570	8866	2401	(K,X,Y,R); 6. DIG; typ: circle
56 - 60	300	1481	9120	1045	(K,X,Y,R); 7. DIG; typ: circle
61 - 65	314	1362	9278	561	(K,X,Y,R); 8. DIG; typ: circle
66 - 70	300	1203	9387	657	(K,X,Y,R); 9. DIG; typ: circle

233

WORDNO.	CONTENT	COMMENT
1	0	Records length of character
2	458	Words

NAME SECTION

3	3	Length of name section
4	303	Character number
5	0	Number of following part

SETTING INFORMATION

6	12	Length of setting information
7	1	Character type = letter
8	89	Number of DI-points
9	7407	Total set width (T=L+W+R)
10	749	Left side bearing (L)
11	6249	Width (W)
12	409	Right side bearing (R)
13	0	X-minimum
14	6249	X-maximum
15	-150	Y-minimum
16	7150	Y-maximum
17	1	Unit is 1/100mm

CONTOUR INDEX

18	0	Records length of contour index
19	8	Words
20	0	Record pointer for 1. contour: 0
21	3	Word pointer : 28
22	-1	Sense of rotation of contour = clockwise
23	0	Nesting: outer 1. order
24	0	Colour inside: transparent
25	89	Number of digitizations

IMAGE INFORMATION

26			0	Records lenght of image information	
27			433	Words	
28 - 30	112	6002	1442		(K,X,Y); 1. DIG; typ: STRP
31 - 33	213	6172	1112		(K,X,Y); 2. DIG; typ: vector
34 - 36	200	5958	894		(K,X,Y); 3. DIG; typ: vector
37 - 39	214	5847	789		(K,X,Y); 4. DIG; typ: vector
40 - 44	300	5521	531	-3219	(K,X,Y,R); 5. DIG; typ: circle
45 - 49	314	5144	304	-3597	(K,X,Y,R); 6. DIG; typ: circle
50 - 54	300	4723	116	-3769	(K,X,Y,R); 7. DIG; typ: circle
55 - 59	314	4257	-29	-4218	(K,X,Y,R); 8. DIG; typ: circle
60 - 64	300	3760	-121	-4220	(K,X,Y,R); 9. DIG; typ: circle
65 - 69	314	3282	-150	-3779	(K,X,Y,R); 10. DIG; typ: circle
70 - 74	300	2671	-96	-3596	(K,X,Y,R); 11. DIG; typ: circle
75 - 79	314	2116	55	-3161	(K,X,Y,R); 12. DIG; typ: circle
80 - 84	300	1558	330	-3073	(K,X,Y,R); 13. DIG; typ: circle
85 - 89	314	1080	703	-2923	(K,X,Y,R); 14. DIG; typ: circle
90 - 94	300	622	1261	-3097	(K,X,Y,R); 15. DIG; typ: circle
95 - 99	314	280	1950	-3520	(K,X,Y,R); 16. DIG; typ: circle

234

WORDNO.	CONTENT				COMMENT	
393 -397	300	1921	1692	2384	(K,X,Y,R);	76. DIG; typ: circle
398 -402	314	2307	1196	2391	(K,X,Y,R);	77. DIG; typ: circle
403 -407	300	2633	934	2107	(K,X,Y,R);	78. DIG; typ: circle
408 -412	314	3008	739	2146	(K,X,Y,R);	79. DIG; typ: circle
413 -417	300	3446	614	2228	(K,X,Y,R);	80. DIG; typ: circle
418 -422	314	3942	573	2668	(K,X,Y,R);	81. DIG; typ: circle
423 -427	300	4227	591	2809	(K,X,Y,R);	82. DIG; typ: circle
428 -432	314	4524	639	3100	(K,X,Y,R);	83. DIG; typ: circle
433 -437	300	4848	727	3111	(K,X,Y,R);	84. DIG; typ: circle
438 -442	314	5144	843	2787	(K,X,Y,R);	85. DIG; typ: circle
443 -447	300	5435	999	2765	(K,X,Y,R);	86. DIG; typ: circle
448 -452	314	5713	1193	2917	(K,X,Y,R);	87. DIG; typ: circle
453 -455	200	5811	1274		(K,X,Y);	88. DIG; typ: vector
456 -458	213	6002	1442		(K,X,Y);	89. DIG; typ: vector

GRAND TOTAL

	WORDS	KBYTES
Length of font:	50362	100.724
Length of font header:	477	0.954
Length of all character headers:	3927	7.854
Length of total image information:	45958	91.916

DIGITIZATIONS	NUMBER
Start points:	227
Straights:	3039
Arcs:	7178
Total:	10444

Characters:	135
Records (a 2048 words):	25

Raster (grid):   15000 X 15000

Digitizations per character:	77
Image information per character:	680 bytes

Appendix K
Description of the VC format

1. Structure of a VC font

The structure of a VC font is as described in appendix G, except that the section "font information" in the font header is expanded by the following:

Expanded font information in the font header

Word	Meaning	Comment
	Font information	
I + 2	Length of font information in words	(J)
I + 3	Identification of a font	= 1
I + 4	Number of characters	
I + 5	Cap height	
I + 6	Body size	
I + 7	x-height	Measured in pixels
I + 8	Position of base line, as distance from lower body line	
I + 9	Line distance for composition	
I + 10	Stroke thickness	
I + 11	Optimum size range	in p
I + 12	Italic angle	in 1/10 degree
I + 13	Average character width related to the cap height	in pixels
	New compared with appendix G	
I + 14	X extension of a pixel	in 1/1000 mm
I + 15	Y extension of a pixel	in 1/1000 mm
I + 16	em resolution in X direction	in pixels
I + 17	em resolution in Y direction	in pixels

Word	Meaning	Comment
I + 18	Scan identification of image data	see below
I + 19	Width of printing window	in pixels
I + 20	Height of printing window	in pixels

The scan identification describes the corner of the em square in which the scanning of the data was actually started, and also the direction in which a scan line will run.
This identification is important for SC, SN, BI and GS formats and is used there.

The following scan identifications are possible:

Decimal value	Scanning direction	Direction of line advance
11	→	(2, 1 lines running right, advancing upward)
12	→	(1, 2 lines running right, advancing downward)
21	↑	(1 2 lines running up, advancing right)
22	↑	(2 1 lines running up, advancing left)

237

Decimal value	Scanning direction	Direction of line advance
−11	←	(line advance diagram) 2 / 1
−12	←	(line advance diagram) 1 / 2
−21	↓	1 2 (line advance diagram)
−22	↓	2 1 (line advance diagram)

Usual values are 21 (CRT machines), 12 (laser printers) and −21 (matrix printers).

The printing window is the frame in which a typesetter can expose. Sometimes laser printers have a smaller printing window than is required for the em of a certain point size. Only then do we describe width and height of the printing window. Normally such details are not necessary.

2. Description of the VC format

The **vector circle format** was created to produce a compressed version of the DI format. The most undesirable and complicated characteristics of the DI format are the double words used to describe radii. Furthermore, it would be advantageous to have a contour format for typesetting machines which corresponded to the maximum resolution of the machine right from the start. Such machines do not have a 15,000 × 15,000 resolution for the em square but usually something like a 1000 × 1000 raster or even less.

238

It is thus appropriate to make three important and basic changes to the DI format: the incremental coding, the use of chord heights (instead of radii) to describe circle segments and finally the use of the so-called switches. The unit for chord heights is in quarters of the font unit system.

The expansion of the font information in the font header also applies to VC, VS, VE, SC, SN, BI and GS formats.

Every character has its own coordinate system, whose X zero point is at the X minimum of the letter and whose Y zero point is at the baseline.

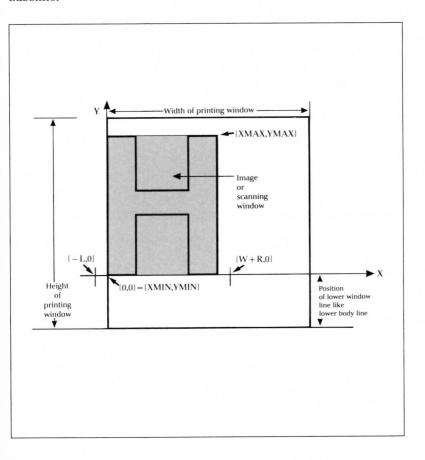

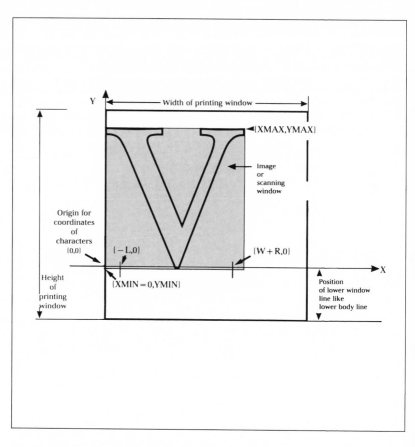

The coding of the straights and circles is done in bytes.

The starting point of the contours is reached with "pen raised" incrementally, with a so-called white vector.

The first white vector of a letter starts at the origin (0,0) of the appropriate coordinate system. The following white vectors start at the ends of preceding contours and lead to following contours in sequence as given in the contour index.

Visible straights are described incrementally as either long or short vectors, circles are described incrementally with a circle vector. We therefore have:

	Switch	ΔX	ΔY	ΔS	Length
W vector		(16 bit)	(16 bit)		= 4 bytes
L vector	127,(7F)	(16 bit)	(16 bit)		= 4(5) bytes
S vector	126,(7E)	(8 bit)	(8 bit)		= 2(3) bytes
C vector	125,(7D)	(8 bit)	(8 bit)	(8 bit)	= 3(4) bytes

The bytes with values 127, 126 and 125 (hexadecimal in brackets) are switches. The vector which is switched on applies until it is switched off.

If an increment cannot be described in 16 bits it is divided into describable 16 bit pieces.

The words (16 bit) and bytes (8 bit) are each given a sign. The words are INTEGER × 2, for the bytes: values 0...120 are counted as positive and values 255...136 are counted as negative, as −1...−120. The values of ΔX (8 bit), ΔY (8 bit) and ΔS (8 bit) are thus to be kept smaller than or equal to 120.

Circles are coded in the form of the above mentioned C vectors. ΔS then means the chord height of the related circle segment. If ΔS is positive, the circle turns in an anti-clockwise direction (mathematically positive), if ΔS is negative then it turns in a clockwise direction. The sketch below shows the circle parameters:

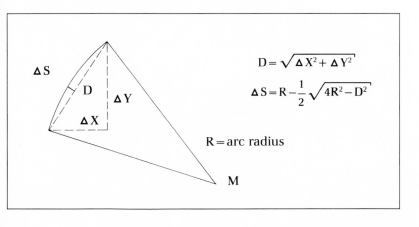

$$D = \sqrt{\Delta X^2 + \Delta Y^2}$$

$$\Delta S = R - \frac{1}{2}\sqrt{4R^2 - D^2}$$

R = arc radius

In order to calculate R (if needed) from △S one should use a look-up table (LUT). With this table one can quickly find R as function of △S and D.

If a circle (in DI format) has △X or △Y > 120, then aid points are set along the circle segment such that △X and △Y ≤ 120.

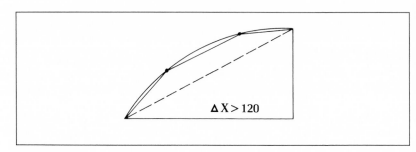

This occurs so rarely that we have not included a long C vector for large circles.

At the start of a contour we therefore always have a white vector which starts at the word boundary. The end of the contour is controlled by the number of vectors (digitizations); these details are found in the contour index. **W, L, S and C vectors are always counted as one digitization.** The end of the character is reached when all contours have been processed.

The end of a font is checked with the character index of the font.

3. Example of a VC format

First of all we represent the lower case letters a, b, c of the typeface "URW Antiqua 2015 normal", with marks. Subsequently the complete font format is reproduced as a data list. The raster is 400 × 400 for the em.

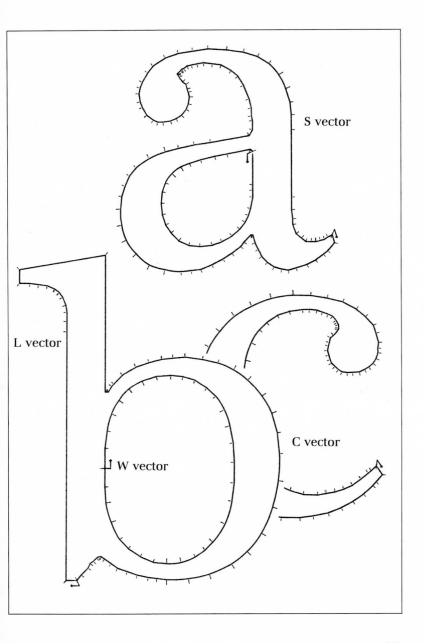

S vector

L vector

C vector

W vector

WORDNO.	CONTENT	COMMENT
1	484	Length of font header

NAME SECTION

2	55	Length of name section
3	825	Number on URW list
4 - 10	AN201512.VC	File name (ASCII)
11 - 49	URW-Antiqua 2000 normal	Font name (ASCII)
50	VC	Data format (ASCII)
51 - 53	20 3 87	Production date: 20-Mar-87
54 - 56	20 3 87	Date of last change: 20-Mar-87

FONT INFORMATION

57	19	Length of font information
58	1	Indicator for font
59	135	Number of characters
60	267	Cap height (in pixels)
61	400	Body size (in pixels)
62	187	x-height (in pixels)
63	100	Distance: base line - lower body line(in pixels)
64	400	Text line distance for setting (in pixels)
65	40	Stem thickness (in pixels)
66	0	Angle of italisation (in 1/10 degree)
67	12	Optimum point size for setting (in p)
68	174	Average character width (in pixels)
69	375	X-extension of a pixel (in 1/1000mm)
70	375	Y-extension of a pixel (in 1/1000mm)
71	400	Em-resolution in X-direction (in pixels)
72	400	Em-resolution in Y-direction (in pixels)
73	21	Scan indicator of image data
74	400	Width of printing window (in pixels)
75	400	Height of printing window (in pixels)

HIERARCHY SECTION

76	1	No hierarchy section in this format

CHARACTER INDEX

77	408	Length of character index
78	9	LENGTH OF FONT IN PHYSICAL RECORDS
79	379	Last word of last record
80	101	Character number: 1
81	1	Pointer to record containing start of character
82	485	Word pointer to start of character
83	102	Ch. no.: 2
84	1	Record pointer
85	588	Word pointer
86- 88	103 1 759	No., record pointer, word pointer of ch.: 3
89- 91	104 1 884	No., record pointer, word pointer of ch.: 4
92- 94	105 1 1011	No., record pointer, word pointer of ch.: 5

WORDNO.	CONTENT			COMMENT	
272- 274	331	5	1116	No., record pointer, word pointer of ch.:	65
275- 277	401	5	1185	No., record pointer, word pointer of ch.:	66
278- 280	408	5	1434	No., record pointer, word pointer of ch.:	67
281- 283	413	5	1699	No., record pointer, word pointer of ch.:	68
284- 286	436	5	1875	No., record pointer, word pointer of ch.:	69
287- 289	449	6	21	No., record pointer, word pointer of ch.:	70
290- 292	501	6	200	No., record pointer, word pointer of ch.:	71
293- 295	502	6	281	No., record pointer, word pointer of ch.:	72
296- 298	503	6	418	No., record pointer, word pointer of ch.:	73
299- 301	504	6	552	No., record pointer, word pointer of ch.:	74
302- 304	505	6	618	No., record pointer, word pointer of ch.:	75
305- 307	506	6	768	No., record pointer, word pointer of ch.:	76
308- 310	507	6	940	No., record pointer, word pointer of ch.:	77
311- 313	508	6	1017	No., record pointer, word pointer of ch.:	78
314- 316	509	6	1218	No., record pointer, word pointer of ch.:	79
317- 319	510	6	1395	No., record pointer, word pointer of ch.:	80
320- 322	511	6	1522	No., record pointer, word pointer of ch.:	81
323- 325	512	6	1752	No., record pointer, word pointer of ch.:	82
326- 328	513	6	1975	No., record pointer, word pointer of ch.:	83
329- 331	601	7	80	No., record pointer, word pointer of ch.:	84
332- 334	602	7	122	No., record pointer, word pointer of ch.:	85
335- 337	603	7	185	No., record pointer, word pointer of ch.:	86
338- 340	604	7	227	No., record pointer, word pointer of ch.:	87
341- 343	605	7	269	No., record pointer, word pointer of ch.:	88
344- 346	606	7	311	No., record pointer, word pointer of ch.:	89
347- 349	607	7	395	No., record pointer, word pointer of ch.:	90
350- 352	608	7	470	No., record pointer, word pointer of ch.:	91
353- 355	609	7	566	No., record pointer, word pointer of ch.:	92
356- 358	610	7	641	No., record pointer, word pointer of ch.:	93
359- 361	611	7	716	No., record pointer, word pointer of ch.:	94
362- 364	612	7	845	No., record pointer, word pointer of ch.:	95
365- 367	613	7	974	No., record pointer, word pointer of ch.:	96
368- 370	614	7	1103	No., record pointer, word pointer of ch.:	97
371- 373	615	7	1206	No., record pointer, word pointer of ch.:	98
374- 376	616	7	1309	No., record pointer, word pointer of ch.:	99
377- 379	617	7	1448	No., record pointer, word pointer of ch.:	100
380- 382	618	7	1587	No., record pointer, word pointer of ch.:	101
383- 385	619	7	1638	No., record pointer, word pointer of ch.:	102
386- 388	620	7	1689	No., record pointer, word pointer of ch.:	103

WORDNO.	CONTENT			COMMENT	
449- 451	704	8	1662	No., record pointer, word pointer of ch.:	124
452- 454	705	8	1709	No., record pointer, word pointer of ch.:	125
455- 457	706	8	1756	No., record pointer, word pointer of ch.:	126
458- 460	709	8	1792	No., record pointer, word pointer of ch.:	127
461- 463	711	8	1879	No., record pointer, word pointer of ch.:	128
464- 466	751	8	1950	No., record pointer, word pointer of ch.:	129
467- 469	753	8	2037	No., record pointer, word pointer of ch.:	130
470- 472	754	9	92	No., record pointer, word pointer of ch.:	131
473- 475	755	9	139	No., record pointer, word pointer of ch.:	132
476- 478	756	9	186	No., record pointer, word pointer of ch.:	133
479- 481	759	9	222	No., record pointer, word pointer of ch.:	134
482- 484	761	9	309	No., record pointer, word pointer of ch.:	135

WORDNO.	CONTENT	COMMENT
1	0	Records length of character
2	183	Words

NAME SECTION

3	3	Length of name section
4	301	Character number
5	0	Number of following part

SETTING INFORMATION

6	12	Length of setting information
7	1	Character type = letter
8	136	Number of vectors
9	206	Total set width (T=L+W+R)
10	15	Left side bearing (L)
11	194	Width (W)
12	-3	Right side bearing (R)
13	0	X-minimum
14	194	X-maximum
15	-4	Y-minimum
16	191	Y-maximum
17	1	Unit is 1 pixel

CONTOUR INDEX

18	0	Records length of contour index
19	14	Words
20	0	Record pointer for 1. contour: 0
21	3	Word pointer : 34
22	-1	Sense of rotation of contour = clockwise
23	0	Nesting: outer 1. order
24	0	Colour inside: transparent
25	108	Number of digitizations
26	0	Record pointer for 2. contour: 0
27	121	Word pointer : 152
28	-1	Sense of rotation of contour = clockwise
29	1	Nesting: inner 1. order
30	0	Colour inside: transparent
31	28	Number of digitizations

IMAGE INFORMATION

32	0	Records length of image information
33	152	Words

34 -151		192	28	192	28	(dX,dY)	1.DIG w-vector
36 1	7E	02	F9	126	2 -7	(K,dX,dY)	2.DIG s-vector
37 2		FA	F9		-6 -7	(dX,dY)	3.DIG s-vector
38 2		FC	FD		-4 -3	(dX,dY)	4.DIG s-vector
39 2		F9	FB		-7 -5	(dX,dY)	5.DIG s-vector
40 2		F8	FC		-8 -4	(dX,dY)	6.DIG s-vector
41 2		F6	FD		-10 -3	(dX,dY)	7.DIG s-vector
42 2		F9	FE		-7 -2	(dX,dY)	8.DIG s-vector
43 2		FA	01		-6 1	(dX,dY)	9.DIG s-vector

246

WORDNO.	CONTENT	COMMENT
44 2	F9 02	-7 2 (dX,dY) 10.DIG s-vector
45 2	FA 04	-6 4 (dX,dY) 11.DIG s-vector
46 2	FB 05	-5 5 (dX,dY) 12.DIG s-vector
47 2	FD 06	-3 6 (dX,dY) 13.DIG s-vector
48 2	FD 06	-3 6 (dX,dY) 14.DIG s-vector
49 2	FE 07	-2 7 (dX,dY) 15.DIG s-vector
50 2	FE 00	-2 0 (dX,dY) 16.DIG s-vector
51 2	FA FA	-6 -6 (dX,dY) 17.DIG s-vector
52 2	FD FC	-3 -4 (dX,dY) 18.DIG s-vector
53 2	F8 FA	-8 -6 (dX,dY) 19.DIG s-vector
54 2	F8 FB	-8 -5 (dX,dY) 20.DIG s-vector
55 2	F6 FB	-10 -5 (dX,dY) 21.DIG s-vector
56 2	F6 FC	-10 -4 (dX,dY) 22.DIG s-vector
57 2	F7 FF	-9 -1 (dX,dY) 23.DIG s-vector
58 2	F7 FF	-9 -1 (dX,dY) 24.DIG s-vector
59 2	7D F1 02 FE	125 -15 2 -2 (K,dX,dY,dS) 25.DIG c-vector
61 2	F2 04 FE	-14 4 -2 (dX,dY,dS) 26.DIG c-vector
63 1	F4 0A FD	-12 10 -3 (dX,dY,dS) 27.DIG c-vector
64 2	F7 0C FD	-9 12 -3 (dX,dY,dS) 28.DIG c-vector
66 1	FC 0D FE	-4 13 -2 (dX,dY,dS) 29.DIG c-vector
67 2	FF 0E FE	-1 14 -2 (dX,dY,dS) 30.DIG c-vector
69 1	7E 01 0B	126 1 11 (K,dX,dY) 31.DIG s-vector
70 2	03 09	3 9 (dX,dY) 32.DIG s-vector
71 2	04 09	4 9 (dX,dY) 33.DIG s-vector
72 2	06 07	6 7 (dX,dY) 34.DIG s-vector
73 2	7D 0C 08 FE	125 12 8 -2 (K,dX,dY,dS) 35.DIG c-vector
75 2	0F 06 FE	15 6 -2 (dX,dY,dS) 36.DIG c-vector
77 1	7E 0C 03	126 12 3 (K,dX,dY) 37.DIG s-vector
78 2	0E 03	14 3 (dX,dY) 38.DIG s-vector
79 2	0F 02	15 2 (dX,dY) 39.DIG s-vector
80 2	23 06	35 6 (dX,dY) 40.DIG s-vector
81 2	03 05	3 5 (dX,dY) 41.DIG s-vector
82 2	00 08	0 8 (dX,dY) 42.DIG s-vector
83 2	FF 04	-1 4 (dX,dY) 43.DIG s-vector
84 2	00 07	0 7 (dX,dY) 44.DIG s-vector
85 2	FE 08	-2 8 (dX,dY) 45.DIG s-vector
86 2	FB 0C	-5 12 (dX,dY) 46.DIG s-vector
87 2	FB 08	-5 8 (dX,dY) 47.DIG s-vector
88 2	FA 05	-6 5 (dX,dY) 48.DIG s-vector
89 2	F7 05	-9 5 (dX,dY) 49.DIG s-vector
90 2	F8 01	-8 1 (dX,dY) 50.DIG s-vector
91 2	F8 01	-8 1 (dX,dY) 51.DIG s-vector
92 2	FA FF	-6 -1 (dX,dY) 52.DIG s-vector
93 2	FB FF	-5 -1 (dX,dY) 53.DIG s-vector
94 2	FC FF	-4 -1 (dX,dY) 54.DIG s-vector
95 2	FD FE	-3 -2 (dX,dY) 55.DIG s-vector
96 2	FE FF	-2 -1 (dX,dY) 56.DIG s-vector
97 2	FF FF	-1 -1 (dX,dY) 57.DIG s-vector
98 2	FE FE	-2 -2 (dX,dY) 58.DIG s-vector
99 2	FF FF	-1 -1 (dX,dY) 59.DIG s-vector
100 2	01 FF	1 -1 (dX,dY) 60.DIG s-vector
101 2	01 FE	1 -2 (dX,dY) 61.DIG s-vector
102 2	03 FC	3 -4 (dX,dY) 62.DIG s-vector
103 2	03 FE	3 -2 (dX,dY) 63.DIG s-vector
104 2	01 FC	1 -4 (dX,dY) 64.DIG s-vector
105 2	01 FD	1 -3 (dX,dY) 65.DIG s-vector
106 2	01 FC	1 -4 (dX,dY) 66.DIG s-vector
107 2	FF FA	-1 -6 (dX,dY) 67.DIG s-vector
108 2	FE FB	-2 -5 (dX,dY) 68.DIG s-vector

WORDNO.	CONTENT					COMMENT			
109 2		FC	FB			-4	-5		(dX,dY)	69.DIG s-vector
110 2		FB	FD			-5	-3		(dX,dY)	70.DIG s-vector
111 2		FB	FE			-5	-2		(dX,dY)	71.DIG s-vector
112 2		F9	FF			-7	-1		(dX,dY)	72.DIG s-vector
113 2		FB	00			-5	0		(dX,dY)	73.DIG s-vector
114 2		FC	02			-4	2		(dX,dY)	74.DIG s-vector
115 2		FA	04			-6	4		(dX,dY)	75.DIG s-vector
116 2		FC	07			-4	7		(dX,dY)	76.DIG s-vector
117 2		FE	05			-2	5		(dX,dY)	77.DIG s-vector
118 2		FF	07			-1	7		(dX,dY)	78.DIG s-vector
119 2		01	05			1	5		(dX,dY)	79.DIG s-vector
120 2		02	05			2	5		(dX,dY)	80.DIG s-vector
121 2		05	08			5	8		(dX,dY)	81.DIG s-vector
122 2		05	06			5	6		(dX,dY)	82.DIG s-vector
123 2		0B	07			11	7		(dX,dY)	83.DIG s-vector
124 2		0C	04			12	4		(dX,dY)	84.DIG s-vector
125 2		0D	02			13	2		(dX,dY)	85.DIG s-vector
126 2		0E	02			14	2		(dX,dY)	86.DIG s-vector
127 2		11	FF			17	-1		(dX,dY)	87.DIG s-vector
128 2		0F	FE			15	-2		(dX,dY)	88.DIG s-vector
129 2		0D	FC			13	-4		(dX,dY)	89.DIG s-vector
130 2		0A	FA			10	-6		(dX,dY)	90.DIG s-vector
131 2	7D	09	F6	FE	125	9	-10	-2	(K,dX,dY,dS)	91.DIG c-vector
133 2		06	F4	FE		6	-12	-2	(dX,dY,dS)	92.DIG c-vector
135 1	7E	04	F4		126	4	-12		(K,dX,dY)	93.DIG s-vector
136 2		01	F5			1	-11		(dX,dY)	94.DIG s-vector
137 2		00	F3			0	-13		(dX,dY)	95.DIG s-vector
138 2		00	C5			0	-59		(dX,dY)	96.DIG s-vector
139 2		00	F5			0	-11		(dX,dY)	97.DIG s-vector
140 2		01	F8			1	-8		(dX,dY)	98.DIG s-vector
141 2		00	FB			0	-5		(dX,dY)	99.DIG s-vector
142 2		03	F8			3	-8		(dX,dY)	100.DIG s-vector
143 2		05	FC			5	-4		(dX,dY)	101.DIG s-vector
144 2		04	FD			4	-3		(dX,dY)	102.DIG s-vector
145 2		05	00			5	0		(dX,dY)	103.DIG s-vector
146 2		04	00			4	0		(dX,dY)	104.DIG s-vector
147 2		04	01			4	1		(dX,dY)	105.DIG s-vector
148 2		04	01			4	1		(dX,dY)	106.DIG s-vector
149 2		03	02			3	2		(dX,dY)	107.DIG s-vector
150 2		04	02			4	2		(dX,dY)	108.DIG s-vector
152 -183		-72		73		-72		73	(dX,dY)	109.DIG w-vector
154 1	7E	00	E3		126	0	-29		(K,dX,dY)	110.DIG s-vector
155 2		00	FB			0	-5		(dX,dY)	111.DIG s-vector
156 2		00	FA			0	-6		(dX,dY)	112.DIG s-vector
157 2		FE	F6			-2	-10		(dX,dY)	113.DIG s-vector
158 2		FE	FA			-2	-6		(dX,dY)	114.DIG s-vector
159 2		FD	FA			-3	-6		(dX,dY)	115.DIG s-vector
160 2		FB	FA			-5	-6		(dX,dY)	116.DIG s-vector
161 2		F9	FA			-7	-6		(dX,dY)	117.DIG s-vector
162 2		F7	FB			-9	-5		(dX,dY)	118.DIG s-vector
163 2		F7	FD			-9	-3		(dX,dY)	119.DIG s-vector
164 2		F5	FF			-11	-1		(dX,dY)	120.DIG s-vector
165 2		F6	01			-10	1		(dX,dY)	121.DIG s-vector
166 2		F7	04			-9	4		(dX,dY)	122.DIG s-vector
167 2		F9	07			-7	7		(dX,dY)	123.DIG s-vector
168 2		FB	07			-5	7		(dX,dY)	124.DIG s-vector
169 2		FD	09			-3	9		(dX,dY)	125.DIG s-vector
170 2		FF	0A			-1	10		(dX,dY)	126.DIG s-vector
171 2		01	0A			1	10		(dX,dY)	127.DIG s-vector

248

WORDNO.	CONTENT	COMMENT
1	0	Records length of character
2	147	Words

NAME SECTION

3	3	Length of name section
4	302	Character number
5	0	Number of following part

SETTING INFORMATION

6	12	Length of setting information
7	1	Character type = letter
8	89	Number of vectors
9	257	Total set width (T=L+W+R)
10	0	Left side bearing (L)
11	237	Width (W)
12	20	Right side bearing (R)
13	0	X-minimum
14	237	X-maximum
15	-5	Y-minimum
16	280	Y-maximum
17	1	Unit is 1 pixel

CONTOUR INDEX

18	0	Records length of contour index
19	14	Words
20	0	Record pointer for 1. contour: 0
21	3	Word pointer : 34
22	-1	Sense of rotation of contour = clockwise
23	0	Nesting: outer 1. order
24	0	Colour inside: transparent
25	56	Number of digitizations
26	0	Record pointer for 2. contour: 0
27	71	Word pointer : 102
28	-1	Sense of rotation of contour = clockwise
29	1	Nesting: inner 1. order
30	0	Colour inside: transparent
31	33	Number of digitizations

IMAGE INFORMATION

32			0	Records		length of image information			
33			116	Words					
34 -101		53	-5		53	-5	(dX,dY)	1.DIG w-vector	
36 1	7E	F6	00	126	-10	0	(K,dX,dY)	2.DIG s-vector	
37 2	7F	0	218	127	0	218	(K,dX,dY)	3.DIG l-vector	
40 1	7E	00	09	126	0	9	(K,dX,dY)	4.DIG s-vector	
41 2		00	08		0	8	(dX,dY)	5.DIG s-vector	
42 2		FF	06		-1	6	(dX,dY)	6.DIG s-vector	
43 2		FD	07		-3	7	(dX,dY)	7.DIG s-vector	
44 2		FD	04		-3	4	(dX,dY)	8.DIG s-vector	
45 2		FC	03		-4	3	(dX,dY)	9.DIG s-vector	

249

WORDNO.	CONTENT	COMMENT
1	0	Records length of character
2	130	Words

NAME SECTION

3	3	Length of name section
4	303	Character number
5	0	Number of following part

SETTING INFORMATION

6	12	Length of setting information
7	1	Character type = letter
8	89	Number of vectors
9	198	Total set width (T=L+W+R)
10	20	Left side bearing (L)
11	167	Width (W)
12	11	Right side bearing (R)
13	0	X-minimum
14	167	X-maximum
15	-4	Y-minimum
16	191	Y-maximum
17	1	Unit is 1 pixel

CONTOUR INDEX

18	0	Records length of contour index
19	8	Words
20	0	Record pointer for 1. contour: 0
21	3	Word pointer : 28
22	-1	Sense of rotation of contour = clockwise
23	0	Nesting: outer 1. order
24	0	Colour inside: transparent
25	89	Number of digitizations

IMAGE INFORMATION

26	0	Records length of image information
27	105	Words

28 -130		160		38		160	38		(dX,dY)	1.DIG w-vector
30 1	7E	05	F8		126	5	-8		(K,dX,dY)	2.DIG s-vector
31 2		FA	FA			-6	-6		(dX,dY)	3.DIG s-vector
32 2		FD	FD			-3	-3		(dX,dY)	4.DIG s-vector
33 2		F7	F9			-9	-7		(dX,dY)	5.DIG s-vector
34 2		F6	FA			-10	-6		(dX,dY)	6.DIG s-vector
35 2		F5	FB			-11	-5		(dX,dY)	7.DIG s-vector
36 2		F4	FC			-12	-4		(dX,dY)	8.DIG s-vector
37 2		F2	FE			-14	-2		(dX,dY)	9.DIG s-vector
38 2		F4	FF			-12	-1		(dX,dY)	10.DIG s-vector
39 2		EF	01			-17	1		(dX,dY)	11.DIG s-vector
40 2		F1	04			-15	4		(dX,dY)	12.DIG s-vector
41 2	7D	F2	08	FE	125	-14	8	-2	(K,dX,dY,dS)	13.DIG c-vector
43 2		F3	0A	FE		-13	10	-2	(dX,dY,dS)	14.DIG c-vector
45 1		F4	0F	FE		-12	15	-2	(dX,dY,dS)	15.DIG c-vector
46 2		F6	12	FE		-10	18	-2	(dX,dY,dS)	16.DIG c-vector

WORDNO.	CONTENT				COMMENT				
114 2	7D	06	F0	02	125	6	-16	2 (K,dX,dY,dS)	76.DIG c-vector
116 2		0B	F3	02		11	-13	2 (dX,dY,dS)	77.DIG c-vector
118 1	7E	08	F9		126	8	-7	(K,dX,dY)	78.DIG s-vector
119 2		0A	FB			10	-5	(dX,dY)	79.DIG s-vector
120 2		0C	FC			12	-4	(dX,dY)	80.DIG s-vector
121 2		0D	FF			13	-1	(dX,dY)	81.DIG s-vector
122 2		08	01			8	1	(dX,dY)	82.DIG s-vector
123 2		08	01			8	1	(dX,dY)	83.DIG s-vector
124 2		08	02			8	2	(dX,dY)	84.DIG s-vector
125 2		08	03			8	3	(dX,dY)	85.DIG s-vector
126 2		08	05			8	5	(dX,dY)	86.DIG s-vector
127 2		07	05			7	5	(dX,dY)	87.DIG s-vector
128 2		03	02			3	2	(dX,dY)	88.DIG s-vector
129 2		05	04			5	4	(dX,dY)	89.DIG s-vector

GRAND TOTAL

	WORDS	KBYTES
Length of font:	16763	33.526
Length of font header:	484	0.968
Length of all character headers:	3927	7.854
Length of total image information:	12352	24.704

DIGITIZATIONS	NUMBER
White vectors:	227
L-vectors:	137
S-vectors:	8694
C-vectors:	1380
Total:	10438

Characters:	135
Records (a 2048 words):	9

Raster (grid):	400 X 400

Digitizations per character:	77
Image information per character:	182 bytes

VC - CHORD HEIGHT - STATISTICS
(Unit is quarter pixel)

Number of chords with height	2 =	140
Number of chords with height	3 =	22
Number of chords with height	4 =	4
Number of chords with height	-2 =	800
Number of chords with height	-3 =	224
Number of chords with height	-4 =	30
Number of chords with height	-5 =	16
Number of chords with height	-6 =	8
Number of chords with height	-7 =	24
Number of chords with height	-8 =	96
Number of chords with height	-9 =	8
Number of chords with height	-10 =	6
Number of chords with height	-11 =	2

Appendix L
Description of the VS format

1. Structure of a VS font

The structure of the **vector scaling font** is exactly the same as that of the VC format, as described in appendix K.

2. Description of the VS format

The vector scaling format was created as a master format for the URW raster image processor (RIP), a software capable of performing fast, intelligent scaling. The URW RIP produces high quality SC data from VS format in a wide range of point sizes for various resolutions. "Intelligent scaling" especially means that similar stems in different characters of a given typeface will all have exactly the same width in the SC data. Also, for example, all upper case characters without overhang will have the same cap height, and all serifs will retain the same shape in all characters.

The VS format is an extended VC format. To enable intelligent scaling, it has two additional features, compared to the VC format:

1. It contains extra information about the position of vertical and horizontal straight lines (stem edges), curved stems, locations of serifs and peak positions.
2. The width of similar stems, cap height, length of serifs and similar quantities are set to the same value in all characters. This is done by using a two-step fit procedure when creating VS format. The VS format is normally created in only one master size, typically 720×720 or 1080×1080 for the em square.

The additional information is stored at two different locations:

a) The positions of straight lines (either vertical or horizontal) and curved stems (vertical and horizontal) are stored in the setting information of the character record. The positions are either absolute, or relative to the last value in the sequence of positions. In order to conserve stem width during the rastering process, stems are represented by one absolute and one relative straight line.

The features of the additional data items in the character headers are demonstrated in a simple character. Here, only vertical and horizontal straight lines are present, but the same holds true also for curved stems. By marking descender line, baseline, meanline, and cap height as horizontal straight lines, we ensure that the heights are preserved during RIP processing. By marking each stem with one absolute and one relative value we make sure that stem widths are treated correctly when scaled down to the (SC) target grid.

In most characters, only one set of stem edges (consisting of horizontal/vertical curve extrema) is needed, because they only have one contour with hierarchy level zero (outer contour 1st order). In some characters, though, there are more contours with hierarchy level one side by side (as in the case for percent or permille symbols) or on top of each other (i, j, characters with accents). In order to manipulate these different parts of the characters independently, the RIP needs a separate set of stems (stem block) for each of them.

Format of stem block (extension of character record, see also appendix G)

Word	Meaning	Comment
N1 + N2 +3	Number of K contours for which the first stem block applies.	K > 0 stem block applies to reset K contours. K < 0 stem block is empty, length of stem block is 1. For an i, for example, there are two stem blocks, each for one contour.
+4	Number of vertical straight lines	NV1 (may be = 0)

Word	Meaning	Comment
NV1 words	Positions of vertical straight lines	If value is >8192: absolute position $=$ value $-16{,}384$. In all other cases: relative position $=$ value.
$+$ NV1 $+$ 5	Number of vertical curve extrema	NV2 (may be $=0$)
NV2 words	Positions of vertical curve extrema	Same as above
$+$ NV1 $+$ NV2 $+6$	Number of horizontal straight lines	NV3 (may be $=0$)
NV3 words	Positions of horizontal straight lines	Same as above
$+$ NV1 $+$ NV2 $+$ NV3 $+7$	Number of horizontal curve extrema	NV4 (may be $=0$)
NV4 words	Positions of horizontal curve extrema	Same as above
$+$ NV1 $+$ NV2 $+$ NV3 $+$ NV4 $+7$	Last data word in first stem block	
$+$ NV1 $+$ NV2 $+$ NV3 $+$ NV4 $+8$	Number of K contours for which the second stem block applies.	
. .	Second stem block	

N2 (length of setting information) is therefore changed to:
$$\sum (NV1_i + NV2_i + NV3_i + NV4_i) + 5n$$
$i = 1, \ldots n$; $n =$ number of stem blocks

b) While the positions of horizontal and vertical edges are stored in the character header, other information is incorporated directly into the image information. In the description of the VC format it was pointed out that bytes with an absolute value of > 120 are interpreted as switches. Compared to the VC format, VS has four additional switches which mark special parts of the character.

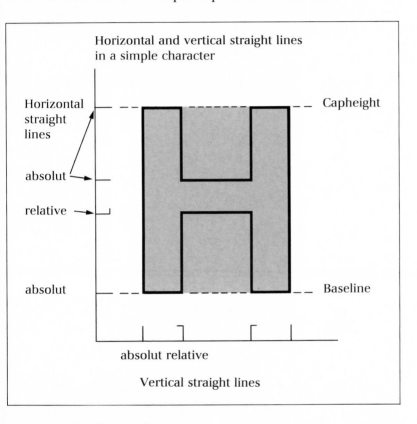

Horizontal and vertical straight lines in a simple character

3. Example of a VS format

First of all we represent the lower case letters a, b, c of the typeface "URW Antiqua 2015 normal", with marks. Subsequently the complete font format is reproduced as a data list. The raster is 1080 × 1080 for the em.

255

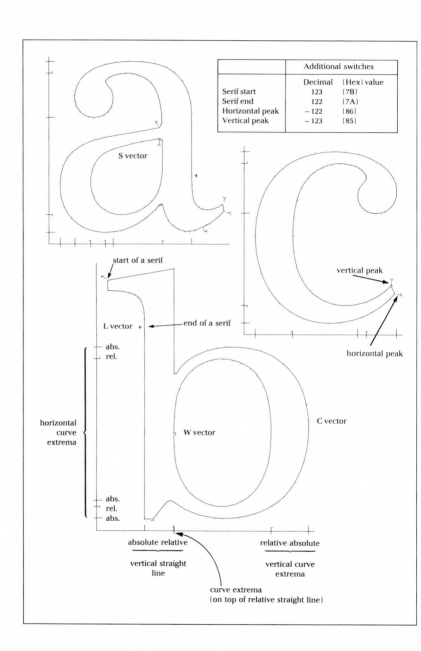

	Additional switches	
	Decimal	(Hex) value
Serif start	123	(7B)
Serif end	122	(7A)
Horizontal peak	−122	(86)
Vertical peak	−123	(85)

S vector

vertical peak

start of a serif

end of a serif

L vector

horizontal peak

abs.
rel.

horizontal
curve
extrema

W vector

C vector

abs.
rel.
abs.

absolute relative   relative absolute

vertical straight
line

vertical curve
extrema

curve extrema
(on top of relative straight line)

```
--------- ------------------ ---------------------------------------------
 WORDNO. |    CONTENT       |                COMMENT
--------- ------------------ ---------------------------------------------
    1    |             484  | Length of font header
--------- ------------------ ---------------------------------------------
```

       NAME SECTION

```
    2    |              55  | Length of name section
    3    |             825  | Number on URW list
  4 - 10 | AN201512.VS      | File name (ASCII)

 11 - 49 |  URW-Antiqua 2000            | Font name (ASCII)
         |         normal

   50    |              VS  | Data format (ASCII)
 51 - 53 |        26  2 87  | Production date:     26-Feb-87
 54 - 56 |        26  2 87  | Date of last change: 26-Feb-87
--------- ------------------ ---------------------------------------------
```

       FONT INFORMATION

```
   57    |              19  | Length of font information
   58    |               1  | Indicator for font
   59    |             135  | Number of characters
   60    |             720  | Cap height (in pixels)
   61    |            1080  | Body size (in pixels)
   62    |             504  | x-height (in pixels)
   63    |             270  | Distance: base line - lower body line(in pixels)
   64    |            1080  | Text line distance for setting (in pixels)
   65    |             108  | Stem thickness (in pixels)
   66    |               0  | Angle of italisation (in 1/10 degree)
   67    |              12  | Optimum point size for setting (in p)
   68    |             469  | Average character width (in pixels)
   69    |             139  | X-extension of a pixel (in 1/1000mm)
   70    |             139  | Y-extension of a pixel (in 1/1000mm)
   71    |            1080  | Em-resolution in X-direction (in pixels)
   72    |            1080  | Em-resolution in Y-direction (in pixels)
   73    |              21  | Scan indicator of image data
   74    |            1080  | Width of printing window (in pixels)
   75    |            1080  | Height of printing window (in pixels)
--------- ------------------ ---------------------------------------------
```

       HIERARCHY SECTION

```
   76    |               1  | No hierarchy section in this format
--------- ------------------ ---------------------------------------------
```

       CHARACTER INDEX

```
   77    |             408  | Length of character index
   78    |              11  | LENGTH OF FONT IN PHYSICAL RECORDS
   79    |            1000  | Last word of last record

   80    |             101  | Character number:  1
   81    |               1  | Pointer to record containing start of character
   82    |             485  | Word pointer to start of character

   83    |             102  | Ch. no.: 2
   84    |               1  | Record pointer
   85    |             622  | Word pointer

 86- 88  |   103   1  842  | No., record pointer, word pointer of ch.:    3
 89- 91  |   104   1  991  | No., record pointer, word pointer of ch.:    4
 92- 94  |   105   1 1145  | No., record pointer, word pointer of ch.:    5
--------- ------------------ ---------------------------------------------
```

WORDNO.	CONTENT			COMMENT	
272- 274	331	6	1547	No., record pointer, word pointer of ch.:	65
275- 277	401	6	1640	No., record pointer, word pointer of ch.:	66
278- 280	408	6	1976	No., record pointer, word pointer of ch.:	67
281- 283	413	7	287	No., record pointer, word pointer of ch.:	68
284- 286	436	7	503	No., record pointer, word pointer of ch.:	69
287- 289	449	7	747	No., record pointer, word pointer of ch.:	70
290- 292	501	7	997	No., record pointer, word pointer of ch.:	71
293- 295	502	7	1095	No., record pointer, word pointer of ch.:	72
296- 298	503	7	1286	No., record pointer, word pointer of ch.:	73
299- 301	504	7	1464	No., record pointer, word pointer of ch.:	74
302- 304	505	7	1548	No., record pointer, word pointer of ch.:	75
305- 307	506	7	1755	No., record pointer, word pointer of ch.:	76
308- 310	507	7	1975	No., record pointer, word pointer of ch.:	77
311- 313	508	8	32	No., record pointer, word pointer of ch.:	78
314- 316	509	8	287	No., record pointer, word pointer of ch.:	79
317- 319	510	8	513	No., record pointer, word pointer of ch.:	80
320- 322	511	8	660	No., record pointer, word pointer of ch.:	81
323- 325	512	8	990	No., record pointer, word pointer of ch.:	82
326- 328	513	8	1292	No., record pointer, word pointer of ch.:	83
329- 331	601	8	1483	No., record pointer, word pointer of ch.:	84
332- 334	602	8	1533	No., record pointer, word pointer of ch.:	85
335- 337	603	8	1608	No., record pointer, word pointer of ch.:	86
338- 340	604	8	1658	No., record pointer, word pointer of ch.:	87
341- 343	605	8	1708	No., record pointer, word pointer of ch.:	88
344- 346	606	8	1758	No., record pointer, word pointer of ch.:	89
347- 349	607	8	1858	No., record pointer, word pointer of ch.:	90
350- 352	608	8	1953	No., record pointer, word pointer of ch.:	91
353- 355	609	9	25	No., record pointer, word pointer of ch.:	92
356- 358	610	9	120	No., record pointer, word pointer of ch.:	93
359- 361	611	9	215	No., record pointer, word pointer of ch.:	94
362- 364	612	9	380	No., record pointer, word pointer of ch.:	95
365- 367	613	9	545	No., record pointer, word pointer of ch.:	96
368- 370	614	9	710	No., record pointer, word pointer of ch.:	97
371- 373	615	9	828	No., record pointer, word pointer of ch.:	98
374- 376	616	9	947	No., record pointer, word pointer of ch.:	99
377- 379	617	9	1134	No., record pointer, word pointer of ch.:	100
380- 382	618	9	1321	No., record pointer, word pointer of ch.:	101
383- 385	619	9	1388	No., record pointer, word pointer of ch.:	102

WORDNO.	CONTENT			COMMENT	
449- 451	704	11	8	No., record pointer, word pointer of ch.:	124
452- 454	705	11	68	No., record pointer, word pointer of ch.:	125
455- 457	706	11	128	No., record pointer, word pointer of ch.:	126
458- 460	709	11	176	No., record pointer, word pointer of ch.:	127
461- 463	711	11	283	No., record pointer, word pointer of ch.:	128
464- 466	751	11	370	No., record pointer, word pointer of ch.:	129
467- 469	753	11	493	No., record pointer, word pointer of ch.:	130
470- 472	754	11	639	No., record pointer, word pointer of ch.:	131
473- 475	755	11	699	No., record pointer, word pointer of ch.:	132
476- 478	756	11	759	No., record pointer, word pointer of ch.:	133
479- 481	759	11	807	No., record pointer, word pointer of ch.:	134
482- 484	761	11	914	No., record pointer, word pointer of ch.:	135

258

WORDNO.	CONTENT	COMMENT
1	0	Records length of character
2	239	Words

NAME SECTION

3	3	Length of name section
4	301	Character number
5	0	Number of following part

SETTING INFORMATION

6	29	Length of setting information
7	11	Character type = small letter
8	136	Number of vectors
9	555	Total set width (T=L+W+R)
10	40	Left side bearing (L)
11	524	Width (W)
12	-9	Right side bearing (R)
13	0	X-minimum
14	524	X-maximum
15	-11	Y-minimum
16	515	Y-maximum
17	1	Unit is 1 pixel
18	2	Stem information for contours 1 - 2
19	2	Number of vertical straight lines
20	16803	Absolute value (in pixels) 419
21	-94	Relative value (in pixels)
22	5	Number of vertical curve extrema
23	16384	Absolute value (in pixels) 0
24	97	Relative value (in pixels)
25	16431	Absolute value (in pixels) 47
26	97	Relative value (in pixels)
27	16553	Absolute value (in pixels) 169
28	0	Number of horizontal straight lines
29	5	Number of horizontal curve extrema
30	16373	Absolute value (in pixels) -11
31	54	Relative value (in pixels)
32	16899	Absolute value (in pixels) 515
33	-36	Relative value (in pixels)
34	16727	Absolute value (in pixels) 343

CONTOUR INDEX

35	0	Records length of contour index
36	14	Words
37	0	Record pointer for 1. contour: 0
38	3	Word pointer : 51
39	-1	Sense of rotation of contour = clockwise
40	0	Nesting: outer 1. order
41	0	Colour inside: transparent
42	108	Number of digitizations
43	0	Record pointer for 2. contour: 0
44	153	Word pointer : 201
45	1	Sense of rotation of contour = counterclockwise
46	1	Nesting: inner 1. order
47	0	Colour inside: transparent
48	28	Number of digitizations

259

WORDNO.	CONTENT			COMMENT				
IMAGE INFORMATION								
49			0	Records		length of image information		
50			191	Words				
51 -200		325	76		325	76	(dX,dY)	1.DIG w-vector
53 1	7E	FA	00	126	-6	0	(K,dX,dY)	2.DIG s-vector
54 2		EF	EE		-17	-18	(dX,dY)	3.DIG s-vector
55 2		F7	F8		-9	-8	(dX,dY)	4.DIG s-vector
56 2		EC	EF		-20	-17	(dX,dY)	5.DIG s-vector
57 2		EA	F1		-22	-15	(dX,dY)	6.DIG s-vector
58 2	7D	E5	F3 FE	125	-27	-13 -2	(K,dX,dY,dS)	7.DIG c-vector
60 2		E4	F6 FE		-28	-10 -2	(dX,dY,dS)	8.DIG c-vector
62 1	7E	E8	FC	126	-24	-4	(K,dX,dY)	9.DIG s-vector
63 2		E8	FE		-24	-2	(dX,dY)	10.DIG s-vector
64 2	7D	D7	04 FB	125	-41	4 -5	(K,dX,dY,dS)	11.DIG c-vector
66 2		DC	0D FB		-36	13 -5	(dX,dY,dS)	12.DIG c-vector
68 1		DE	1A F9		-34	26 -7	(dX,dY,dS)	13.DIG c-vector
69 2		E9	22 F9		-23	34 -7	(dX,dY,dS)	14.DIG c-vector
71 1		F5	22 FC		-11	34 -4	(dX,dY,dS)	15.DIG c-vector
72 2		FD	26 FC		-3	38 -4	(dX,dY,dS)	16.DIG c-vector
74 1		03	1D FE		3	29 -2	(dX,dY,dS)	17.DIG c-vector
75 2		07	19 FE		7	25 -2	(dX,dY,dS)	18.DIG c-vector
77 1		0D	19 FD		13	25 -3	(dX,dY,dS)	19.DIG c-vector
78 2		10	12 FD		16	18 -3	(dX,dY,dS)	20.DIG c-vector
80 1		20	16 FC		32	22 -4	(dX,dY,dS)	21.DIG c-vector
81 2		27	10 FC		39	16 -4	(dX,dY,dS)	22.DIG c-vector
83 1	7E	21	08	126	33	8	(K,dX,dY)	23.DIG s-vector
84 2		27	07		39	7	(dX,dY)	24.DIG s-vector
85 2		29	06		41	6	(dX,dY)	25.DIG s-vector
86 2		5C	11		92	17	(dX,dY)	26.DIG s-vector
87 2	85			-123				is a vertical peak
88 1		08	0C		8	12	(dX,dY)	27.DIG s-vector
89 1		00	15		0	21	(dX,dY)	28.DIG s-vector
90 1		00	0B		0	11	(dX,dY)	29.DIG s-vector
91 1		FD	14		-3	20	(dX,dY)	30.DIG s-vector
92 1		FC	14		-4	20	(dX,dY)	31.DIG s-vector
93 1	7D	F4	21 03	125	-12	33 3	(K,dX,dY,dS)	32.DIG c-vector
95 1		F2	15 03		-14	21 3	(dX,dY,dS)	33.DIG c-vector
96 2		F0	0D 03		-16	13 3	(dX,dY,dS)	34.DIG c-vector
98 1		E7	0B 03		-25	11 3	(dX,dY,dS)	35.DIG c-vector
99 2		EB	05 02		-21	5 2	(dX,dY,dS)	36.DIG c-vector
101 1		EB	01 02		-21	1 2	(dX,dY,dS)	37.DIG c-vector
102 2	7E	F0	FE	126	-16	-2	(K,dX,dY)	38.DIG s-vector
104 1		F2	FD		-14	-3	(dX,dY)	39.DIG s-vector
105 1		F6	FD		-10	-3	(dX,dY)	40.DIG s-vector
106 1		F9	FD		-7	-3	(dX,dY)	41.DIG s-vector
107 1		FB	FD		-5	-3	(dX,dY)	42.DIG s-vector
108 1		FB	FC		-5	-4	(dX,dY)	43.DIG s-vector
109 1		FB	FB		-5	-5	(dX,dY)	44.DIG s-vector
110 1		FF	FD		-1	-3	(dX,dY)	45.DIG s-vector
111 1		01	FD		1	-3	(dX,dY)	46.DIG s-vector
112 1		03	FB		3	-5	(dX,dY)	47.DIG s-vector
113 1		08	F7		8	-9	(dX,dY)	48.DIG s-vector
114 1		06	F9		6	-7	(dX,dY)	49.DIG s-vector
115 1		04	F7		4	-9	(dX,dY)	50.DIG s-vector
116 1		02	F7		2	-9	(dX,dY)	51.DIG s-vector

WORDNO.	CONTENT			COMMENT				
117 1	01	F6			1	-10		(dX,dY)	52.DIG s-vector
118 1	7D	FE	F2	FE	125	-2 -14	-2	(K,dX,dY,dS)	53.DIG c-vector
120 1		FB	F2	FE		-5 -14	-2	(dX,dY,dS)	54.DIG c-vector
121 2		F6	F3	FD		-10 -13	-3	(dX,dY,dS)	55.DIG c-vector
123 1		F3	F6	FD		-13 -10	-3	(dX,dY,dS)	56.DIG c-vector
124 2		F0	FB	FE		-16 -5	-2	(dX,dY,dS)	57.DIG c-vector
126 1		EF	FE	FE		-17 -2	-2	(dX,dY,dS)	58.DIG c-vector
127 2	7E	F1	02		126	-15 2		(K,dX,dY)	59.DIG s-vector
129 1		F6	03			-10 3		(dX,dY)	60.DIG s-vector
130 1	7D	F0	0C	FC	125	-16 12	-4	(K,dX,dY,dS)	61.DIG c-vector
132 1		F4	11	FC		-12 17	-4	(dX,dY,dS)	62.DIG c-vector
133 2		FB	10	FE		-5 16	-2	(dX,dY,dS)	63.DIG c-vector
135 1		FF	11	FE		-1 17	-2	(dX,dY,dS)	64.DIG c-vector
136 2	7E	02	0F		126	2 15		(K,dX,dY)	65.DIG s-vector
138 1		05	0E			5 14		(dX,dY)	66.DIG s-vector
139 1	7D	0C	15	FD	125	12 21	-3	(K,dX,dY,dS)	67.DIG c-vector
141 1		10	10	FD		16 16	-3	(dX,dY,dS)	68.DIG c-vector
142 2		1D	12	FC		29 18	-4	(dX,dY,dS)	69.DIG c-vector
144 1		21	0B	FC		33 11	-4	(dX,dY,dS)	70.DIG c-vector
145 2		23	07	FE		35 7	-2	(dX,dY,dS)	71.DIG c-vector

WORDNO.	CONTENT			COMMENT				
199 1		F9	13			-7	19	(dX,dY)	107.DIG s-vector
200 1		FB	12			-5	18	(dX,dY)	108.DIG s-vector
201 -239		0		198		0	198	(dX,dY)	109.DIG w-vector
203 1	7E	F9	04		126	-7	4	(K,dX,dY)	110.DIG s-vector
204 2	85				-123				is a vertical peak
205 1		C6	F6			-58	-10	(dX,dY)	111.DIG s-vector
206 1		E3	FA			-29	-6	(dX,dY)	112.DIG s-vector
207 1		DD	F7			-35	-9	(dX,dY)	113.DIG s-vector
208 1		E4	F8			-28	-8	(dX,dY)	114.DIG s-vector
209 1		EB	F7			-21	-9	(dX,dY)	115.DIG s-vector
210 1	7D	EA	F0	04	125	-22 -16	4	(K,dX,dY,dS)	116.DIG c-vector
212 1		F0	EA	04		-16 -22	4	(dX,dY,dS)	117.DIG c-vector
213 2		F8	EB	03		-8 -21	3	(dX,dY,dS)	118.DIG c-vector
215 1		FC	E2	03		-4 -30	3	(dX,dY,dS)	119.DIG c-vector
216 2		02	E6	03		2 -26	3	(dX,dY,dS)	120.DIG c-vector
218 1		0B	E8	03		8 -24	3	(dX,dY,dS)	121.DIG c-vector
219 2		0D	EA	04		13 -22	4	(dX,dY,dS)	122.DIG c-vector
221 1		15	EF	04		21 -17	4	(dX,dY,dS)	123.DIG c-vector
222 2		18	F5	04		24 -11	4	(dX,dY,dS)	124.DIG c-vector
224 1		1D	FC	04		29 -4	4	(dX,dY,dS)	125.DIG c-vector
225 2		1C	03	03		28 3	3	(dX,dY,dS)	126.DIG c-vector
227 1		1A	08	03		26 8	3	(dX,dY,dS)	127.DIG c-vector
228 2		18	0E	03		24 14	3	(dX,dY,dS)	128.DIG c-vector
230 1		14	11	03		20 17	3	(dX,dY,dS)	129.DIG c-vector
231 2		0D	11	02		13 17	2	(dX,dY,dS)	130.DIG c-vector
233 2		08	10	02		8 16	2	(dX,dY,dS)	131.DIG c-vector
234 2	7E	06	13		126	6 19		(K,dX,dY)	132.DIG s-vector
236 1		04	1A			4	26	(dX,dY)	133.DIG s-vector
237 1		02	11			2	17	(dX,dY)	134.DIG s-vector
238 1		00	0F			0	15	(dX,dY)	135.DIG s-vector
239 1		00	4F			0	79	(dX,dY)	136.DIG s-vector

WORDNO.	CONTENT	COMMENT
1	0	Records length of character
2	179	Words

NAME SECTION

3	3	Length of name section
4	302	Character number
5	0	Number of following part

SETTING INFORMATION

6	27	Length of setting information
7	11	Character type = small letter
8	89	Number of vectors
9	694	Total set width (T=L+W+R)
10	0	Left side bearing (L)
11	640	Width (W)
12	54	Right side bearing (R)
13	0	X-minimum
14	640	X-maximum
15	-14	Y-minimum
16	756	Y-maximum
17	1	Unit is 1 pixel
18	2	Stem information for contours 1 - 2
19	2	Number of vertical straight lines
20	16501	Absolute value (in pixels) 117
21	94	Relative value (in pixels)
22	3	Number of vertical curve extrema
23	17024	Absolute value (in pixels) 640
24	-119	Relative value (in pixels)
25	16594	Absolute value (in pixels) 210
26	0	Number of horizontal straight lines
27	5	Number of horizontal curve extrema
28	16373	Absolute value (in pixels) -11
29	36	Relative value (in pixels)
30	16899	Absolute value (in pixels) 515
31	-36	Relative value (in pixels)
32	16427	Absolute value (in pixels) 43

CONTOUR INDEX

33	0	Records length of contour index
34	14	Words
35	0	Record pointer for 1. contour: 0
36	3	Word pointer : 49
37	-1	Sense of rotation of contour = clockwise
38	0	Nesting: outer 1. order
39	0	Colour inside: transparent
40	56	Number of digitizations
41	0	Record pointer for 2. contour: 0
42	84	Word pointer : 130
43	1	Sense of rotation of contour = counterclockwise
44	1	Nesting: inner 1. order
45	0	Colour inside: transparent
46	33	Number of digitizations

WORDNO.	CONTENT				COMMENT				
121 2	7D	FB	FE	02	125	-5	-2	2	(K,dX,dY,dS)	51.DIG c-vector
123 2		F6	F8	02		-10	-8	2	(dX,dY,dS)	52.DIG c-vector
125 1	7E	FA	F9		126	-6	-7		(K,dX,dY)	53.DIG s-vector
126 2		F8	F7			-8	-9		(dX,dY)	54.DIG s-vector
127 2		F2	EE			-14	-18		(dX,dY)	55.DIG s-vector
128 2		F5	F3			-11	-13		(dX,dY)	56.DIG s-vector
130 -179		66		266		66	266		(dX,dY)	57.DIG w-vector
132 1	7E	01	D4		126	1	-44		(K,dX,dY)	58.DIG s-vector
133 2		03	DB			3	-37		(dX,dY)	59.DIG s-vector
134 2	7D	0D	D0	06	125	13	-48	6	(K,dX,dY,dS)	60.DIG c-vector
136 2		16	D7	06		22	-41	6	(dX,dY,dS)	61.DIG c-vector
138 1		15	EA	04		21	-22	4	(dX,dY,dS)	62.DIG c-vector
139 2		1D	ED	04		29	-19	4	(dX,dY,dS)	63.DIG c-vector
141 1		20	F4	04		32	-12	4	(dX,dY,dS)	64.DIG c-vector
142 2		1F	FC	04		31	-4	4	(dX,dY,dS)	65.DIG c-vector
144 1		21	04	04		33	4	4	(dX,dY,dS)	66.DIG c-vector
145 2		21	0D	04		33	13	4	(dX,dY,dS)	67.DIG c-vector
147 1		19	10	03		25	16	3	(dX,dY,dS)	68.DIG c-vector
148 2		14	14	03		20	20	3	(dX,dY,dS)	69.DIG c-vector
150 1		1A	2C	07		26	44	7	(dX,dY,dS)	70.DIG c-vector
151 2		10	35	07		16	53	7	(dX,dY,dS)	71.DIG c-vector
153 1		05	2D	02		5	45	2	(dX,dY,dS)	72.DIG c-vector
154 2		01	31	02		1	49	2	(dX,dY,dS)	73.DIG c-vector
156 1		FD	2E	02		-3	46	2	(dX,dY,dS)	74.DIG c-vector
157 2		F9	29	02		-7	41	2	(dX,dY,dS)	75.DIG c-vector
159 1		F3	27	04		-13	39	4	(dX,dY,dS)	76.DIG c-vector
160 2		EC	21	04		-20	33	4	(dX,dY,dS)	77.DIG c-vector
162 1		EB	15	04		-21	21	4	(dX,dY,dS)	78.DIG c-vector
163 2		E2	11	04		-30	17	4	(dX,dY,dS)	79.DIG c-vector
165 1		E4	09	03		-28	9	3	(dX,dY,dS)	80.DIG c-vector
166 2		E2	04	03		-30	4	3	(dX,dY,dS)	81.DIG c-vector
168 1		DD	FD	04		-35	-3	4	(dX,dY,dS)	82.DIG c-vector
169 2		DE	F4	04		-34	-12	4	(dX,dY,dS)	83.DIG c-vector
171 1		E1	EC	05		-31	-20	5	(dX,dY,dS)	84.DIG c-vector
172 2		E8	E6	05		-24	-26	5	(dX,dY,dS)	85.DIG c-vector
174 1		EE	DF	05		-18	-33	5	(dX,dY,dS)	86.DIG c-vector
175 2		F5	D6	05		-11	-42	5	(dX,dY,dS)	87.DIG c-vector
177 1		FC	D7	02		-4	-41	2	(dX,dY,dS)	88.DIG c-vector
178 2		FE	CE	02		-2	-50	2	(dX,dY,dS)	89.DIG c-vector

WORDNO.	CONTENT	COMMENT
1	0	Records length of character
2	161	Words

NAME SECTION

3	3	Length of name section
4	303	Character number
5	0	Number of following part

SETTING INFORMATION

6	27	Length of setting information
7	11	Character type = small letter
8	89	Number of vectors
9	533	Total set width (T=L+W+R)
10	54	Left side bearing (L)
11	450	Width (W)
12	29	Right side bearing (R)
13	0	X-minimum
14	450	X-maximum
15	-11	Y-minimum
16	515	Y-maximum
17	1	Unit is 1 pixel
18	1	Stem information for contours 1 - 1
19	0	Number of vertical straight lines
20	5	Number of vertical curve extrema
21	16384	Absolute value (in pixels) 0
22	119	Relative value (in pixels)
23	16834	Absolute value (in pixels) 450
24	-97	Relative value (in pixels)
25	16709	Absolute value (in pixels) 325
26	0	Number of horizontal straight lines
27	5	Number of horizontal curve extrema
28	16373	Absolute value (in pixels) -11
29	54	Relative value (in pixels)
30	16899	Absolute value (in pixels) 515
31	-36	Relative value (in pixels)
32	16710	Absolute value (in pixels) 326

CONTOUR INDEX

33	0	Records length of contour index
34	8	Words
35	0	Record pointer for 1. contour: 0
36	3	Word pointer : 43
37	-1	Sense of rotation of contour = clockwise
38	0	Nesting: outer 1. order
39	0	Colour inside: transparent
40	89	Number of digitizations

IMAGE INFORMATION

41		0	Records length of image information
42		121	Words
43 -161	432 104	432 104 (dX,dY) 1.DIG w-vector
45 1	85	-123 is a vertical peak

WORDNO.	CONTENT				COMMENT				
45 2	7E	0C	E8		126	12	−24	(K,dX,dY)	2.DIG s-vector
47 1	86				−122				is a horizontal peak
47 2		F1	F0			−15	−16	(dX,dY)	3.DIG s-vector
48 2		F8	F9			−8	−7	(dX,dY)	4.DIG s-vector
49 2	7D	E8	ED	FE	125	−24	−19	−2 (K,dX,dY,dS)	5.DIG c-vector
51 2		E5	F0	FE		−27	−16	−2 (dX,dY,dS)	6.DIG c-vector
53 1		E2	F2	FE		−30	−14	−2 (dX,dY,dS)	7.DIG c-vector
54 2		DF	F6	FE		−33	−10	−2 (dX,dY,dS)	8.DIG c-vector
56 1		DC	F9	FE		−36	−7	−2 (dX,dY,dS)	9.DIG c-vector
57 2		DD	FE	FE		−35	−2	−2 (dX,dY,dS)	10.DIG c-vector
59 1		D4	04	FC		−44	4	−4 (dX,dY,dS)	11.DIG c-vector
60 2		D8	0B	FC		−40	11	−4 (dX,dY,dS)	12.DIG c-vector
62 1		D8	14	FB		−40	20	−5 (dX,dY,dS)	13.DIG c-vector
63 2		DE	1A	FB		−34	26	−5 (dX,dY,dS)	14.DIG c-vector
65 1		DF	29	FA		−33	41	−6 (dX,dY,dS)	15.DIG c-vector
66 2		E7	31	FA		−25	49	−6 (dX,dY,dS)	16.DIG c-vector
68 1		F1	38	FB		−15	56	−5 (dX,dY,dS)	17.DIG c-vector
69 2		FB	3B	FB		−5	59	−5 (dX,dY,dS)	18.DIG c-vector
71 1		04	37	FB		4	55	−5 (dX,dY,dS)	19.DIG c-vector
72 2		0E	34	FB		14	52	−5 (dX,dY,dS)	20.DIG c-vector

WORDNO.	CONTENT				COMMENT				
122 2		F8	08			−8	8	(dX,dY)	60.DIG s-vector
123 2		F7	07			−9	7	(dX,dY)	61.DIG s-vector
124 2		F4	06			−12	6	(dX,dY)	62.DIG s-vector
125 2		F1	04			−15	4	(dX,dY)	63.DIG s-vector
126 2		F0	03			−16	3	(dX,dY)	64.DIG s-vector
127 2		EF	01			−17	1	(dX,dY)	65.DIG s-vector
128 2	7D	E2	FD	03	125	−30	−3	3 (K,dX,dY,dS)	66.DIG c-vector
130 2		E3	F6	03		−29	−10	3 (dX,dY,dS)	67.DIG c-vector
132 1		E6	F1	03		−26	−15	3 (dX,dY,dS)	68.DIG c-vector
133 2		EF	F0	03		−17	−16	3 (dX,dY,dS)	69.DIG c-vector
135 1		EB	E2	04		−21	−30	4 (dX,dY,dS)	70.DIG c-vector
136 2		F1	D9	04		−15	−39	4 (dX,dY,dS)	71.DIG c-vector
138 1		F6	CA	04		−10	−54	4 (dX,dY,dS)	72.DIG c-vector
139 2		FD	C9	04		−3	−55	4 (dX,dY,dS)	73.DIG c-vector
141 1		03	CE	03		3	−50	3 (dX,dY,dS)	74.DIG c-vector
142 2		09	D5	03		9	−43	3 (dX,dY,dS)	75.DIG c-vector
144 1		11	D7	06		17	−41	6 (dX,dY,dS)	76.DIG c-vector
145 2		1B	DC	06		27	−36	6 (dX,dY,dS)	77.DIG c-vector
147 1		17	EE	03		23	−18	3 (dX,dY,dS)	78.DIG c-vector
148 2		1A	F2	03		26	−14	3 (dX,dY,dS)	79.DIG c-vector
150 1		1E	F7	03		30	−9	3 (dX,dY,dS)	80.DIG c-vector
151 2		23	FD	03		35	−3	3 (dX,dY,dS)	81.DIG c-vector
153 1	7E	13	01		126	19	1	(K,dX,dY)	82.DIG s-vector
154 2		15	04			21	4	(dX,dY)	83.DIG s-vector
155 2		17	06			23	6	(dX,dY)	84.DIG s-vector
156 2		14	08			20	8	(dX,dY)	85.DIG s-vector
157 2		15	0B			21	11	(dX,dY)	86.DIG s-vector
158 2		13	0D			19	13	(dX,dY)	87.DIG s-vector
159 2		07	06			7	6	(dX,dY)	88.DIG s-vector
160 2		0D	0C			13	12	(dX,dY)	89.DIG s-vector

```
                            GRAND TOTAL
                            -----------
                                                WORDS        KBYTES
                                                -----        ------
   Length of font:                              21480        42.960
   Length of font header:                         484         0.968
   Length of all character headers:              5546        11.092
   Length of total image information:           15450        30.900
```

```
              DIGITIZATIONS                      NUMBER
              -------------                      ------
              White vectors:                       227
              L-vectors:                            441
              S-vectors:                           4242
              C-vectors:                           5528
                                                 ======
              Total:                              10438
```

```
              Serif starts:                        150
              Serif ends:                          150
              Horizontal peaks:                     81
              Vertical peaks:                      107
```

```
              Characters:                          135
              Records (a 2048 words):               11
```

```
              Raster (grid):              1080 X  1080
```

```
              Digitizations per character:          77
              Image information per character:     228 bytes
```

```
                    VS - CHORD HEIGHT - STATISTICS
                       (Unit is quarter pixel)

              Number of chords with height    2 =    1011
              Number of chords with height    3 =     825
              Number of chords with height    4 =     323
              Number of chords with height    5 =     145
              Number of chords with height    6 =      92
              Number of chords with height    7 =      74
              Number of chords with height    8 =      24
              Number of chords with height    9 =      10
              Number of chords with height   10 =       6
              Number of chords with height   17 =       4
              Number of chords with height   18 =       4
              Number of chords with height   -2 =    1175
              Number of chords with height   -3 =     745
              Number of chords with height   -4 =     362
              Number of chords with height   -5 =     244
              Number of chords with height   -6 =     120
              Number of chords with height   -7 =      90
              Number of chords with height   -8 =      54
              Number of chords with height   -9 =      45
              Number of chords with height  -10 =      15
              Number of chords with height  -11 =       6

              Number of chords with height  -21 =      80
              Number of chords with height  -22 =       4
              Number of chords with height  -23 =       8
              Number of chords with height  -24 =       8
              Number of chords with height  -28 =       8
```

266

Appendix M
Description of the VE format

1. Structure of a VE font

For the structure of a VE font see appendices G and K, extended structure.

2. Description of the VE format

The **vector format** is a simplified form of the VC format. The arcs are no longer described as circles but divided into vectors and then coded.

The curved sections of an IK type font comprise almost 90% of the image information. As already mentioned (chapter 5.1.4), raster images seldom have long straight sections in curved parts with more than 13 contour pixels.

This fact has led to an incremental coding in which an 8 bit byte is sufficient for a vector. Such vectors are known as V vectors. The left 4 bits (higher value) describe the X increment of the V vector, the right 4 bits (lower value) the Y increment.

The amounts ΔX and ΔY of the V vectors are kept smaller than 14. The sign is determined specially for each case.

As in the case of a VC format, there are also white vectors which run to the start of the contours with pen "raised". They start on the word boundary at the beginning of the contour data. The associated ΔX and ΔY values are INTEGER $\times 2$ with sign. The first white vector starts at the zero point of the appropriate coordinate system of the character. The subsequent white vectors then start at the ends of the preceding contours and lead to the following contour in a sequence as given by the contour index.

Longer straights cannot, of course, be described with V vectors. For this reason we have introduced the following system (hexadecimal notation).

The vectors E0...ED indicate that the X components are first described in the following byte. In doing so the byte values 1...120 are taken as positive and the values 255...136 are counted as negative, as $-1...-120$. We call this the S vector method.

From now on the X components of the vectors have the sign given here. Vectors F0...FD are in effect the same and additionally change the sign of the following Y components.

If the following byte is coded with 80 then the coding, as INTE-GER × 2 with sign, follows in the next 2 bytes (16 bit). We call this the L vector method. The sign of the components also applies to the subsequent V vectors.

Correspondingly the vectors OE...DE and OF...DF mean that the Y components are first described in the following byte or following 3 bytes. Byte EE, EF, FE or FF mean that first the X, and then the Y components are described as discussed previously.

The switch-over of the sign for the short increments ΔX and ΔY of the V vectors is carried out by calling up the longer code (either 8 or 16 bit) for one or, in some cases, both components. The stating of F0...FD or 0F...DF allows simultaneous switching of the sign of the other respective component. This switch-over first applies, however, from the next V vector onwards and not for the vector currently being dealt with.

Coding examples: sequence of increments

Increment	Hexadecimal (INTEGER × 2)	Status of sign XY	Comments
5,5	55	+ +	Normal V vector
− 10,0	E0,F6	− +	Sign change in X
− 14,10	EA,F2	− +	S vector method for X
− 10,14	AE,0E	− +	S vector method for Y
− 1000,0	E0,80,(− 1000)	− +	L vector method for X
− 10, − 1000	AF,80,(− 1000)	− −	L vector method for Y
		+ −	Sign change for X
10,10	AE,0A	+ +	Sign change for Y

Increment	Hexadecimal (INTEGER × 2)	Status of sign XY	Comments
200,200	FF,80,(200), 80,(200)	+ + − −	L method for X and Y with double sign change
− 10, − 10	AA		
5, − 5	F5,05	+ − + +	Sign change in X Sign change in Y
4,4	4F,04		
− 3,3	33	− +	Sign change in X

The switch-over of the other component respectively in the case of longer components, is particularly very favourable when digitizing curves; because at the extremes one component is long whereas the other is short and often changes its sign.

The end of the contour is controlled by the number of vectors (digitizations), details of this are found in the contour index. **W, S, L and V vectors are each counted as one digitization.** The end of a character is reached when all contours have been processed. The end of a font is checked with the character index of that font.

3. Example of a VE format

First of all we represent the lower case letters a, b, c of the typeface "URW Antiqua 2015 normal", with marks.

Subsequently the complete type font format is reproduced as a data list. The raster is 400×400 for the em.

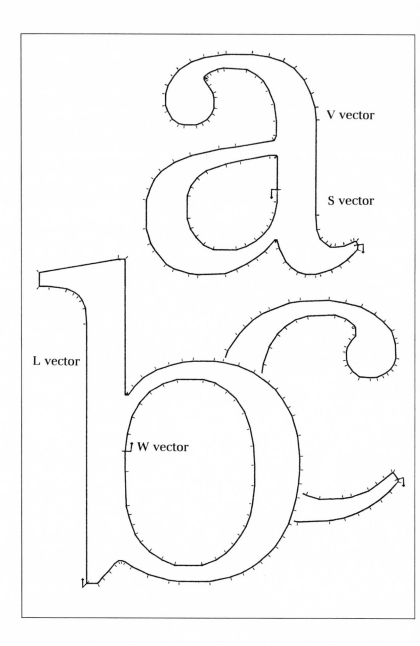

WORDNO.	CONTENT	COMMENT
1	484	Length of font header

NAME SECTION

2	55	Length of name section
3	825	Number on URW list
4 - 10	AN201512.VE	File name (ASCII)
11 - 49	URW-Antiqua 2000 normal	Font name (ASCII)
50	VE	Data format (ASCII)
51 - 53	7 1 87	Production date: 7-Jan-87
54 - 56	7 1 87	Date of last change: 7-Jan-87

FONT INFORMATION

57	19	Length of font information
58	1	Indicator for font
59	135	Number of characters
60	267	Cap height (in pixels)
61	400	Body size (in pixels)
62	187	x-height (in pixels)
63	100	Distance: base line - lower body line(in pixels)
64	400	Text line distance for setting (in pixels)
65	40	Stem thickness (in pixels)
66	0	Angle of italisation (in 1/10 degree)
67	1	Optimum point size for setting (in p)
68	174	Average character width (in pixels)
69	375	X-extension of a pixel (in 1/1000mm)
70	375	Y-extension of a pixel (in 1/1000mm)
71	400	Em-resolution in X-direction (in pixels)
72	400	Em-resolution in Y-direction (in pixels)
73	0	Scan indicator of image data
74	0	Width of printing window (in pixels)
75	0	Height of printing window (in pixels)

HIERARCHY SECTION

76	1	No hierarchy section in this format

CHARACTER INDEX

77	408	Length of character index
78	6	LENGTH OF FONT IN PHYSICAL RECORDS
79	1478	Last word of last record
80	101	Character number: 1
81	1	Pointer to record containing start of character
82	485	Word pointer to start of character
83	102	Ch. no.: 2
84	1	Record pointer
85	566	Word pointer
86- 88	103 1 680	No., record pointer, word pointer of ch.: 3
89- 91	104 1 779	No., record pointer, word pointer of ch.: 4
92- 94	105 1 872	No., record pointer, word pointer of ch.: 5

WORDNO.	CONTENT		COMMENT	
95- 97	106	1 951	No., record pointer, word pointer of ch.:	6
98- 100	107	1 1022	No., record pointer, word pointer of ch.:	7
101- 103	108	1 1134	No., record pointer, word pointer of ch.:	8
104- 106	109	1 1220	No., record pointer, word pointer of ch.:	9
107- 109	110	1 1274	No., record pointer, word pointer of ch.:	10
110- 112	111	1 1334	No., record pointer, word pointer of ch.:	11
113- 115	112	1 1419	No., record pointer, word pointer of ch.:	12
116- 118	113	1 1480	No., record pointer, word pointer of ch.:	13
119- 121	114	1 1564	No., record pointer, word pointer of ch.:	14
122- 124	115	1 1641	No., record pointer, word pointer of ch.:	15
125- 127	116	1 1753	No., record pointer, word pointer of ch.:	16
128- 130	117	1 1845	No., record pointer, word pointer of ch.:	17
131- 133	118	1 1979	No., record pointer, word pointer of ch.:	18
134- 136	119	2 41	No., record pointer, word pointer of ch.:	19
137- 139	120	2 141	No., record pointer, word pointer of ch.:	20
140- 142	121	2 206	No., record pointer, word pointer of ch.:	21
143- 145	122	2 294	No., record pointer, word pointer of ch.:	22
146- 148	123	2 357	No., record pointer, word pointer of ch.:	23
149- 151	124	2 435	No., record pointer, word pointer of ch.:	24
152- 154	125	2 529	No., record pointer, word pointer of ch.:	25
155- 157	126	2 601	No., record pointer, word pointer of ch.:	26
158- 160	127	2 663	No., record pointer, word pointer of ch.:	27
161- 163	128	2 773	No., record pointer, word pointer of ch.:	28
164- 166	129	2 899	No., record pointer, word pointer of ch.:	29
167- 169	201	2 1039	No., record pointer, word pointer of ch.:	30
170- 172	208	2 1160	No., record pointer, word pointer of ch.:	31
173- 175	210	2 1283	No., record pointer, word pointer of ch.:	32
176- 178	237	2 1404	No., record pointer, word pointer of ch.:	33
179- 181	251	2 1556	No., record pointer, word pointer of ch.:	34
182- 184	301	2 1684	No., record pointer, word pointer of ch.:	35
185- 187	302	2 1791	No., record pointer, word pointer of ch.:	36
188- 190	303	2 1888	No., record pointer, word pointer of ch.:	37
191- 193	304	2 1969	No., record pointer, word pointer of ch.:	38
194- 196	305	3 23	No., record pointer, word pointer of ch.:	39
197- 199	306	3 115	No., record pointer, word pointer of ch.:	40
200- 202	307	3 192	No., record pointer, word pointer of ch.:	41
203- 205	308	3 330	No., record pointer, word pointer of ch.:	42
206- 208	309	3 410	No., record pointer, word pointer of ch.:	43
209- 211	310	3 480	No., record pointer, word pointer of ch.:	44
212- 214	311	3 565	No., record pointer, word pointer of ch.:	45
215- 217	312	3 642	No., record pointer, word pointer of ch.:	46
218- 220	313	3 693	No., record pointer, word pointer of ch.:	47
221- 223	314	3 798	No., record pointer, word pointer of ch.:	48
224- 226	315	3 874	No., record pointer, word pointer of ch.:	49
227- 229	316	3 964	No., record pointer, word pointer of ch.:	50
230- 232	317	3 1066	No., record pointer, word pointer of ch.:	51
233- 235	318	3 1167	No., record pointer, word pointer of ch.:	52
236- 238	319	3 1237	No., record pointer, word pointer of ch.:	53
239- 241	320	3 1322	No., record pointer, word pointer of ch.:	54
242- 244	321	3 1382	No., record pointer, word pointer of ch.:	55
245- 247	322	3 1453	No., record pointer, word pointer of ch.:	56
248- 250	323	3 1512	No., record pointer, word pointer of ch.:	57
251- 253	324	3 1584	No., record pointer, word pointer of ch.:	58
254- 256	325	3 1666	No., record pointer, word pointer of ch.:	59
257- 259	326	3 1750	No., record pointer, word pointer of ch.:	60
260- 262	327	3 1809	No., record pointer, word pointer of ch.:	61
263- 265	328	3 1956	No., record pointer, word pointer of ch.:	62
266- 268	329	4 46	No., record pointer, word pointer of ch.:	63
269- 271	330	4 162	No., record pointer, word pointer of ch.:	64

WORDNO.	CONTENT	COMMENT
1	0	Records length of character
2	107	Words

NAME SECTION

3	3	Length of name section
4	301	Character number
5	0	Number of following part

SETTING INFORMATION

6	12	Length of setting information
7	1	Character type = letter
8	113	Number of vectors
9	206	Total set width (T=L+W+R)
10	15	Left side bearing (L)
11	194	Width (W)
12	-3	Right side bearing (R)
13	0	X-minimum
14	194	X-maximum
15	-4	Y-minimum
16	191	Y-maximum
17	1	Unit is 1 pixel

CONTOUR INDEX

18	0	Records length of contour index
19	14	Words
20	0	Record pointer for 1. contour: 0
21	3	Word pointer : 34
22	-1	Turn sense of contour = clockwise
23	0	Nesting: outer 1. order
24	0	Colour inside: transparent
25	89	Number of digitizations
26	0	Record pointer for 2. contour: 0
27	60	Word pointer : 91
28	-1	Turn sense of contour = clockwise
29	1	Nesting: inner 1. order
30	0	Colour inside: transparent
31	24	Number of digitizations

IMAGE INFORMATION

32		0	Records length of image information		
33		76	Words		
34 - 90	193 24		193 24 (dX,dY)	1.DIG w-vector
36 1	OF FC		0 -4 (dx,dY)	2.DIG s-vector
37 1	99		-9 -9 (dx,dY)	3.DIG v-vector
37 2	75		-7 -5 (dx,dy)	4.DIG v-vector
38 1	84		-8 -4 (dx,dy)	5.DIG v-vector
38 2	A3		-10 -3 (dx,dy)	6.DIG v-vector
39 1	41		-4 -1 (dx,dy)	7.DIG v-vector
39 2	F0 F7		-9 0 (dX,dy)	8.DIG s-vector
40 2	72		-7 2 (dx,dy)	9.DIG v-vector

273

WORDNO.	CONTENT	COMMENT
41 1	64	-6	4 (dx,dy)	10.DIG v-vector
41 2	55	-5	5 (dx,dy)	11.DIG v-vector
42 1	6C	-6	12 (dx,dy)	12.DIG v-vector
42 2	27	-2	7 (dx,dy)	13.DIG v-vector
43 1	F0 FE	-2	0 (dX,dy)	14.DIG s-vector
44 1	9A	-9	-10 (dx,dy)	15.DIG v-vector
44 2	86	-8	-6 (dx,dy)	16.DIG v-vector
45 1	85	-8	-5 (dx,dy)	17.DIG v-vector
45 2	A5	-10	-5 (dx,dy)	18.DIG v-vector
46 1	A4	-10	-4 (dx,dy)	19.DIG v-vector
46 2	F1 E7	-25	-1 (dX,dy)	20.DIG s-vector
47 2	81	-8	1 (dx,dy)	21.DIG v-vector
48 1	E4 F2	-14	4 (dX,dy)	22.DIG s-vector
49 1	74	-7	4 (dx,dy)	23.DIG v-vector
49 2	AC	-10	12 (dx,dy)	24.DIG v-vector
50 1	46	-4	6 (dx,dy)	25.DIG v-vector
50 2	4D	-4	13 (dx,dy)	26.DIG v-vector
51 1	0F 19	0	25 (dx,dY)	27.DIG s-vector
52 1	39	3	9 (dx,dy)	28.DIG v-vector
52 2	49	4	9 (dx,dy)	29.DIG v-vector
53 1	67	6	7 (dx,dy)	30.DIG v-vector
53 2	C8	12	8 (dx,dy)	31.DIG v-vector
54 1	E6 0F	15	6 (dX,dy)	32.DIG s-vector
55 1	E6 1A	26	6 (dX,dy)	33.DIG s-vector
56 1	E2 0F	15	2 (dX,dy)	34.DIG s-vector
57 1	E6 23	35	6 (dX,dy)	35.DIG s-vector
58 1	24	2	4 (dx,dy)	36.DIG v-vector
58 2	0F 0D	0	13 (dx,dY)	37.DIG s-vector
59 2	2E 0F	-2	15 (dx,dY)	38.DIG s-vector
60 2	5C	-5	12 (dx,dy)	39.DIG v-vector
61 1	58	-5	8 (dx,dy)	40.DIG v-vector
61 2	65	-6	5 (dx,dy)	41.DIG v-vector
62 1	95	-9	5 (dx,dy)	42.DIG v-vector
62 2	F1 EB	-21	1 (dX,dy)	43.DIG s-vector
63 2	61	-6	-1 (dx,dy)	44.DIG v-vector
64 1	73	-7	-3 (dx,dy)	45.DIG v-vector
64 2	32	-3	-2 (dx,dy)	46.DIG v-vector
65 1	22	-2	-2 (dx,dy)	47.DIG v-vector
65 2	0F FE	0	-2 (dx,dY)	48.DIG s-vector
66 2	12	1	-2 (dx,dy)	49.DIG v-vector
67 1	34	3	-4 (dx,dy)	50.DIG v-vector
67 2	46	4	-6 (dx,dy)	51.DIG v-vector
68 1	14	1	-4 (dx,dy)	52.DIG v-vector
68 2	0F F7	0	-9 (dx,dY)	53.DIG s-vector
69 2	25	-2	-5 (dx,dy)	54.DIG v-vector
70 1	45	-4	-5 (dx,dy)	55.DIG v-vector
70 2	53	-5	-3 (dx,dy)	56.DIG v-vector
71 1	52	-5	-2 (dx,dy)	57.DIG v-vector
71 2	F0 F5	-11	0 (dX,dy)	58.DIG s-vector
72 2	51	-5	1 (dx,dy)	59.DIG v-vector
73 1	64	-6	4 (dx,dy)	60.DIG v-vector
73 2	47	-4	7 (dx,dy)	61.DIG v-vector
74 1	25	-2	5 (dx,dy)	62.DIG v-vector
74 2	0F 0A	0	10 (dx,dY)	63.DIG s-vector
75 2	27	2	7 (dx,dy)	64.DIG v-vector
76 1	58	5	8 (dx,dy)	65.DIG v-vector
76 2	56	5	6 (dx,dy)	66.DIG v-vector
77 1	B7	11	7 (dx,dy)	67.DIG v-vector
77 2	C4	12	4 (dx,dy)	68.DIG v-vector

274

WORDNO.	CONTENT	COMMENT
1	0	Records length of character
2	97	Words

NAME SECTION

3	3	Length of name section
4	302	Character number
5	0	Number of following part

SETTING INFORMATION

6	12	Length of setting information
7	1	Character type = letter
8	90	Number of vectors
9	257	Total set width (T=L+W+R)
10	0	Left side bearing (L)
11	237	Width (W)
12	20	Right side bearing (R)
13	0	X-minimum
14	237	X-maximum
15	-5	Y-minimum
16	280	Y-maximum
17	1	Unit is 1 pixel

CONTOUR INDEX

18	0	Records length of contour index
19	14	Words
20	0	Record pointer for 1. contour: 0
21	3	Word pointer : 34
22	-1	Turn sense of contour = clockwise
23	0	Nesting: outer 1. order
24	0	Colour inside: transparent
25	56	Number of digitizations
26	0	Record pointer for 2. contour: 0
27	43	Word pointer : 74
28	-1	Turn sense of contour = clockwise
29	1	Nesting: inner 1. order
30	0	Colour inside: transparent
31	34	Number of digitizations

IMAGE INFORMATION

32		0	Records length of image information
33		66	Words
34 – 73	43 -5	43 -5 (dX,dY)	1.DIG w-vector
36 1	0F 80 227	0 227 (dx,dY)	2.DIG l-vector
38 1	1E 0E	-1 14 (dx,dY)	3.DIG s-vector
39 1	37	-3 7 (dx,dy)	4.DIG v-vector
39 2	34	-3 4 (dx,dy)	5.DIG v-vector
40 1	43	-4 3 (dx,dy)	6.DIG v-vector
40 2	73	-7 3 (dx,dy)	7.DIG v-vector
41 1	E2 F0	-16 2 (dX,dy)	8.DIG s-vector
42 1	90	-9 0 (dx,dy)	9.DIG v-vector

WORDNO.	CONTENT	COMMENT			
83 1	5E F2	5	-14	(dx,dY)	69.DIG s-vector
84 1	3E F1	3	-15	(dx,dY)	70.DIG s-vector
85 1	1E EF	1	-17	(dx,dY)	71.DIG s-vector
86 1	0F EE	0	-18	(dx,dY)	72.DIG s-vector
87 1	2E F0	-2	-16	(dx,dY)	73.DIG s-vector
88 1	2A	-2	-10	(dx,dy)	74.DIG v-vector
88 2	4A	-4	-10	(dx,dy)	75.DIG v-vector
89 1	58	-5	-8	(dx,dy)	76.DIG v-vector
89 2	68	-6	-8	(dx,dy)	77.DIG v-vector
90 1	77	-7	-7	(dx,dy)	78.DIG v-vector
90 2	96	-9	-6	(dx,dy)	79.DIG v-vector
91 1	D5	-13	-5	(dx,dy)	80.DIG v-vector
91 2	F0 E7	-25	0	(dX,dy)	81.DIG s-vector
92 2	C5	-12	5	(dx,dy)	82.DIG v-vector
93 1	B7	-11	7	(dx,dy)	83.DIG v-vector
93 2	88	-8	8	(dx,dy)	84.DIG v-vector
94 1	57	-5	7	(dx,dy)	85.DIG v-vector
94 2	38	-3	8	(dx,dy)	86.DIG v-vector
95 1	39	-3	9	(dx,dy)	87.DIG v-vector
95 2	28	-2	8	(dx,dy)	88.DIG v-vector
96 1	1E 1E	-1	30	(dx,dY)	89.DIG s-vector
97 1	0E 12	0	18	(dx,dY)	90.DIG s-vector

WORDNO.	CONTENT		COMMENT
1	0		Records length of character
2	81		Words

NAME SECTION

3	3		Length of name section
4	303		Character number
5	0		Number of following part

SETTING INFORMATION

6	12		Length of setting information
7	1		Character type = letter
8	78		Number of vectors
9	198		Total set width (T=L+W+R)
10	20		Left side bearing (L)
11	167		Width (W)
12	11		Right side bearing (R)
13	0		X-minimum
14	167		X-maximum
15	-4		Y-minimum
16	191		Y-maximum
17	1		Unit is 1 pixel

CONTOUR INDEX

18	0		Records length of contour index
19	8		Words
20	0		Record pointer for 1. contour: 0
21	3		Word pointer : 28
22	-1		Turn sense of contour = clockwise
23	0		Nesting: outer 1. order
24	0		Colour inside: transparent
25	78		Number of digitizations

IMAGE INFORMATION

26		0	Records length of image information			
27		56	Words			
28 - 81	164	31	164	31 (dX,dY)	1.DIG	w-vector
30 1	0F FE		0	-2 (dx,dY)	2.DIG	s-vector
31 1	88		-8	-8 (dx,dy)	3.DIG	v-vector
31 2	97		-9	-7 (dx,dy)	4.DIG	v-vector
32 1	A6		-10	-6 (dx,dy)	5.DIG	v-vector
32 2	B5		-11	-5 (dx,dy)	6.DIG	v-vector
33 1	C4		-12	-4 (dx,dy)	7.DIG	v-vector
33 2	E2 F2		-14	-2 (dX,dy)	8.DIG	s-vector
34 2	F0 E3		-29	0 (dX,dy)	9.DIG	s-vector
35 2	E4 F1		-15	4 (dX,dy)	10.DIG	s-vector
36 2	E8 F2		-14	8 (dX,dy)	11.DIG	s-vector
37 2	DA		-13	10 (dx,dy)	12.DIG	v-vector
38 1	77		-7	7 (dx,dy)	13.DIG	v-vector
38 2	58		-5	8 (dx,dy)	14.DIG	v-vector
39 1	AE 12		-10	18 (dx,dY)	15.DIG	s-vector
40 1	5E 15		-5	21 (dx,dY)	16.DIG	s-vector

WORDNO.	CONTENT	COMMENT
41 1	1B	-1 11 (dx,dy) 17.DIG v-vector
41 2	OF 14	0 20 (dx,dY) 18.DIG s-vector
42 2	1B	1 11 (dx,dy) 19.DIG v-vector
43 1	5E 13	5 19 (dx,dY) 20.DIG s-vector
44 1	6E OF	6 15 (dx,dY) 21.DIG s-vector
45 1	AD	10 13 (dx,dy) 22.DIG v-vector
45 2	77	7 7 (dx,dy) 23.DIG v-vector
46 1	76	7 6 (dx,dy) 24.DIG v-vector
46 2	85	8 5 (dx,dy) 25.DIG v-vector
47 1	83	8 3 (dx,dy) 26.DIG v-vector
47 2	E6 12	18 6 (dx,dy) 27.DIG s-vector
48 2	A1	10 1 (dx,dy) 28.DIG v-vector
49 1	FO 1A	26 0 (dX,dy) 29.DIG s-vector
50 1	E3 OF	15 -3 (dX,dy) 30.DIG s-vector
51 1	E4 OE	14 -4 (dX,dy) 31.DIG s-vector
52 1	C7	12 -7 (dx,dy) 32.DIG v-vector
52 2	87	8 -7 (dx,dy) 33.DIG v-vector
53 1	78	7 -8 (dx,dy) 34.DIG v-vector
53 2	27	2 -7 (dx,dy) 35.DIG v-vector
54 1	14	1 -4 (dx,dy) 36.DIG v-vector
54 2	OF F3	0 -13 (dx,dY) 37.DIG s-vector
55 2	25	-2 -5 (dx,dy) 38.DIG v-vector
56 1	34	-3 -4 (dx,dy) 39.DIG v-vector
56 2	43	-4 -3 (dx,dy) 40.DIG v-vector
57 1	42	-4 -2 (dx,dy) 41.DIG v-vector
57 2	52	-5 -2 (dx,dy) 42.DIG v-vector
58 1	FO FA	-6 0 (dX,dy) 43.DIG s-vector
59 1	A1	-10 1 (dx,dy) 44.DIG v-vector
59 2	65	-6 5 (dx,dy) 45.DIG v-vector
60 1	46	-4 6 (dx,dy) 46.DIG v-vector
60 2	14	-1 4 (dx,dy) 47.DIG v-vector
61 1	OF 07	0 7 (dx,dY) 48.DIG s-vector
62 1	14	1 4 (dx,dy) 49.DIG v-vector
62 2	46	4 6 (dx,dy) 50.DIG v-vector
63 1	44	4 4 (dx,dy) 51.DIG v-vector
63 2	OF 07	0 7 (dx,dY) 52.DIG s-vector
64 2	12	-1 2 (dx,dy) 53.DIG v-vector
65 1	76	-7 6 (dx,dy) 54.DIG v-vector
65 2	A4	-10 4 (dx,dy) 55.DIG v-vector
66 1	FO E7	-25 0 (dX,dy) 56.DIG s-vector
67 1	B3	-11 -3 (dx,dy) 57.DIG v-vector
67 2	A6	-10 -6 (dx,dy) 58.DIG v-vector
68 1	76	-7 -6 (dx,dy) 59.DIG v-vector
68 2	8B	-8 -11 (dx,dy) 60.DIG v-vector
69 1	6E F1	-6 -15 (dx,dY) 61.DIG s-vector
70 1	4E EC	-4 -20 (dx,dY) 62.DIG s-vector
71 1	OF D9	0 -39 (dx,dY) 63.DIG s-vector
72 1	4E FO	4 -16 (dx,dY) ·64.DIG s-vector
73 1	6E FO	6 -16 (dx,dY) 65.DIG s-vector
74 1	57	5 -7 (dx,dy) 66.DIG v-vector
74 2	66	6 -6 (dx,dy) 67.DIG v-vector
75 1	87	8 -7 (dx,dy) 68.DIG v-vector
75 2	A5	10 -5 (dx,dy) 69.DIG v-vector
76 1	C4	12 -4 (dx,dy) 70.DIG v-vector
76 2	FO 15	21 0 (dX,dy) 71.DIG s-vector
77 2	81	8 1 (dx,dy) 72.DIG v-vector
78 1	E5 10	16 5 (dX,dy) 73.DIG s-vector
79 1	85	8 5 (dx,dy) 74.DIG v-vector
79 2	75	7 5 (dx,dy) 75.DIG v-vector

WORDNO.	CONTENT	COMMENT
80 1	75	7 5 (dx,dy) 76.DIG v-vector
80 2	F0 01	1 0 (dX,dy) 77.DIG s-vector
81 2	46	4 -6 (dx,dy) 78.DIG v-vector

GRAND TOTAL

	WORDS	KBYTES
Length of font:	11718	23.436
Length of font header:	484	0.968
Length of all character headers:	3927	7.854
Length of total image information:	7307	14.614

DIGITIZATIONS	NUMBER
White vectors:	227
L-vectors:	163
S-vectors:	3002
V-vectors:	6141
	======
Total:	9533

| Characters: | 135 |
| Records (a 2048 words): | 6 |

| Raster (grid): | 400 X 400 |

| Digitizations per character: | 71 |
| Image information per character: | 108 bytes |

Appendix N
Description of the SC format

1. Structure of an SC font

The structure of an SC font is as described in appendix G together with the extended structure as in appendix K.

2. Description of the SC format

The scan identification (word number I + 18 in the font header) in the **scanline format** determines in which direction a line progresses and where the following lines are.

The image line start is found, depending on scanning identification, at one of the sides of the square, which is given by XMIN, XMAX, YMIN and YMAX (words N1 + 10 up to N1 + 13). This is further standardized in that XMIN is taken to be 0 pixels and YMIN and YMAX are respective to the baseline and given in pixels (see also the sketches in appendix K).

The lines scan (hence scanlines) across the em square, scanning a series of transitions from white to black and vice versa. The distance from one transition to the next is known as a run length. One assumes that the first run length of each line crosses a white area. It is therefore natural to allow run length 0 to be at the start of a line for those exceptions when the line starts with a "black" run length. In the middle of the line, run lengths are always $\neq 0$. This means that run length = 0 can be, and is, used as the line end indicator, i.e. bytes 00 00 represent an empty line.

The run lengths are coded with 7, 14 or 22 bits as follows:

run length up to 127 with one byte 00...7F; run lengths up to 16,383 with 2 bytes, whereby the higher valued 7 bits are in the first byte and coded from 80 to FF. The highest value (left) bit indicates that another byte follows with 7 lower valued bits, coded as 00...7F. The two 7 bit groups form the 14 bit representation of the run length.

Still longer run lengths are coded with 22 bits and describe in theory lengths up to 4,194,303 points. They are indicated by the second byte with coding 80...FF. The highest value (left) bit indicates that an additional byte follows, i.e. we have then $7 + 7 + 8$ bits available for coding. The first byte supplies bits 21...15, the second bits 14...8 and the third bits 7...0 for the 22 bit coding.

Coding examples

Bytes	Coded run length	Comment
00	0	Either black line start (non-white) or scanline end
00 00	0	Empty scanline
01	1	7 bit run length
0F	15	7 bit run length
7F	127	7 bit run length
81 00	128	14 bit run length
81 7F	255	14 bit run length
FF 7F	16,383	14 bit run length
80 C0 00	16,384	22 bit run length
82 80 00	65,538	22 bit run length
FF FF FE	4,194,303	22 bit run length

The number of line repetitions is written just behind the run lengths of a scanline, if applicable. As a scanline always has to have an even number of run lengths, this notation gives an odd number and can be easily recognized.

The end of the character is controlled using the line index and correspondingly, the end of a font is checked in the character index.

One run length, no matter whether coded with 7, 14 or 22 bits, is counted as one digitization.

3. Example of an SC format

First of all we represent the lower case letters a, b, c of the typeface "URW Antiqua 2015 normal", as a raster image. The scanning identification is 21 (CRT machines). The raster is 100 × 100 for the em. Subsequently the type font format is reproduced as a data list.

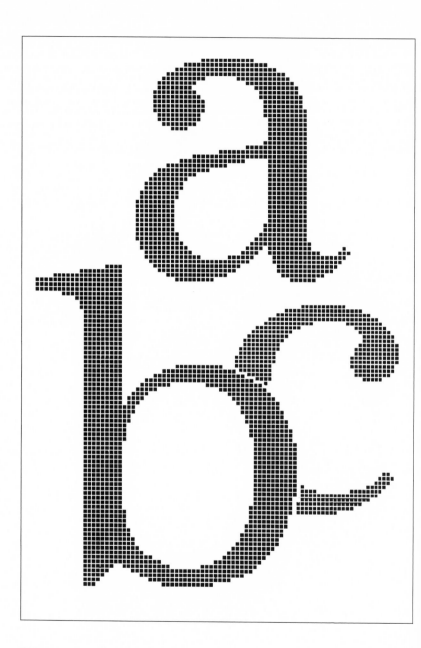

WORDNO.	CONTENT	COMMENT
1	484	Length of font header

NAME SECTION

2	55	Length of name section
3	825	Number on URW list
4 - 10	AN201512.SC	File name (ASCII)
11 - 49	URW-Antiqua 2000 normal	Font name (ASCII)
50	SC	Data format (ASCII)
51 - 53	20 3 87	Production date: 20-Mar-87
54 - 56	3 4 87	Date of last change: 3-Apr-87

FONT INFORMATION

57	19	Length of font information
58	1	Indicator for font
59	135	Number of characters
60	67	Cap height (in pixels)
61	100	Body size (in pixels)
62	47	x-height (in pixels)
63	25	Distance: base line - lower body line(in pixels)
64	100	Text line distance for setting (in pixels)
65	10	Stem thickness (in pixels)
66	0	Angle of italisation (in 1/10 degree)
67	12	Optimum point size for setting (in p)
68	43	Average character width (in pixels)
69	1500	X-extension of a pixel (in 1/1000mm)
70	1500	Y-extension of a pixel (in 1/1000mm)
71	100	Em-resolution in X-direction (in pixels)
72	100	Em-resolution in Y-direction (in pixels)
73	21	Scan indicator of image data
74	0	Width of printing window (in pixels)
75	0	Height of printing window (in pixels)

HIERARCHY SECTION

76	1	No hierarchy section in this format

CHARACTER INDEX

77	408	Length of character index
78	8	LENGTH OF FONT IN PHYSICAL RECORDS
79	647	Last word of last record
80	101	Character number: 1
81	1	Pointer to record containing start of character
82	485	Word pointer to start of character
83	102	Ch. no.: 2
84	1	Record pointer
85	649	Word pointer
86- 88	103 1 759	No., record pointer, word pointer of ch.: 3
89- 91	104 1 901	No., record pointer, word pointer of ch.: 4
92- 94	105 1 1003	No., record pointer, word pointer of ch.: 5

WORDNO.	CONTENT			COMMENT
95- 97	106	1	1110	No., record pointer, word pointer of ch.: 6
98- 100	107	1	1205	No., record pointer, word pointer of ch.: 7
101- 103	108	1	1364	No., record pointer, word pointer of ch.: 8
104- 106	109	1	1456	No., record pointer, word pointer of ch.: 9
107- 109	110	1	1506	No., record pointer, word pointer of ch.: 10
110- 112	111	1	1580	No., record pointer, word pointer of ch.: 11
113- 115	112	1	1748	No., record pointer, word pointer of ch.: 12
116- 118	113	1	1819	No., record pointer, word pointer of ch.: 13
119- 121	114	1	1980	No., record pointer, word pointer of ch.: 14
122- 124	115	2	73	No., record pointer, word pointer of ch.: 15
125- 127	116	2	223	No., record pointer, word pointer of ch.: 16
128- 130	117	2	322	No., record pointer, word pointer of ch.: 17
131- 133	118	2	536	No., record pointer, word pointer of ch.: 18
134- 136	119	2	673	No., record pointer, word pointer of ch.: 19
137- 139	120	2	828	No., record pointer, word pointer of ch.: 20
140- 142	121	2	912	No., record pointer, word pointer of ch.: 21
143- 145	122	2	1028	No., record pointer, word pointer of ch.: 22
146- 148	123	2	1169	No., record pointer, word pointer of ch.: 23
149- 151	124	2	1353	No., record pointer, word pointer of ch.: 24
152- 154	125	2	1546	No., record pointer, word pointer of ch.: 25
155- 157	126	2	1696	No., record pointer, word pointer of ch.: 26
158- 160	127	2	1894	No., record pointer, word pointer of ch.: 27
161- 163	128	3	52	No., record pointer, word pointer of ch.: 28
164- 166	129	3	223	No., record pointer, word pointer of ch.: 29
167- 169	201	3	452	No., record pointer, word pointer of ch.: 30
170- 172	208	3	640	No., record pointer, word pointer of ch.: 31
173- 175	210	3	832	No., record pointer, word pointer of ch.: 32
176- 178	237	3	1013	No., record pointer, word pointer of ch.: 33
179- 181	251	3	1196	No., record pointer, word pointer of ch.: 34
182- 184	301	3	1336	No., record pointer, word pointer of ch.: 35
185- 187	302	3	1474	No., record pointer, word pointer of ch.: 36
188- 190	303	3	1588	No., record pointer, word pointer of ch.: 37
191- 193	304	3	1692	No., record pointer, word pointer of ch.: 38
194- 196	305	3	1806	No., record pointer, word pointer of ch.: 39
197- 199	306	3	1932	No., record pointer, word pointer of ch.: 40
200- 202	307	3	2021	No., record pointer, word pointer of ch.: 41
203- 205	308	4	151	No., record pointer, word pointer of ch.: 42
206- 208	309	4	261	No., record pointer, word pointer of ch.: 43
209- 211	310	4	318	No., record pointer, word pointer of ch.: 44

WORDNO.	CONTENT			COMMENT
449- 451	704	7	1986	No., record pointer, word pointer of ch.: 124
452- 454	705	7	2042	No., record pointer, word pointer of ch.: 125
455- 457	706	8	50	No., record pointer, word pointer of ch.: 126
458- 460	709	8	124	No., record pointer, word pointer of ch.: 127
461- 463	711	8	190	No., record pointer, word pointer of ch.: 128
464- 466	751	8	241	No., record pointer, word pointer of ch.: 129
467- 469	753	8	288	No., record pointer, word pointer of ch.: 130
470- 472	754	8	345	No., record pointer, word pointer of ch.: 131
473- 475	755	8	401	No., record pointer, word pointer of ch.: 132
476- 478	756	8	457	No., record pointer, word pointer of ch.: 133
479- 481	759	8	531	No., record pointer, word pointer of ch.: 134
482- 484	761	8	597	No., record pointer, word pointer of ch.: 135

284

WORDNO.	CONTENT	COMMENT
1	0	Records length of character
2	138	Words

NAME SECTION

3	3	Length of name section
4	301	Character number
5	0	Number of following part

SETTING INFORMATION

6	12	Length of setting information
7	1	Character type = letter
8	198	Number of transitions
9	51	Total set width (T=L+W+R)
10	4	Left side bearing (L)
11	49	Width (W)
12	-2	Right side bearing (R)
13	1	X-minimum
14	49	X-maximum
15	0	Y-minimum
16	48	Y-maximum
17	1	Unit is 1 pixel

LINE INDEX

18	0	Records
19	2	Words No line index in this format

IMAGE INFORMATION

20	0	Records length of image information
21	119	Words

		Run lengths:	
22- 23	09 09 00	10 19	1.L.
23- 24	07 0D 00	8 21	2.L.
25- 26	05 11 00	6 23	3.L.
26- 27	04 13 00	5 24	4.L.
28- 30	03 15 0D 05 00	4 25 38 43	5.L.
30- 32	02 17 0A 09 00	3 26 36 45	6.L.
33- 35	02 17 09 0B 00	3 26 35 46	7.L.
35- 37	01 19 08 0C 00	2 27 35 47	8.L.
38- 40	01 19 07 0D 00	2 27 34 47	9.L.
40- 43	00 0B 07 08 07 0E 00	1 12 19 27 34 48	10.L.
44- 47	00 09 0B 07 06 0E 00	1 10 21 28 34 48	11.L.
47- 50	00 08 0E 05 06 0F 00	1 9 23 28 34 49	12.L.
51- 54	00 07 10 04 07 0E 00	1 8 24 28 35 49	13.L.
54- 58	00 06 11 05 06 08 01 05 00	1 7 24 29 35 43 44 49	14.L.
59- 63	00 06 12 04 07 06 03 04 00	1 7 25 29 36 42 45 49	15.L.
63- 67	00 05 13 04 09 03 04 05 00	1 6 25 29 38 41 45 50	16.L.
68- 71	00 05 13 04 11 04 00	1 6 25 29 46 50	17.L.
71- 74	00 05 14 03 11 04 00	1 6 26 29 46 50	18.L.
75- 78	01 04 14 03 11 04 00	2 6 26 29 46 50	19.L.
78- 82	01 04 14 04 10 04	2 6 26 30 46 50	20.L.
	01 00	1 Repeated line	
82- 86	02 04 14 03 10 04	3 7 27 30 46 50	22.L.

285

WORDNO.	CONTENT	COMMENT	
	01 00	1 Repeated line	
86- 89	03 03 14 03 0F 05 00	4 7 27 30 45 50	24.L.
90- 93	04 03 13 03 0F 05 00	5 8 27 30 45 50	25.L.
93- 96	04 04 13 03 0D 06 00	5 9 28 31 44 50	26.L.
97- 100	05 04 12 03 0D 06 00	6 10 28 31 44 50	27.L.
100- 103	06 04 11 03 0C 06 00	7 11 28 31 43 49	28.L.
104- 107	07 04 10 03 0A 08 00	8 12 28 31 41 49	29.L.
107- 110	08 05 0E 04 05 0C 00	9 14 28 32 37 49	30.L.
111- 112	06 29 00	7 48	31.L.
112- 113	04 2B 00	5 48	32.L.
114- 115	02 2C 00	3 47	33.L.
115- 116	01 2D 00	2 47	34.L.
117- 118	01 2C 00	2 46	35.L.
118- 119	00 2C 00	1 45	36.L.
120- 121	00 2B 00	1 44	37.L.
121- 122	00 29 00	1 42	38.L.
123- 124	00 26 00	1 39	39.L.
124- 125	00 09 00	1 10	40.L.
126- 127	00 07 00	1 8	41.L.
127- 128	01 06 00	2 8	42.L.
129- 130	01 05 00	2 7	43.L.
130- 132	02 04	3 7	44.L.
	01 00	1 Repeated line	

WORDNO.	CONTENT	COMMENT
1	0	Records length of character
2	114	Words
NAME SECTION		
3	3	Length of name section
4	302	Character number
5	0	Number of following part
SETTING INFORMATION		
6	12	Length of setting information
7	1	Character type = letter
8	180	Number of transitions
9	65	Total set width (T=L+W+R)
10	0	Left side bearing (L)
11	60	Width (W)
12	5	Right side bearing (R)
13	1	X-minimum
14	60	X-maximum
15	0	Y-minimum
16	70	Y-maximum
17	1	Unit is 1 pixel
LINE INDEX		
18	0	Records
19	2	Words No line index in this format

```
---------  ------------------------------  ------------------------------------
WORDNO.           CONTENT                           COMMENT
---------  ------------------------------  ------------------------------------
 56-  58   01 06 24 03 00                  2 8 44 47                       27.L.
 58-  60   01 05 25 04 00                  2 7 44 48                       28.L.
 61-  63   01 05 26 03 00                  2 7 45 48                       29.L.
 63-  66   00 05 27 04                     1 6 45 49                       30.L.
           01 00                               1 Repeated line
 66-  68   00 04 29 03 00                  1 5 46 49                       32.L.
 69-  71   00 04 29 04                     1 5 46 50                       33.L.
           05 00                               5 Repeated lines
 72-  74   00 05 28 04 00                  1 6 46 50                       39.L.
 74-  77   00 05 27 05                     1 6 45 50                       40.L.
           01 00                               1 Repeated line
 77-  79   01 05 26 05 00                  2 7 45 50                       42.L.
 80-  82   01 05 25 06 00                  2 7 44 50                       43.L.
 82-  84   01 06 24 05 00                  2 8 44 49                       44.L.
 85-  87   01 07 22 06 00                  2 9 43 49                       45.L.
 87-  89   02 07 20 07 00                  3 10 42 49                      46.L.
 90-  92   02 08 1E 07 00                  3 11 41 48                      47.L.
 92-  94   02 0A 1A 09 00                  3 13 39 48                      48.L.
 95-  97   03 0B 16 0A 00                  4 15 37 47                      49.L.
 97-  99   03 0F 0F 0D 00                  4 19 34 47                      50.L.
100- 101   04 29 00                        5 46                            51.L.
101- 102   05 28 00                        6 46                            52.L.
103- 104   06 26 00                        7 45                            53.L.
104- 105   07 24 00                        8 44                            54.L.
106- 107   08 22 00                        9 43                            55.L.
107- 108   09 20 00                        10 42                           56.L.
109- 110   0B 1C 00                        12 40                           57.L.
110- 111   0D 18 00                        14 38                           58.L.
112- 113   10 13 00                        17 36                           59.L.
113- 114   14 0C 00                        21 33                           60.L.
```

287

WORDNO.	CONTENT	COMMENT
1	0	Records length of character
2	104	Words

NAME SECTION

3	3	Length of name section
4	303	Character number
5	0	Number of following part

SETTING INFORMATION

6	12	Length of setting information
7	1	Character type = letter
8	152	Number of transitions
9	50	Total set width (T=L+W+R)
10	5	Left side bearing (L)
11	42	Width (W)
12	3	Right side bearing (R)
13	1	X-minimum
14	42	X-maximum
15	0	Y-minimum
16	48	Y-maximum
17	1	Unit is 1 pixel

LINE INDEX

| 18 | 0 | Records |
| 19 | 2 | Words   No line index in this format |

IMAGE INFORMATION

| 20 | 0 | Records   length of image information |
| 21 | 85 | Words |

			Run lengths:	
22-	23	13 0B 00	20 31	1.L.
23-	24	0F 13 00	16 35	2.L.
25-	26	0D 18 00	14 38	3.L.
26-	27	0B 1C 00	12 40	4.L.
28-	29	09 20 00	10 42	5.L.
29-	30	08 22 00	9 43	6.L.
31-	32	06 25 00	7 44	7.L.
32-	34	05 27	6 45	8.L.
		01 00	1 Repeated line	
34-	35	04 29 00	5 46	10.L.
36-	38	03 10 0C 0F 00	4 20 32 47	11.L.
38-	40	03 0C 14 0B 00	4 16 36 47	12.L.
41-	43	02 0B 19 09 00	3 14 39 48	13.L.
43-	45	02 09 1D 07 00	3 12 41 48	14.L.
46-	48	01 09 1F 07 00	2 11 42 49	15.L.
48-	50	01 08 21 06 00	2 10 43 49	16.L.
51-	53	01 07 23 05 00	2 9 44 49	17.L.
53-	55	00 07 24 05 00	1 8 44 49	18.L.
56-	58	00 07 25 05 00	1 8 45 50	19.L.
58-	61	00 06 26 05	1 7 45 50	20.L.
		01 00	1 Repeated line	
61-	63	00 06 27 04 00	1 7 46 50	22.L.

```
---------|----------------------------|-------------------------------------
WORDNO. |           CONTENT          |                COMMENT
---------|----------------------------|-------------------------------------
  64- 66 | 00 05 28 04                | 1 6 46 50                        23.L.
         | 04 00                      |    4 Repeated lines
  67- 69 | 01 04 28 04                | 2 6 46 50                        28.L.
         | 01 00                      |    1 Repeated line
  70- 72 | 01 04 27 04 00             | 2 6 45 49                        30.L.
  72- 75 | 01 05 1C 03 07 04 00       | 2 7 35 38 45 49                  31.L.
  76- 79 | 02 04 1A 07 04 05 00       | 3 7 33 40 44 49                  32.L.
  79- 82 | 02 04 1A 08 02 06 00       | 3 7 33 41 43 49                  33.L.
  83- 85 | 03 03 19 10 00             | 4 7 32 48                        34.L.
  85- 87 | 03 04 18 10 00             | 4 8 32 48                        35.L.
  88- 90 | 04 03 18 0F 00             | 5 8 32 47                        36.L.
  90- 92 | 04 04 17 0F 00             | 5 9 32 47                        37.L.
  93- 95 | 05 04 16 0E 00             | 6 10 32 46                       38.L.
  95- 97 | 06 04 16 0C 00             | 7 11 33 45                       39.L.
  98-100 | 07 03 16 0B 00             | 8 11 33 44                       40.L.
 100-102 | 08 01 18 09 00             | 9 10 34 43                       41.L.
 103-104 | 23 05 00                   | 36 41                            42.L.
---------|----------------------------|-------------------------------------
```

```
                         GRAND TOTAL
                         -----------
                                        WORDS        KBYTES
                                        -----        ------
       Length of font:                  14983        29.966
       Length of font header:             484         0.968
       Length of all character headers:  2565         5.130
       Length of total image information: 11934      23.868


           DIGITIZATIONS                    NUMBER
           -------------                    ------
           Lines:                            6429
           Total of transitions:            22481
           ----------------------------------------
           Characters:                        135
           Records (a 2048 words):              8
           ----------------------------------------
           Raster (grid):              100 X 100
           ----------------------------------------
           Digitizations per line:           3.50
           Lines per character:                48
           Image information per character:  177 bytes
```

Appendix O
Description of the SN format

1. Structure of an SN font
The structure of an SN font is as described in appendix G together with the extended structure as in appendix K.

2. Description of the SN format
The **scanline nibble format** is a variation of the SC format especially suited for rasters between 30×30 up to 140×140. We propose to use this format instead of bitmaps in laser printers. It needs less storage capacity (see grand total of SC and SN format).

Basically, a byte is replaced by a halfbyte, the nibble. So, one has described a very short run length by a nibble. The nibbles 8...F indicate that the high value three bits are given with this nibble, and the low value three bits follow in the next nibble. One uses as many nibbles as are needed. Each further nibble gives three bits more. The later a nibble occurs in a sequence for one run length, the lower is its value.

Coding examples

Nibbles	Coded run length	Comment
0	0	Either black line start (non-white) or scanline end
00	0	Empty scanline
1	1	3 bit run length
7	7	3 bit run length
90	8	6 bit run length
F7	63	6 bit run length
980	64	9 bit run length
FF7	511	9 bit run length

Nibbles	Coded run length	Comment
9880	512	12 bit run length
FFF7	4095	12 bit run length
98880	4096	15 bit run length
⋮	⋮	⋮
etc.	etc.	etc.

The number of line repetitions is written just behind the run lengths of a scanline, if applicable. As a scanline always has to have an even number of run lengths, this notation gives an odd number and can be easily recognized.

The end of the character is controlled using the line index and correspondingly, the end of a font is checked in the character index.

One run length, no matter whether coded with 3, 6, 9, 12 or 15 bits, is counted as one digitization.

3. Example of an SN format

First of all we represent the lower case letters a, b, c of the typeface "URW Antiqua 2015 normal", as a raster image. The scanning identification is 21 (CRT machines). The raster is 100 × 100 for the em. Subsequently the type font format is reproduced as a data list.

```
---------  ------------------  --------------------------------------------------
WORDNO.       CONTENT                          COMMENT
---------  ------------------  --------------------------------------------------
    1                    484   Length of font header
---------  ------------------  --------------------------------------------------
      NAME SECTION
      ------------
    2                     55   Length of name section
    3                    825   Number on URW list
  4 - 10      AN201512.SN      File name (ASCII)

 11 - 49      URW-Antiqua 2000                 | Font name (ASCII)
                  normal

   50                     SN   Data format (ASCII)
 51 - 53          20  3 87     Production date:    20-Mar-87
 54 - 56           3  4 87     Date of last change:  3-Apr-87
---------  ------------------  --------------------------------------------------
      FONT INFORMATION
      ----------------
   57                     19   Length of font information
   58                      1   Indicator for font
   59                    135   Number of characters
   60                     67   Cap height (in pixels)
   61                    100   Body size (in pixels)
   62                     47   x-height (in pixels)
   63                     25   Distance: base line - lower body line(in pixels)
   64                    100   Text line distance for setting (in pixels)
   65                     10   Stem thickness (in pixels)
   66                      0   Angle of italisation (in 1/10 degree)
   67                     12   Optimum point size for setting (in p)
   68                     43   Average character width (in pixels)
   69                   1500   X-extension of a pixel (in 1/1000mm)
   70                   1500   Y-extension of a pixel (in 1/1000mm)
   71                    100   Em-resolution in X-direction (in pixels)
   72                    100   Em-resolution in Y-direction (in pixels)
   73                     21   Scan indicator of image data
   74                      0   Width of printing window (in pixels)
   75                      0   Height of printing window (in pixels)
---------  ------------------  --------------------------------------------------
      HIERARCHY SECTION
      -----------------
   76                      1   No hierarchy section in this format
---------  ------------------  --------------------------------------------------
      CHARACTER INDEX
      ---------------
   77                    408   Length of character index
   78                      6   LENGTH OF FONT IN PHYSICAL RECORDS
   79                   1323   Last word of last record

   80                    101   Character number:  1
   81                      1   Pointer to record containing start of character
   82                    485   Word pointer to start of character

   83                    102   Ch. no.: 2
   84                      1   Record pointer
   85                    606   Word pointer

 86-  88    103    1  692     No., record pointer, word pointer of ch.:    3
 89-  91    104    1  798     No., record pointer, word pointer of ch.:    4
 92-  94    105    1  876     No., record pointer, word pointer of ch.:    5
---------  ------------------  --------------------------------------------------
```

293

WORDNO.	CONTENT	COMMENT
95- 97	106 1 957	No., record pointer, word pointer of ch.: 6
98- 100	107 1 1029	No., record pointer, word pointer of ch.: 7
101- 103	108 1 1147	No., record pointer, word pointer of ch.: 8
104- 106	109 1 1213	No., record pointer, word pointer of ch.: 9
107- 109	110 1 1252	No., record pointer, word pointer of ch.: 10
110- 112	111 1 1314	No., record pointer, word pointer of ch.: 11
113- 115	112 1 1437	No., record pointer, word pointer of ch.: 12
116- 118	113 1 1489	No., record pointer, word pointer of ch.: 13
119- 121	114 1 1609	No., record pointer, word pointer of ch.: 14
122- 124	115 1 1719	No., record pointer, word pointer of ch.: 15
125- 127	116 1 1834	No., record pointer, word pointer of ch.: 16
128- 130	117 1 1911	No., record pointer, word pointer of ch.: 17
131- 133	118 2 32	No., record pointer, word pointer of ch.: 18
134- 136	119 2 133	No., record pointer, word pointer of ch.: 19
137- 139	120 2 254	No., record pointer, word pointer of ch.: 20
140- 142	121 2 319	No., record pointer, word pointer of ch.: 21
143- 145	122 2 406	No., record pointer, word pointer of ch.: 22
146- 148	123 2 520	No., record pointer, word pointer of ch.: 23
149- 151	124 2 667	No., record pointer, word pointer of ch.: 24
152- 154	125 2 811	No., record pointer, word pointer of ch.: 25
155- 157	126 2 925	No., record pointer, word pointer of ch.: 26
158- 160	127 2 1072	No., record pointer, word pointer of ch.: 27
161- 163	128 2 1223	No., record pointer, word pointer of ch.: 28
164- 166	129 2 1351	No., record pointer, word pointer of ch.: 29
167- 169	201 2 1529	No., record pointer, word pointer of ch.: 30
170- 172	208 2 1673	No., record pointer, word pointer of ch.: 31
173- 175	210 2 1813	No., record pointer, word pointer of ch.: 32
176- 178	237 2 1952	No., record pointer, word pointer of ch.: 33
179- 181	251 3 43	No., record pointer, word pointer of ch.: 34
182- 184	301 3 148	No., record pointer, word pointer of ch.: 35
185- 187	302 3 245	No., record pointer, word pointer of ch.: 36
188- 190	303 3 331	No., record pointer, word pointer of ch.: 37
191- 193	304 3 409	No., record pointer, word pointer of ch.: 38
194- 196	305 3 492	No., record pointer, word pointer of ch.: 39
197- 199	306 3 587	No., record pointer, word pointer of ch.: 40
200- 202	307 3 655	No., record pointer, word pointer of ch.: 41
203- 205	308 3 789	No., record pointer, word pointer of ch.: 42
206- 208	309 3 865	No., record pointer, word pointer of ch.: 43
209- 211	310 3 910	No., record pointer, word pointer of ch.: 44
212- 214	311 3 970	No., record pointer, word pointer of ch.: 45
215- 217	312 3 1070	No., record pointer, word pointer of ch.: 46
218- 220	313 3 1108	No., record pointer, word pointer of ch.: 47
221- 223	314 3 1212	No., record pointer, word pointer of ch.: 48
224- 226	315 3 1279	No., record pointer, word pointer of ch.: 49
227- 229	316 3 1353	No., record pointer, word pointer of ch.: 50
230- 232	317 3 1446	No., record pointer, word pointer of ch.: 51
233- 235	318 3 1532	No., record pointer, word pointer of ch.: 52
236- 238	319 3 1588	No., record pointer, word pointer of ch.: 53
239- 241	320 3 1679	No., record pointer, word pointer of ch.: 54
242- 244	321 3 1723	No., record pointer, word pointer of ch.: 55
245- 247	322 3 1786	No., record pointer, word pointer of ch.: 56
248- 250	323 3 1877	No., record pointer, word pointer of ch.: 57
251- 253	324 3 2001	No., record pointer, word pointer of ch.: 58
254- 256	325 4 66	No., record pointer, word pointer of ch.: 59
257- 259	326 4 183	No., record pointer, word pointer of ch.: 60
260- 262	327 4 293	No., record pointer, word pointer of ch.: 61
263- 265	328 4 444	No., record pointer, word pointer of ch.: 62
266- 268	329 4 583	No., record pointer, word pointer of ch.: 63
269- 271	330 4 693	No., record pointer, word pointer of ch.: 64

WORDNO.	CONTENT			COMMENT
272- 274	331	4	805	No., record pointer, word pointer of ch.: 65
275- 277	401	4	838	No., record pointer, word pointer of ch.: 66
278- 280	408	4	959	No., record pointer, word pointer of ch.: 67
281- 283	413	4	1086	No., record pointer, word pointer of ch.: 68
284- 286	436	4	1185	No., record pointer, word pointer of ch.: 69
287- 289	449	4	1294	No., record pointer, word pointer of ch.: 70
290- 292	501	4	1386	No., record pointer, word pointer of ch.: 71
293- 295	502	4	1431	No., record pointer, word pointer of ch.: 72
296- 298	503	4	1548	No., record pointer, word pointer of ch.: 73
299- 301	504	4	1664	No., record pointer, word pointer of ch.: 74
302- 304	505	4	1736	No., record pointer, word pointer of ch.: 75
305- 307	506	4	1840	No., record pointer, word pointer of ch.: 76
308- 310	507	4	1941	No., record pointer, word pointer of ch.: 77
311- 313	508	4	2034	No., record pointer, word pointer of ch.: 78
314- 316	509	5	89	No., record pointer, word pointer of ch.: 79
317- 319	510	5	188	No., record pointer, word pointer of ch.: 80
320- 322	511	5	260	No., record pointer, word pointer of ch.: 81
323- 325	512	5	399	No., record pointer, word pointer of ch.: 82
326- 328	513	5	521	No., record pointer, word pointer of ch.: 83
329- 331	601	5	607	No., record pointer, word pointer of ch.: 84
332- 334	602	5	637	No., record pointer, word pointer of ch.: 85
335- 337	603	5	675	No., record pointer, word pointer of ch.: 86
338- 340	604	5	706	No., record pointer, word pointer of ch.: 87
341- 343	605	5	737	No., record pointer, word pointer of ch.: 88
344- 346	606	5	768	No., record pointer, word pointer of ch.: 89
347- 349	607	5	817	No., record pointer, word pointer of ch.: 90
350- 352	608	5	859	No., record pointer, word pointer of ch.: 91
353- 355	609	5	916	No., record pointer, word pointer of ch.: 92
356- 358	610	5	958	No., record pointer, word pointer of ch.: 93
359- 361	611	5	999	No., record pointer, word pointer of ch.: 94
362- 364	612	5	1062	No., record pointer, word pointer of ch.: 95
365- 367	613	5	1123	No., record pointer, word pointer of ch.: 96
368- 370	614	5	1186	No., record pointer, word pointer of ch.: 97
371- 373	615	5	1235	No., record pointer, word pointer of ch.: 98
374- 376	616	5	1284	No., record pointer, word pointer of ch.: 99
377- 379	617	5	1367	No., record pointer, word pointer of ch.: 100
380- 382	618	5	1446	No., record pointer, word pointer of ch.: 101
383- 385	619	5	1515	No., record pointer, word pointer of ch.: 102
386- 388	620	5	1584	No., record pointer, word pointer of ch.: 103

WORDNO.	CONTENT			COMMENT
449- 451	704	6	804	No., record pointer, word pointer of ch.: 124
452- 454	705	6	847	No., record pointer, word pointer of ch.: 125
455- 457	706	6	890	No., record pointer, word pointer of ch.: 126
458- 460	709	6	941	No., record pointer, word pointer of ch.: 127
461- 463	711	6	986	No., record pointer, word pointer of ch.: 128
464- 466	751	6	1024	No., record pointer, word pointer of ch.: 129
467- 469	753	6	1061	No., record pointer, word pointer of ch.: 130
470- 472	754	6	1104	No., record pointer, word pointer of ch.: 131
473- 475	755	6	1147	No., record pointer, word pointer of ch.: 132
476- 478	756	6	1190	No., record pointer, word pointer of ch.: 133
479- 481	759	6	1241	No., record pointer, word pointer of ch.: 134
482- 484	761	6	1286	No., record pointer, word pointer of ch.: 135

```
---------|------------------|-------------------------------------------
WORDNO.  |     CONTENT      |                    COMMENT
---------|------------------|-------------------------------------------
   1     |               0  | Records     length of character
   2     |              97  | Words
---------|------------------|-------------------------------------------
         | NAME SECTION
         | ------------
   3     |               3  | Length of name section
   4     |             301  | Character number
   5     |               0  | Number of following part
---------|------------------|-------------------------------------------
         | SETTING INFORMATION
         | -------------------
   6     |              12  | Length of setting information
   7     |               1  | Character type = letter
   8     |             198  | Number of transitions
   9     |              51  | Total set width (T=L+W+R)
  10     |               4  | Left side bearing (L)
  11     |              49  | Width (W)
  12     |              -2  | Right side bearing (R)
  13     |               1  | X-minimum
  14     |              49  | X-maximum
  15     |               0  | Y-minimum
  16     |              48  | Y-maximum
  17     |               1  | Unit is 1 pixel
---------|------------------|-------------------------------------------
         | LINE INDEX
         | ----------
  18     |               0  | Records
  19     |               2  | Words     No line index in this format
---------|------------------|-------------------------------------------
         | IMAGE INFORMATION
         | -----------------
  20     |               0  | Records     length of image information
  21     |              78  | Words
         |                  |
         |                  | Run lengths:
 22-  23 | 91 91 0          | 10 19                            1.L.
 23-  24 | 7  95 0          | 8 21                             2.L.
 24-  25 | 5  A1 0          | 6 23                             3.L.
 25-  26 | 4  A3 0          | 5 24                             4.L.
 26-  27 | 3  A5 95 5  0    | 4 25 38 43                       5.L.
 28-  29 | 2  A7 92 91 0    | 3 26 36 45                       6.L.
 30-  31 | 2  A7 91 93 0    | 3 26 35 46                       7.L.
 32-  33 | 1  B1 90 94 0    | 2 27 35 47                       8.L.
 34-  35 | 1  B1 7  95 0    | 2 27 34 47                       9.L.
 35-  38 | 0  93 7  90 7   96 0       | 1 12 19 27 34 48      10.L.
 38-  40 | 0  91 93 7   6   96 0      | 1 10 21 28 34 48      11.L.
 40-  43 | 0  90 96 5   6   97 0      | 1 9 23 28 34 49       12.L.
 43-  45 | 0  7  A0 4   7   96 0      | 1 8 24 28 35 49       13.L.
 45-  48 | 0  6  A1 5   6   90 1  5  0 | 1 7 24 29 35 43 44 49 14.L.
 48-  50 | 0  6  A2 4   7   6  3  4  0 | 1 7 25 29 36 42 45 49 15.L.
 50-  53 | 0  5  A3 4   91 3   4  5  0 | 1 6 25 29 38 41 45 50 16.L.
 53-  55 | 0  5  A3 4   A1 4   0      | 1 6 25 29 46 50       17.L.
 55-  57 | 0  5  A4 3   A1 4   0      | 1 6 26 29 46 50       18.L.
 58-  60 | 1  4  A4 3   A1 4   0      | 2 6 26 29 46 50       19.L.
 60-  62 | 1  4  A4 4   A0 4          | 2 6 26 30 46 50       20.L.
         | 1  0                        |    1 Repeated line
 62-  65 | 2  4  A4 3   A0 4          | 3 7 27 30 46 50       22.L.
---------|------------------------------|-------------------------------------
```

WORDNO.	CONTENT	COMMENT	
	1 0	1 Repeated line	
65- 67	3 3 A4 3 97 5 0	4 7 27 30 45 50	24.L.
67- 69	4 3 A3 3 97 5 0	5 8 27 30 45 50	25.L.
69- 71	4 4 A3 3 95 6 0	5 9 28 31 44 50	26.L.
72- 74	5 4 A2 3 95 6 0	6 10 28 31 44 50	27.L.
74- 76	6 4 A1 3 94 6 0	7 11 28 31 43 49	28.L.
76- 78	7 4 A0 3 92 90 0	8 12 28 31 41 49	29.L.
79- 81	90 5 96 4 5 94 0	9 14 28 32 37 49	30.L.
81- 82	6 D1 0	7 48	31.L.
82- 83	4 D3 0	5 48	32.L.
83- 84	2 D4 0	3 47	33.L.
84- 85	1 D5 0	2 47	34.L.
85- 86	1 D4 0	2 46	35.L.
86- 87	0 D4 0	1 45	36.L.
87- 88	0 D3 0	1 44	37.L.
88- 89	0 D1 0	1 42	38.L.
89- 90	0 C6 0	1 39	39.L.
90- 91	0 91 0	1 10	40.L.
91- 92	0 7 0	1 8	41.L.
92- 92	1 6 0	2 8	42.L.
93- 93	1 5 0	2 7	43.L.
93- 94	2 4	3 7	44.L.
	1 0	1 Repeated line	
94- 95	3 3 0	4 7	46.L.
95- 96	4 3 0	5 8	47.L.
96- 96	5 3 0	6 9	48.L.
97- 97	6 1 0	7 8	49.L.

297

WORDNO.	CONTENT	COMMENT
1	0	Records length of character
2	86	Words

NAME SECTION

3	3	Length of name section
4	302	Character number
5	0	Number of following part

SETTING INFORMATION

6	12	Length of setting information
7	1	Character type = letter
8	180	Number of transitions
9	65	Total set width (T=L+W+R)
10	0	Left side bearing (L)
11	60	Width (W)
12	5	Right side bearing (R)
13	1	X-minimum
14	60	X-maximum
15	0	Y-minimum
16	70	Y-maximum
17	1	Unit is 1 pixel

LINE INDEX

18	0	Records
19	2	Words No line index in this format

IMAGE INFORMATION

20		0	Records length of image information
21		67	Words
			Run lengths:
22- 23	98 3	66 69	1.L.
	3 0	3 Repeated lines	
23- 24	98 4	66 70	5.L.
	1 0	1 Repeated line	
25- 26	98 5	65 70	7.L.
	2 0	2 Repeated lines	
26- 27	F7 6 0	64 70	10.L.
27- 28	F5 91 0	62 71	11.L.
28- 30	0 98	1 71	12.L.
	2 0	2 Repeated lines	
30- 31	1 98 0	2 71	15.L.
31- 32	2 98 0	3 71	16.L.
32- 33	3 98 0	4 72	17.L.
34- 35	4 98 0	5 72	18.L.
35- 36	5 98	6 72	19.L.
	1 0	1 Repeated line	
36- 38	4 95 97 90 0	5 18 33 41	21.L.
38- 40	4 91 A7 6 0	5 14 37 43	22.L.
40- 42	3 90 B3 5 0	4 12 39 44	23.L.
42- 43	3 6 B7 4 0	4 10 41 45	24.L.
43- 45	2 6 C1 4 0	3 9 42 46	25.L.
45- 46	2 5 C3 4 0	3 8 43 47	26.L.

WORDNO.		CONTENT				COMMENT	
46- 48	1	6	C4	3	0	2 8 44 47	27.L.
48- 49	1	5	C5	4	0	2 7 44 48	28.L.
49- 51	1	5	C6	3	0	2 7 45 48	29.L.
51- 52	0	5	C7	4		1 6 45 49	30.L.
	1	0				1 Repeated line	
53- 54	0	4	D1	3	0	1 5 46 49	32.L.
54- 56	0	4	D1	4		1 5 46 50	33.L.
	5	0				5 Repeated lines	
56- 57	0	5	D0	4	0	1 6 46 50	39.L.
57- 59	0	5	C7	5		1 6 45 50	40.L.
	1	0				1 Repeated line	
59- 60	1	5	C6	5	0	2 7 45 50	42.L.
61- 62	1	5	C5	6	0	2 7 44 50	43.L.
62- 63	1	6	C4	5	0	2 8 44 49	44.L.
64- 65	1	7	C2	6	0	2 9 43 49	45.L.
65- 66	2	7	C0	7	0	3 10 42 49	46.L.
67- 68	2	90	B6	7	0	3 11 41 48	47.L.
68- 70	2	92	B2	91	0	3 13 39 48	48.L.
70- 72	3	93	A6	92	0	4 15 37 47	49.L.
72- 74	3	97	97	95	0	4 19 34 47	50.L.
74- 75	4	D1	0			5 46	51.L.
75- 76	5	D0	0			6 46	52.L.
76- 77	6	C6	0			7 45	53.L.
77- 78	7	C4	0			8 44	54.L.
78- 79	90	C2	0			9 43	55.L.
80- 81	91	C0	0			10 42	56.L.
81- 82	93	B4	0			12 40	57.L.
82- 83	95	B0	0			14 38	58.L.
83- 84	A0	A3	0			17 36	59.L.
85- 86	A4	94	0			21 33	60.L.

WORDNO.	CONTENT	COMMENT
1	0	Records length of character
2	78	Words

NAME SECTION

3	3	Length of name section
4	303	Character number
5	0	Number of following part

SETTING INFORMATION

6	12	Length of setting information
7	1	Character type = letter
8	152	Number of transitions
9	50	Total set width (T=L+W+R)
10	5	Left side bearing (L)
11	42	Width (W)
12	3	Right side bearing (R)
13	1	X-minimum
14	42	X-maximum
15	0	Y-minimum
16	48	Y-maximum
17	1	Unit is 1 pixel

LINE INDEX

18	0	Records
19	2	Words No line index in this format

IMAGE INFORMATION

20		0	Records length of image information
21		59	Words
			Run lengths:
22–	23	A3 93 0	20 31	1.L.
23–	24	97 A3 0	16 35	2.L.
24–	25	95 B0 0	14 38	3.L.
25–	26	93 B4 0	12 40	4.L.
27–	28	91 C0 0	10 42	5.L.
28–	29	90 C2 0	9 43	6.L.
29–	30	6 C5 0	7 44	7.L.
30–	31	5 C7	6 45	8.L.
		1 0	1 Repeated line	
31–	32	4 D1 0	5 46	10.L.
32–	34	3 A0 94 97 0	4 20 32 47	11.L.
34–	36	3 94 A4 93 0	4 16 36 47	12.L.
36–	38	2 93 B1 91 0	3 14 39 48	13.L.
38–	40	2 91 B5 7 0	3 12 41 48	14.L.
40–	42	1 91 B7 7 0	2 11 42 49	15.L.
42–	43	1 90 C1 6 0	2 10 43 49	16.L.
44–	45	1 7 C3 5 0	2 9 44 49	17.L.
45–	46	0 7 C4 5 0	1 8 44 49	18.L.
47–	48	0 7 C5 5 0	1 8 45 50	19.L.
48–	50	0 6 C6 5	1 7 45 50	20.L.
		1 0	1 Repeated line	
50–	51	0 6 C7 4 0	1 7 46 50	22.L.

```
---------|-----------------------------|-----------------------------------------
WORDNO. |          CONTENT            |              COMMENT
---------|-----------------------------|-----------------------------------------
 51-  53| 0   5   D0  4               | 1  6  46  50                      23.L.
         | 4   0                       |        4 Repeated lines
 53-  55| 1   4   D0  4               | 2  6  46  50                      28.L.
         | 1   0                       |        1 Repeated line
 55-  56| 1   4   C7  4   0           | 2  6  45  49                      30.L.
 56-  58| 1   5   B4  3   7   4   0   | 2  7  35  38  45  49              31.L.
 58-  60| 2   4   B2  7   4   5   0   | 3  7  33  40  44  49              32.L.
 60-  62| 2   4   B2  90  2   6   0   | 3  7  33  41  43  49              33.L.
 63-  64| 3   3   B1  A0  0           | 4  7  32  48                      34.L.
 64-  66| 3   4   B0  A0  0           | 4  8  32  48                      35.L.
 66-  68| 4   3   B0  97  0           | 5  8  32  47                      36.L.
 68-  69| 4   4   A7  97  0           | 5  9  32  47                      37.L.
 70-  71| 5   4   A6  96  0           | 6  10  32  46                     38.L.
 71-  73| 6   4   A6  94  0           | 7  11  33  45                     39.L.
 73-  75| 7   3   A6  93  0           | 8  11  33  44                     40.L.
 75-  77| 90  1   B0  91  0           | 9  10  34  43                     41.L.
 77-  78| C3  5   0                   | 36  41                            42.L.
---------|-----------------------------|-----------------------------------------
```

GRAND TOTAL

	WORDS	KBYTES
Length of font:	11563	23.126
Length of font header:	484	0.968
Length of all character headers:	2565	5.130
Length of total image information:	8514	17.028

DIGITIZATIONS	NUMBER
Lines:	6416
Total of transitions:	22481
Characters:	135
Records (a 2048 words):	6
Raster (grid):	100 X 100
Digitizations per line:	3.51
Lines per character:	48
Image information per character:	126 bytes

301

Appendix P
Description of the BI format

1. Structure of a BI font

The structure of the BI font is as described in appendix G with the extended structure as in appendix K.

Word	Meaning	Comment
	Extended setting informa-tion in character record	
N1 + N2 + 15	Number of zero bytes at the start	
N1 + N2 + 16	Number of zero bytes at the end	
N1 + N2 + 17	Number of non zero bytes in the lines	New information, particular to BI and GS format
N1 + N2 + 18	Number of empty lines at the start	
N1 + N2 + 19	Number of empty lines at the end	

2. Description of the BI format

The scan identification (word number I + 18 in the font header) determines in which direction a line progresses and where the following lines are.

As in the SC format the **bitmap format** is based on a rastered em square.

Bit value = 0 describes a white pixel, and bit value = 1 describes a black pixel.

Every sequence of 8 bits in one line is coded as a byte. In doing so, higher value bits are thus points further to the left in the line and lower value bits are points lying further to the right of the line. The terms left and right are geometrically correct in the case of scanning identifications 11 and 12, and in the case of identifications − 11 and − 12 they are correspondingly reversed. In the case of identifications 21 and 22, left means below and right means above, in identifications − 21 and − 22 this is correspondingly reversed.

The width and height of the printing window (word numbers I + 19 and I + 20 in the font header) give the length of the lines in bytes and the number of lines.

The number of bytes for one line is constant for all lines of any particular character. If the first bytes of all lines are equal to 0 then they are not coded as bits but rather, the number of bytes is written in the extended setting information in the character record, and similarly the number of the last bytes, which are equal to 0 in all lines. Also, the extended setting information contains the constant number of bytes for a character in which the actual image information is contained in the form of black pixels. The total number of bytes in one line is then calculated by rounding up. If, for example, in a printing window 17 dots form one line then the total number of bytes is 3. However, only the first 17 bits are relevant (see sketch).

One byte is counted as one digitization.

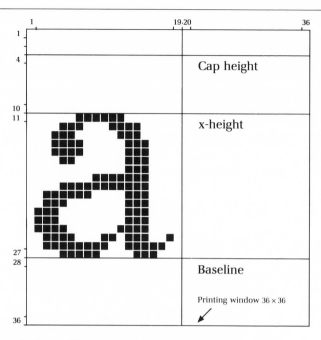

Example for additional setting information

Scanning code −21 (⁞.) results in:
Number of zero bytes at start: 1
Number of zero bytes at end: 1
Number of non zero bytes: 3
Number of empty lines at start: 1
Number of empty lines at end: 18

Scanning code 12 (⁞➝) results in:
Number of zero bytes at start: 0
Number of zero bytes at end: 2
Number of non zero bytes: 3
Number of empty lines at start: 10
Number of empty lines at end: 9

3. Example of a BI format

First of all we represent the lower case letters a, b, c of the typeface "URW Antiqua 2015 normal", as a raster image. The scanning identification is 12 (laser printer). The raster is 32×24 for the em. The printing window correspondingly has a height of 24 and a length of 32. This relationship is not imperative, however. Subsequently, the type font format is reproduced as a data list.

```
--------- ------------------ ----------------------------------------------------
WORDNO. |    CONTENT       |                   COMMENT
--------- ------------------ ----------------------------------------------------
   1    |            484   | Length of font header
--------- ------------------ ----------------------------------------------------
        NAME SECTION
        ------------
   2    |             55   | Length of name section
   3    |            825   | Number on URW list
 4 - 10 |   AN201512.BI    | File name (ASCII)

11 - 49 |   URW-Antiqua 2000           | Font name (ASCII)
        |         normal

  50    |             BI   | Data format (ASCII)
51 - 53 |        29  1 87  | Production date:     29-Jan-87
54 - 56 |        29  1 87  | Date of last change: 29-Jan-87
--------- ------------------ ----------------------------------------------------
        FONT INFORMATION
        ----------------
  57    |             19   | Length of font information
  58    |              1   | Indicator for font
  59    |            135   | Number of characters
  60    |             16   | Cap height (in pixels)
  61    |             24   | Body size (in pixels)
  62    |             12   | x-height (in pixels)
  63    |              6   | Distance: base line - lower body line(in pixels)
  64    |             24   | Text line distance for setting (in pixels)
  65    |              3   | Stem thickness (in pixels)
  66    |              0   | Angle of italisation (in 1/10 degree)
  67    |             12   | Optimum point size for setting (in p)
  68    |             13   | Average character width (in pixels)
  69    |           4688   | X-extension of a pixel (in 1/1000mm)
  70    |           6250   | Y-extension of a pixel (in 1/1000mm)
  71    |             32   | Em-resolution in X-direction (in pixels)
  72    |             24   | Em-resolution in Y-direction (in pixels)
  73    |             12   | Scan indicator of image data
  74    |             32   | Width of printing window (in pixels)
  75    |             24   | Height of printing window (in pixels)
--------- ------------------ ----------------------------------------------------
        HIERARCHY SECTION
        -----------------
  76    |              1   | No hierarchy section in this format
--------- ------------------ ----------------------------------------------------
        CHARACTER INDEX
        ----------------
  77    |            408   | Length of character index
  78    |              4   | LENGTH OF FONT IN PHYSICAL RECORDS
  79    |            173   | Last word of last record

  80    |            101   | Character number:  1
  81    |              1   | Pointer to record containing start of character
  82    |            485   | Word pointer to start of character

  83    |            102   | Ch. no.: 2
  84    |              1   | Record pointer
  85    |            537   | Word pointer

86- 88  |   103    1  589  | No., record pointer, word pointer of ch.:    3
89- 91  |   104    1  642  | No., record pointer, word pointer of ch.:    4
92- 94  |   105    1  694  | No., record pointer, word pointer of ch.:    5
--------- ------------------ ----------------------------------------------------
```

307

WORDNO.	CONTENT			COMMENT	
95- 97	106	1	746	No., record pointer, word pointer of ch.:	6
98- 100	107	1	798	No., record pointer, word pointer of ch.:	7
101- 103	108	1	851	No., record pointer, word pointer of ch.:	8
104- 106	109	1	903	No., record pointer, word pointer of ch.:	9
107- 109	110	1	946	No., record pointer, word pointer of ch.:	10
110- 112	111	1	993	No., record pointer, word pointer of ch.:	11
113- 115	112	1	1045	No., record pointer, word pointer of ch.:	12
116- 118	113	1	1097	No., record pointer, word pointer of ch.:	13
119- 121	114	1	1157	No., record pointer, word pointer of ch.:	14
122- 124	115	1	1209	No., record pointer, word pointer of ch.:	15
125- 127	116	1	1262	No., record pointer, word pointer of ch.:	16
128- 130	117	1	1314	No., record pointer, word pointer of ch.:	17
131- 133	118	1	1386	No., record pointer, word pointer of ch.:	18
134- 136	119	1	1438	No., record pointer, word pointer of ch.:	19
137- 139	120	1	1482	No., record pointer, word pointer of ch.:	20
140- 142	121	1	1534	No., record pointer, word pointer of ch.:	21
143- 145	122	1	1586	No., record pointer, word pointer of ch.:	22
146- 148	123	1	1638	No., record pointer, word pointer of ch.:	23
149- 151	124	1	1707	No., record pointer, word pointer of ch.:	24
152- 154	125	1	1759	No., record pointer, word pointer of ch.:	25
155- 157	126	1	1811	No., record pointer, word pointer of ch.:	26
158- 160	127	1	1863	No., record pointer, word pointer of ch.:	27
161- 163	128	1	1923	No., record pointer, word pointer of ch.:	28
164- 166	129	1	1983	No., record pointer, word pointer of ch.:	29
167- 169	201	1	2042	No., record pointer, word pointer of ch.:	30
170- 172	208	2	52	No., record pointer, word pointer of ch.:	31
173- 175	210	2	111	No., record pointer, word pointer of ch.:	32
176- 178	237	2	170	No., record pointer, word pointer of ch.:	33
179- 181	251	2	228	No., record pointer, word pointer of ch.:	34
182- 184	301	2	786	No., record pointer, word pointer of ch.:	35
185- 187	302	2	323	No., record pointer, word pointer of ch.:	36
188- 190	303	2	373	No., record pointer, word pointer of ch.:	37
191- 193	304	2	410	No., record pointer, word pointer of ch.:	38
194- 196	305	2	463	No., record pointer, word pointer of ch.:	39
197- 199	306	2	502	No., record pointer, word pointer of ch.:	40
200- 202	307	2	546	No., record pointer, word pointer of ch.:	41
203- 205	308	2	589	No., record pointer, word pointer of ch.:	42
206- 208	309	2	642	No., record pointer, word pointer of ch.:	43
209- 211	310	2	685	No., record pointer, word pointer of ch.:	44

WORDNO.	CONTENT			COMMENT	
449- 451	704	3	1865	No., record pointer, word pointer of ch.:	124
452- 454	705	3	1894	No., record pointer, word pointer of ch.:	125
455- 457	706	3	1923	No., record pointer, word pointer of ch.:	126
458- 460	709	3	1955	No., record pointer, word pointer of ch.:	127
461- 463	711	3	1985	No., record pointer, word pointer of ch.:	128
464- 466	751	3	2014	No., record pointer, word pointer of ch.:	129
467- 469	753	3	2044	No., record pointer, word pointer of ch.:	130
470- 472	754	4	25	No., record pointer, word pointer of ch.:	131
473- 475	755	4	54	No., record pointer, word pointer of ch.:	132
476- 478	756	4	83	No., record pointer, word pointer of ch.:	133
479- 481	759	4	115	No., record pointer, word pointer of ch.:	134
482- 484	761	4	145	No., record pointer, word pointer of ch.:	135

WORDNO.	CONTENT	COMMENT
1	0	Records length of character
2	37	Words

NAME SECTION

3	3	Length of name section
4	301	Character number
5	0	Number of following part

SETTING INFORMATION

6	17	Length of setting information
7	1	Character type = letter
8	22	Number of bytes
9	16	Total set width (T=L+W+R)
10	1	Left side bearing (L)
11	15	Width (W)
12	0	Right side bearing (R)
13	1	X-minimum
14	15	X-maximum
15	1	Y-minimum
16	11	Y-maximum
17	1	Unit is 1 pixel
18	0	Number of bytes = 0 at the begin
19	2	Number of bytes = 0 at the end
20	2	Number of used bytes for all lines
21	7	Number of lines = 0 at the begin
22	6	Number of lines = 0 at the end

LINE INDEX

23	0	Records
24	2	Words No line index in this format

IMAGE INFORMATION

25	0	Records length of image information
26	13	Words

WORDNO.	CONTENT	COMMENT
27- 27	1F C0	0001111111000000
28- 28	30 70	0011000001110000
29- 29	78 38	0111100000111000
30- 30	30 38	0011000000111000
31- 31	01 F8	0000000111111000
32- 32	1E 38	0001111000111000
33- 33	70 38	0111000000111000
34- 34	E0 38	1110000000111000
35- 35	E0 78	1110000001111000
36- 36	70 BA	0111000010111010
37- 37	3F 1C	0011111100011100

309

WORDNO.	CONTENT	COMMENT
1	0	Records length of character
2	50	Words

NAME SECTION

3	3	Length of name section
4	302	Character number
5	0	Number of following part

SETTING INFORMATION

6	17	Length of setting information
7	1	Character type = letter
8	48	Number of bytes
9	21	Total set width (T=L+W+R)
10	0	Left side bearing (L)
11	19	Width (W)
12	2	Right side bearing (R)
13	1	X-minimum
14	19	X-maximum
15	1	Y-minimum
16	16	Y-maximum
17	1	Unit is 1 pixel
18	0	Number of bytes = 0 at the begin
19	1	Number of bytes = 0 at the end
20	3	Number of used bytes for all lines
21	2	Number of lines = 0 at the begin
22	6	Number of lines = 0 at the end

LINE INDEX

23	0	Records
24	2	Words No line index in this format

WORDNO.	CONTENT	COMMENT
27- 28	FC 00 00	111111000000000000000000
28- 29	1C 00 00	000111000000000000000000
30- 31	1C 00 00	000111000000000000000000
31- 32	1C 00 00	000111000000000000000000
33- 34	1C 00 00	000111000000000000000000
34- 35	1C FE 00	000111001111111000000000
36- 37	1F 87 80	000111111000011110000000
37- 38	1E 01 C0	000111100000000111000000
39- 40	1C 01 C0	000111000000000111000000
40- 41	1C 00 E0	000111000000000011100000
42- 43	1C 00 E0	000111000000000011100000
43- 44	1C 00 E0	000111000000000011100000
45- 46	1C 01 C0	000111000000000111000000
46- 47	1E 01 C0	000111100000000111000000
48- 49	1F 87 80	000111111000011110000000
49- 50	19 FE 00	000110011111111000000000

WORDNO.	CONTENT	COMMENT
1	0	Records length of character
2	37	Words

NAME SECTION

3	3	Length of name section
4	303	Character number
5	0	Number of following part

SETTING INFORMATION

6	17	Length of setting information
7	1	Character type = letter
8	22	Number of bytes
9	16	Total set width (T=L+W+R)
10	2	Left side bearing (L)
11	13	Width (W)
12	1	Right side bearing (R)
13	1	X-minimum
14	13	X-maximum
15	1	Y-minimum
16	11	Y-maximum
17	1	Unit is 1 pixel
18	0	Number of bytes = 0 at the begin
19	2	Number of bytes = 0 at the end
20	2	Number of used bytes for all lines
21	7	Number of lines = 0 at the begin
22	6	Number of lines = 0 at the end

LINE INDEX

23	0	Records
24	2	Words No line index in this format

IMAGE INFORMATION

25	0	Records length of image information
26	13	Words

311

WORDNO.	CONTENT	COMMENT
27- 27	OF E0	0000111111100000
28- 28	38 30	0011100000110000
29- 29	70 78	0111000001111000
30- 30	E0 30	1110000000110000
31- 31	E0 00	1110000000000000
32- 32	E0 00	1110000000000000
33- 33	E0 00	1110000000000000
34- 34	E0 00	1110000000000000
35- 35	70 08	0111000000001000
36- 36	38 30	0011100000110000
37- 37	OF C0	0000111111000000

GRAND TOTAL

	WORDS	KBYTES
Length of font:	6317	12.634
Length of font header:	484	0.968
Length of all character headers:	3240	6.480
Length of total image information:	2593	5.186

DIGITIZATIONS	NUMBER
Lines:	1917
Total of bytes:	4606
Characters:	135
Records (a 2048 words):	4
Raster (grid):	32 X 24
Digitizations per line:	2.40
Lines per character:	14
Image information per character:	38 bytes

Appendix Q
Description of the GS format

1. Structure of a GS font

The structure of a GS font is as described in appendix G with an extended structure as in appendix K.

In the identification for a font (word number 50) the number of gray tones is coded:

G1 for 2 bit, G2 for 3 bit, G3 for 4 bit, G4 for 8 bit etc.

2. Description of the GS format

The **gray scale format** was designed to describe points which are not only black or white but also half tone. In the case of a 4 bit coding with linear interpretation for gray the following gray scales are possible:

Hexadecimal 4 bit value	Black fraction in %	Comment
0	0	white
1	7	.
2	16	light
.	.	.
.	.	.
.	.	.
E	93	dark
F	100	black

The four bits are recorded as a halfbyte and written corresponding to the BI format conventions. With the GS format however, two pixels already form one byte, and we therefore expect four times more data for an equivalent grid resolution.

One byte is considered as one digitization.

3. Example of a GS format

First of all we represent the lower case letters a, b, c of the typeface "URW Antiqua 2015 normal", as graymaps of a 4 bit coding. The scan identification is 12 (laser printer). The raster is 16×16 for the em square. Subsequently, the type font format is reproduced as a data list.

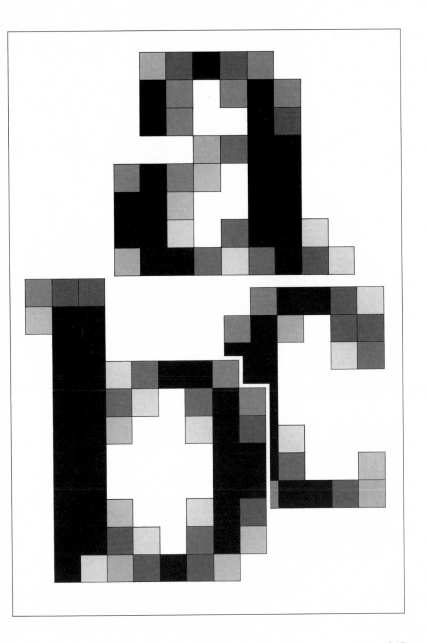

315

```
---------  ------------------  -------------------------------------------------
WORDNO.  |    CONTENT       |                    COMMENT
---------  ------------------  -------------------------------------------------
   1     |             484  | Length of font header
---------  ------------------  -------------------------------------------------
```

NAME SECTION

```
   2     |              55  | Length of name section
   3     |             825  | Number on URW list
 4  - 10 |    AN201512.G3   | File name (ASCII)

11  - 49 |  URW-Antiqua 2000                     | Font name (ASCII)
         |         normal

  50     |              G3  | Data format (ASCII)
51  - 53 |          3  2 87 | Production date:      3-Feb-87
54  - 56 |          3  2 87 | Date of last change:  3-Feb-87
---------  ------------------  -------------------------------------------------
```

FONT INFORMATION

```
  57     |              19  | Length of font information
  58     |               1  | Indicator for font
  59     |             135  | Number of characters
  60     |              11  | Cap height (in pixels)
  61     |              16  | Body size (in pixels)
  62     |               8  | x-height (in pixels)
  63     |               5  | Distance: base line - lower body line(in pixels)
  64     |              16  | Text line distance for setting (in pixels)
  65     |               2  | Stem thickness (in pixels)
  66     |               0  | Angle of italisation (in 1/10 degree)
  67     |              12  | Optimum point size for setting (in p)
  68     |               8  | Average character width (in pixels)
  69     |            9375  | X-extension of a pixel (in 1/1000mm)
  70     |            9375  | Y-extension of a pixel (in 1/1000mm)
  71     |              16  | Em-resolution in X-direction (in pixels)
  72     |              16  | Em-resolution in Y-direction (in pixels)
  73     |              12  | Scan indicator of image data
  74     |              16  | Width of printing window (in pixels)
  75     |              16  | Height of printing window (in pixels)
---------  ------------------  -------------------------------------------------
```

HIERARCHY SECTION

```
  76     |               1  | No hierarchy section in this format
---------  ------------------  -------------------------------------------------
```

CHARACTER INDEX

```
  77     |             408  | Length of character index
  78     |               4  | LENGTH OF FONT IN PHYSICAL RECORDS
  79     |             676  | Last word of last record

  80     |             101  | Character number:  1
  81     |               1  | Pointer to record containing start of character
  82     |             485  | Word pointer to start of character

  83     |             102  | Ch. no.: 2
  84     |               1  | Record pointer
  85     |             544  | Word pointer

86-  88  |   103   1  598   | No., record pointer, word pointer of ch.:   3
89-  91  |   104   1  660   | No., record pointer, word pointer of ch.:   4
92-  94  |   105   1  719   | No., record pointer, word pointer of ch.:   5
---------  ------------------  -------------------------------------------------
```

316

WORDNO.	CONTENT			COMMENT
95- 97	106	1	773	No., record pointer, word pointer of ch.: 6
98- 100	107	1	827	No., record pointer, word pointer of ch.: 7
101- 103	108	1	889	No., record pointer, word pointer of ch.: 8
104- 106	109	1	948	No., record pointer, word pointer of ch.: 9
107- 109	110	1	991	No., record pointer, word pointer of ch.: 10
110- 112	111	1	1038	No., record pointer, word pointer of ch.: 11
113- 115	112	1	1097	No., record pointer, word pointer of ch.: 12
116- 118	113	1	1151	No., record pointer, word pointer of ch.: 13
119- 121	114	1	1221	No., record pointer, word pointer of ch.: 14
122- 124	115	1	1280	No., record pointer, word pointer of ch.: 15
125- 127	116	1	1342	No., record pointer, word pointer of ch.: 16
128- 130	117	1	1396	No., record pointer, word pointer of ch.: 17
131- 133	118	1	1475	No., record pointer, word pointer of ch.: 18
134- 136	119	1	1537	No., record pointer, word pointer of ch.: 19
137- 139	120	1	1587	No., record pointer, word pointer of ch.: 20
140- 142	121	1	1641	No., record pointer, word pointer of ch.: 21
143- 145	122	1	1703	No., record pointer, word pointer of ch.: 22
146- 148	123	1	1762	No., record pointer, word pointer of ch.: 23
149- 151	124	1	1842	No., record pointer, word pointer of ch.: 24
152- 154	125	1	1901	No., record pointer, word pointer of ch.: 25
155- 157	126	1	1960	No., record pointer, word pointer of ch.: 26
158- 160	127	1	2014	No., record pointer, word pointer of ch.: 27
161- 163	128	2	36	No., record pointer, word pointer of ch.: 28
164- 166	129	2	110	No., record pointer, word pointer of ch.: 29
167- 169	201	2	181	No., record pointer, word pointer of ch.: 30
170- 172	208	2	249	No., record pointer, word pointer of ch.: 31
173- 175	210	2	317	No., record pointer, word pointer of ch.: 32
176- 178	237	2	385	No., record pointer, word pointer of ch.: 33
179- 181	251	2	453	No., record pointer, word pointer of ch.: 34
182- 184	301	2	521	No., record pointer, word pointer of ch.: 35
185- 187	302	2	567	No., record pointer, word pointer of ch.: 36
188- 190	303	2	621	No., record pointer, word pointer of ch.: 37
191- 193	304	2	659	No., record pointer, word pointer of ch.: 38
194- 196	305	2	715	No., record pointer, word pointer of ch.: 39
197- 199	306	2	757	No., record pointer, word pointer of ch.: 40
200- 202	307	2	801	No., record pointer, word pointer of ch.: 41
203- 205	308	2	849	No., record pointer, word pointer of ch.: 42
206- 208	309	2	911	No., record pointer, word pointer of ch.: 43
209- 211	310	2	954	No., record pointer, word pointer of ch.: 44

WORDNO.	CONTENT			COMMENT
449- 451	704	4	310	No., record pointer, word pointer of ch.: 124
452- 454	705	4	340	No., record pointer, word pointer of ch.: 125
455- 457	706	4	370	No., record pointer, word pointer of ch.: 126
458- 460	709	4	402	No., record pointer, word pointer of ch.: 127
461- 463	711	4	434	No., record pointer, word pointer of ch.: 128
464- 466	751	4	464	No., record pointer, word pointer of ch.: 129
467- 469	753	4	493	No., record pointer, word pointer of ch.: 130
470- 472	754	4	523	No., record pointer, word pointer of ch.: 131
473- 475	755	4	553	No., record pointer, word pointer of ch.: 132
476- 478	756	4	583	No., record pointer, word pointer of ch.: 133
479- 481	759	4	615	No., record pointer, word pointer of ch.: 134
482- 484	761	4	647	No., record pointer, word pointer of ch.: 135

317

WORDNO.	CONTENT	COMMENT
1	0	Records length of character
2	46	Words

NAME SECTION

3	3	Length of name section
4	301	Character number
5	0	Number of following part

SETTING INFORMATION

6	17	Length of setting information
7	1	Character type = letter
8	40	Number of bytes
9	10	Total set width (T=L+W+R)
10	1	Left side bearing (L)
11	9	Width (W)
12	-1	Right side bearing (R)
13	1	X-minimum
14	9	X-maximum
15	2	Y-minimum
16	9	Y-maximum
17	1	Unit is 1 pixel
18	0	Number of bytes = 0 at the begin
19	3	Number of bytes = 0 at the end
20	5	Number of used bytes for all lines
21	3	Number of lines = 0 at the begin
22	5	Number of lines = 0 at the end

LINE INDEX

23	0	Records
24	2	Words No line index in this format

IMAGE INFORMATION

25	0	Records length of information
26	22	Words

27-	29	06EFE80000	-X#X+
29-	31	0F908F9000	#+ +#+
32-	34	0F904FE000	#+ :#X
34-	36	0046AFF000	:-*##
37-	39	8F800FF000	+#+ ##
39-	41	FF000FF000	## ##
42-	44	FF30AFF100	##. *##.
44-	46	6FFB3BFC20	-##*.*#X.

WORDNO.	CONTENT	COMMENT
1	0	Records length of character
2	54	Words

NAME SECTION

3	3	Length of name section
4	302	Character number
5	0	Number of following part

SETTING INFORMATION

6	17	Length of setting information
7	1	Character type = letter
8	55	Number of bytes
9	10	Total set width (T=L+W+R)
10	0	Left side bearing (L)
11	9	Width (W)
12	1	Right side bearing (R)
13	1	X-minimum
14	9	X-maximum
15	2	Y-minimum
16	12	Y-maximum
17	1	Unit is 1 pixel
18	0	Number of bytes = 0 at the begin
19	3	Number of bytes = 0 at the end
20	5	Number of used bytes for all lines
21	0	Number of lines = 0 at the begin
22	5	Number of lines = 0 at the end

LINE INDEX

23	0	Records
24	2	Words No line index in this format

IMAGE INFORMATION

25	0	Records length of information
26	30	Words
27- 29	9CE0000000	+XX
29- 31	4FF0000000	:##
32- 34	0FF0000000	##
34- 36	0FF1BFF900	##.*##+
37- 39	0FFA20AF80	##*. *#+
39- 41	0FF5001FE0	##: .#X
42- 44	0FF0000FF0	## ##
44- 46	0FF0000FF0	## ##
47- 49	0FF5001FE0	##: .#X
49- 51	0FFD20AF50	##X. *#:
52- 54	0F37EFE500	#.-X#X:

```
--------- ------------------ -----------------------------------------------
 WORDNO.    CONTENT                                       COMMENT
--------- ------------------ -----------------------------------------------
    1               0        Records       length of character
    2              38        Words
--------- ------------------ -----------------------------------------------
        NAME SECTION
        ------------
    3               3        Length of name section
    4             303        Character number
    5               0        Number of following part
--------- ------------------ -----------------------------------------------
        SETTING INFORMATION
        -------------------
    6              17        Length of setting information
    7               1        Character type = letter
    8              24        Number of bytes
    9               7        Total set width (T=L+W+R)
   10               1        Left side bearing (L)
   11               6        Width (W)
   12               0        Right side bearing (R)
   13               1        X-minimum
   14               6        X-maximum
   15               2        Y-minimum
   16               9        Y-maximum
   17               1        Unit is 1 pixel
   18               0        Number of bytes = 0 at the begin
   19               5        Number of bytes = 0 at the end
   20               3        Number of used bytes for all lines
   21               3        Number of lines = 0 at the begin
   22               5        Number of lines = 0 at the end
--------- ------------------ -----------------------------------------------
        LINE INDEX
        ----------
   23               0        Records
   24               2        Words       No line index in this format
--------- ------------------ -----------------------------------------------
        IMAGE INFORMATION
        -----------------
   25                            0       Records    length of information
   26                           14       Words

  27- 28  O9FFC3                    +##X.
  28- 29  8F7OCC                    +#- XX
  30- 31  FFOO1B                    ##  .*
  31- 32  FFOOOO                    ##
  33- 34  FFOOOO                    ##
  34- 35  EF2OOO                    X#.
  36- 37  7FBOO5                    -#*  :
  37- 38  O8FFD6                    +##X-
--------- ------------------ -----------------------------------------------
```

320

```
                        GRAND TOTAL
                        -----------
                                        WORDS        KBYTES
                                        -----        ------
Length of font:                         6820         13.640
Length of font header:                   484          0.968
Length of all character headers:        3240          6.480
Length of total image information:      3096          6.192


        DIGITIZATIONS                        NUMBER
        -------------                        ------
        Lines:                                1275
        Total of bytes:                       5626
        ------------------------------------------
        Characters:                            135
        Records (a 2048 words):                  4
        ------------------------------------------
        Raster (grid):                   16 X  16
        ------------------------------------------
        Digitizations per line:              4.41
        Lines per character:                    9
        Image information per character:      46 bytes
```

Appendix R
Data structure for spacing

1. General

URW currently has four different sorts of letter spacing available:
- traditional (width tables),
- kerning,
- touching,
- overlapping.

The traditional widths are stored in the form of width tables.

For kerning there is a short and a long form of storage. The short form is created from classifications of the left and right side appearance of all characters of any font in question. We use the clustering method which classifies similar side appearances into classes and which allows for example 32 different classes of right side appearance (back classes). The same applies to the left side appearances (front classes). This produces a short kerning table of 32 × 32 values for all possible combinations of left and right side classes.

In the long kerning table all character pairs have individual correction values, i.e. the long table has 100 × 100 values when applied to 100 different characters, and 250 × 250 values when applied to a typeface of 250 characters.

To date we have always kept to the long storage form for touching and overlapping tables.

2. Access

The access to the letter spacing is organized exactly as for a font, i.e. we take the data structure of a font (appendix G) and adjust the contents for the purpose of letter spacing. The widths are known as "character number 1", the short table for kerning as "character number 2", the long table as "number 3" and the touching and overlapping tables as "number 4" and "number 5".

For additional letter spacing variations there is a lot of room from number 6 onwards.

A correction value is stored as INTEGER × 2 (16 bit) and is regarded as a digitization.

The correction values are accessed through a changed contour index as follows:

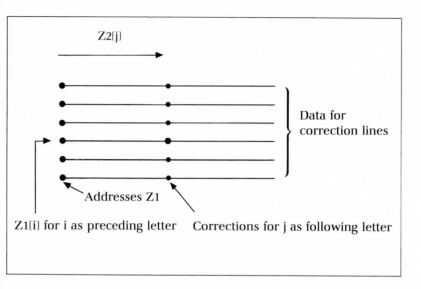

For character number i in position i it contains the start address $Z1(i)$ of the correction line (old image information) with the correction values for letter number i as preceding letter. This first section of the index has a length of $2 \times N4$ (in words).

In addition, the letter spacing index contains for letter number j in position $2 \times N4 + j$ the address $Z2(j)$ in the correction lines, where the correction value for letter number j is stored as the following letter. This is the second section of the index. For character pair (ij) the correction value for the letter spacing is found in position $Z1(i) + Z2(j)$ in the image information.

The length of the index is dependent upon the highest character number of the respective font. Our current concept allows for space for a maximum length of 1000 places per index table. However, this length is a variable and can be adjusted to meet individual needs.

There is a default correction value of 0. This correction has no effect and is assigned to all letter pairs which are not intended to kern, touch, or overlap.

3. Description of the letter spacing header

In this appendix we wish to describe the letter spacing and use a changed font header. The data records for the tables follow in appendices S, T, U and V.

Data carriers are as described in appendix G, point 1.

Spacing header

Word	Meaning	Comment
1	Length of spacing header in words	$= 1 + I + J + L + M$
	Name section	
2	Length of name section	(I)
3	Number on URW list	
4–9	File name	6 words
10–49	Font name in ASCII	40 words
50	Format identification of data	SP (spacing)
51–53	Production date	3 words
54–56	Date of last change	e.g. 16,6,85 for 16th of June 1985. Currently (1985) I has the value 55 at URW.
	Spacing information	
I + 2	Length of spacing data in words	(J)
I + 3	Identification of spacing	= 3
I + 4	Number of tables	Currently = 5
I + 5	Cap height	in units At URW currently (1985) J has the value 4.

Word	Meaning	Comment
I+J+2	**Hierarchy section** Length of hierarchy	(L) = 1 for spacing
I+J+L+2 I+J+L+3 I+J+L+4 I+J+L+5 I+J+L+6 I+J+L+7	**Table index** Length of table index Pointer to last written physi- cal record (= **length of spacing in physical records**) Pointer to last written word of last record Number of first table Record pointer in the spacing which contains the start of the first table Pointer to the first word used in this record	(M) Current length of spacing data Widths
I+J+L+8 I+J+L+9 I+J+L+10	Number Record pointer Word pointer	Short kerning (clustering)
I+J+L+11 I+J+L+12 I+J+L+13	Number Record pointer Word pointer	Long kerning
I+J+L+14 I+J+L+15 I+J+L+16	Number Record pointer Word pointer	Touching
I+J+L+17 I+J+L+18 I+J+L+19	Number Record pointer Word pointer	Overlapping

An adjustment of the letter spacing for all data records can only be carried out together with the associated character number list (see appendix B) of the respective font.

Appendix S
Width table

The width tables could be compressed because one does not actually need access to a matrix, but rather to a simple array. We have decided to ignore this exception. For this reason the width table in letter spacing (see appendix R) has the following structure shown below. An example is reproduced at the end of appendix T, section 4.

1. Width record

Word	Meaning	Comment
1 2	Length of width record in records in words	$2+N1+N2+N3+M$
3 4 5	**Name section** Length of name section Number Following part number	$N1$ (currently $=3$) $=1$ (width) $=0$ (currently)
$N1+3$ $N1+4$ $N1+5$	**Record information** Length of record information Number of widths Unit size	$N2$ (currently $=3$) according to font format
$N1+N2+3$ $N1+N2+4$	**Spacing index** Length of letter spacing index in records in words	$N3=2+N4\times3$

Word	Meaning	Comment
$N1 + N2 + 5$ $N1 + N2 + 6$	Record and word pointer of width of character number 1	The addresses are counted relative to the start of spacing information.
$N1 + N2 + 7$ $N1 + N2 + 8$ . . .	Record and word pointer of width of character number 2 . . .	N4 entries for width line $\triangleq$ Addresses Z1(i) as per appendix R
$N1 + N2 + 4$ $+ N4 \times 2$	Word pointer of width of highest character number of font	
$N1 + N2 + 5$ $+ N4 \times 2$	0	N4 entries for width lines $\triangleq$ Addresses Z2(j) as per appendix R, all N4 entries are given the value 0.
	Letter spacing information	
$N1 + N2 + N3$ $+ 3$	Length of table in records	M
$+ 4$	in words	
$+ 5$	"Width" of the em	Default parameter
$+ 6$	Width of first character with no default width	
$+ 7$	Width of second character with no default width	
. . .	. . .	
$N1 + N2$ $+ N3 + M + 2$	Last width	

Thus, to read the width of character i and the next character j from the table we have the following:

Address: $= Z1(i) + Z2(j)$,

Width: $=$ contents (address).

The details of the next character j are then irrelevant. We do however intend to adjust the access to widths, to that of the method for kerning correction values.

An example of a width table record is shown at the end of appendix T, the table is representing traditional widths for the typeface "URW Antiqua 2015 normal".

Appendix T
Kerning table

There are long and short versions of kerning tables. As already mentioned the short tables are generated by classifying left and right side appearances of characters, and the long tables as kerning corrections for all possible letter pairs of a type font. The short kerning table has the following structure (see also appendix R):

1. Short kerning record

Word	Meaning	Comment
1 2	Length of short kerning record in records in words	$2 + N1 + N2 + N3 + M$
3 4 5	**Name section** Length of name section Number Following part number	N1 (currently = 3) = 2 (short kerning)
N1 + 3 N1 + 4 N1 + 5 N1 + 6	**Record information** Length of record information Number of correction values Unit size Number of corresponding long kerning table	N2 (currently = 4) According to font format
N1 + N2 + 3	**Spacing index** Length of spacing index in records	$N3 = 2 + N4 \times 3$

Word	Meaning	Comment
N1 + N2 + 4	in words	
N1 + N2 + 5	Record and word pointer to	The addresses are
N1 + N2 + 6	correction line for letter pairs,	counted relative to
	in which the first (front) letter	start of spacing
	is character number 1.	information.
N1 + N2 + 7	Record and word pointer to	
N1 + N2 + 8	correction line of the letter	
	pair in which the first (front)	N4 entries for
	letter is character number 2.	correction lines
.	.	$\triangleq$
.	.	Addresses Z1(i) as
.	.	per appendix R
N1 + N2 + 4	Word pointer to correction	
+ N4 × 2	line of the letter pair in which	
	the last character is in front.	
N1 + N2 + 5	Word pointer to the place in	
+ N4 × 2	the correction line for letter	
	pairs in which character	
	number 1 is back.	N4 entries for
		correction lines
.	.	$\triangleq$
.	.	Addresses Z2(j) as
.	.	per appendix R
N1 + N2 + 2	Last pointer for last character	
+ N3	as 2nd (back) letter.	

Word	**Spacing information**	Comment
N1 + N2 + N3	Length of table	M
+ 3	in records	
+ 4	in words	
+ 5	Default correction value line	All = 0
	Pair (none,none)	
+ 6	Pair (none, 1st back class)	1st correction line
		for "none" character
+ 7	Pair (none, 2nd back class)	at front.

Word	Meaning	Comment
. . .	. . .	
N1 + N2 + N3 + N5 + 5 + 6 + 7	Correction value for pair 1st front class, "none" character. Correction value for the pair 1st front class, 1st back class. Correction value for the pair 1st front class, 2nd back class.	= 0 2nd correction line
. . .	. . .	. . .
2 + N1 + N2 + N3 + M	Correction value for the pair (N5,N5)	Last correction for last front class with last back class.

The correction lines all have a constant length. The N4 entries in the letter spacing index usually include empty indicators (indicators to 1st correction line or the first places of the correction line) for character numbers which do not occur in the font in question or which cause no correction, if they are preceding or following a character. In addition, the classification sometimes makes reference to the same place.

Therefore the lengths of the correction lines are shorter than N4. The following applies:

$M = 2 + N5 \times N5$, where N5 is the number of different classes in a font.

In particular N5 is the line length and has e.g. the value 33 (one default correction plus 32 values for 32 different classes).

An example of a short kerning record at the end of this appendix shows short kerning values for the type "URW Antiqua 2015 normal".

3. Long kerning record

Word	Meaning	Comment
1 2	Length of long kerning record in records in words	$2 + N1 + N2 + N3 + M$
3 4 5	**Name section** Length of name section Number Following part number	$N1$ (currently = 3) = 3 (long kerning record)
N1 + 3 N1 + 4 N1 + 5 N1 + 6 N1 + 7 N1 + 8 N1 + 9 N1 + 10 N1 + 11 N1 + 12 N1 + 13 N1 + 14 N1 + 15	**Setting information** Length of setting information Number of lines of correction matrix Number of columns of correction matrix Unit size 1st spacing letter 2nd spacing letter Left side bearing Right side bearing Left side bearing Right side bearing 1st value of minimum distance 2nd value of minimum distance Factor	$N2$ (currently = 19) $N5$ (currently) $N5$ (currently) According to font format Base upper case Base lower case ⎱ of 1st base ⎰ spacing letter ⎱ of 2nd base ⎰ spacing letter on the level of base- lines between baselines (in touching tables = minimum distance for vertical strokes) for compression of white space

Word	Meaning	Comment
N1 + 16	Distance function	= 0 appropriate to geometrical mean = 1 appropriate to arithmetic mean
N1 + 17	Italic angle	in 1/10 degree
N1 + 18	Serif height	in 1/100 mm
N1 + 19	Cap height	(are given especially for kerning calculation)
N1 + 20	x-height	
N1 + 21	Descender length	
	Spacing index Length of spacing	$N3 = 2 + N4 \times 3$
N1 + N2 + 3	in records	
N1 + N2 + 4	in words	
N1 + N2 + 5	Record and word pointer to	The addresses are
N1 + N2 + 6	correction line for letter pairs	counted relative to
	in which the 1st (front) letter	the start of spacing
	is character number 1.	information.
N1 + N2 + 7	Record and word pointer to	N4 entries for
N1 + N2 + 8	correction line of the letter	correction lines
	pairs in which the 1st (front)	
	letter is character number 2.	
.	.	$\cong$
.	.	Addresses Z1(i) as
.	.	per appendix R
N1 + N2 + 4 + N4	Word pointer to correction line of the letter pairs in which the last character is in front.	
N1 + N2 + 5 + N4	Word pointer to the place in correction line for letter pairs in which character number 1 is in 2nd (back) position.	N4 entries for correction lines

Word	Meaning	Comment
. . . $2 + N1 + N2$ $+ N3$	. . . Last word pointer for last character as 2nd (back) letter.	$\triangleq$ Addresses Z2(j) as per appendix R
Spacing information		
$N1 + N2 + N3$	Length of table	M
$+3$	in records	
$+4$	in words	
$+5$	Default correction line first entry for pair (none,none)	All $= 0$ 1st correction line for "none" character at front
$+6$	Pair (none, 1st character)	
$+7$	Pair (none, 2nd character)	
. . .	. . .	2nd correction line
$N1 + N2 + N3$ $+ N5 + 5$	Default correction value	$= 0$ (1st char., none)
$+6$	2nd word of correction line for first character with no default value as front letter.	Contains correction value for pair formation with first character in front.
$+7$	1st with 2nd character	
$+8$	1st with 3rd character	
. . .	. . .	
$2 + N1 + N2$ $+ N3 + M$	Last with last character	Last correction line

The correction value for the kerning of character i with its successor j is read from the table as follows:

Address: $= Z1(i) + Z2(j)$
Correction: $=$ contents (address)

---

kerning
unterschneiden

Examples of kerning

---

4. Examples of spacing records

Here we show tables containing the traditional widths (record 1), the short kerning (record 2), the long kerning (record 3) and widths and bearings (record 6) for the type "URW Antiqua 2015 normal".

Word no	Content	Meaning
1	76	Length of spacing header

NAME SECTION

2	55	Length of name section
3	0	Number on URW list
4 - 10	AN2015.SP	File name
11 - 49		Font name in ASCII
50	SP	Format ident of data
51 - 53	6. 2.87	Production date
54 - 56	17. 2.87	Date of last change

SPACING INFORMATION

57	4	Length of spacing data in words
58	3	Ident of spacing
59	4	Number of tables
60	10000	Cap height (in 1/100 mm)

HIERARCHY SECTION

61	1	Length of hierarchy

TABLE INDEX

62			15	Length of table index	
63			26	LENGTH OF SPACING IN PHYSICAL RECORDS	
64			1453	Last written word of last record	
65			1	Number of 1. table	
66			1	Pointer to record, which cont. start of table	
67			1025	Pointer to first used word in this record	
68			2	Number of 2. table	
69			3	Record pointer	
70			61	Word pointer	
71- 73	3	5	4	No, record pointer, word pointer f. 3. table	
74- 76	6	25	97	No, record pointer, word pointer f. 4. table	

Word no	Content		Meaning
1		1	Records Length of table
2		1084	Words

NAME SECTION

3		3	Length of name section
4		1	Table = widths
5		0	Following part number

RECORD INFORMATION

6		3	Length of record information
7		120	Number of widths
8		1	Unit size is 1/100 mm

SPACING INDEX

9		1	Records Length of spacing index
10		954	Words
211	0	6	Record/wordp. f. width of 101 (abs. 1, 968)
213	0	7	Record/wordp. f. width of 102 (abs. 1, 969)
215	0	8	Record/wordp. f. width of 103 (abs. 1, 970)
217	0	9	Record/wordp. f. width of 104 (abs. 1, 971)
219	0	10	Record/wordp. f. width of 105 (abs. 1, 972)
221	0	11	Record/wordp. f. width of 106 (abs. 1, 973)
223	0	12	Record/wordp. f. width of 107 (abs. 1, 974)
225	0	4	Record/wordp. f. width of 108 (abs. 1, 966)
227	0	13	Record/wordp. f. width of 109 (abs. 1, 975)
229	0	14	Record/wordp. f. width of 110 (abs. 1, 976)
231	0	15	Record/wordp. f. width of 111 (abs. 1, 977)
233	0	16	Record/wordp. f. width of 112 (abs. 1, 978)
235	0	17	Record/wordp. f. width of 113 (abs. 1, 979)
237	0	18	Record/wordp. f. width of 114 (abs. 1, 980)
239	0	19	Record/wordp. f. width of 115 (abs. 1, 981)
241	0	20	Record/wordp. f. width of 116 (abs. 1, 982)
243	0	21	Record/wordp. f. width of 117 (abs. 1, 983)
245	0	22	Record/wordp. f. width of 118 (abs. 1, 984)
247	0	23	Record/wordp. f. width of 119 (abs. 1, 985)
249	0	24	Record/wordp. f. width of 120 (abs. 1, 986)
251	0	25	Record/wordp. f. width of 121 (abs. 1, 987)
253	0	26	Record/wordp. f. width of 122 (abs. 1, 988)
255	0	27	Record/wordp. f. width of 123 (abs. 1, 989)
257	0	28	Record/wordp. f. width of 124 (abs. 1, 990)
259	0	29	Record/wordp. f. width of 125 (abs. 1, 991)
261	0	30	Record/wordp. f. width of 126 (abs. 1, 992)
263	0	31	Record/wordp. f. width of 127 (abs. 1, 993)
265	0	32	Record/wordp. f. width of 128 (abs. 1, 994)
267	0	33	Record/wordp. f. width of 129 (abs. 1, 995)
411	0	34	Record/wordp. f. width of 201 (abs. 1, 996)
425	0	35	Record/wordp. f. width of 208 (abs. 1, 997)
429	0	36	Record/wordp. f. width of 210 (abs. 1, 998)
483	0	37	Record/wordp. f. width of 237 (abs. 1, 999)
511	0	38	Record/wordp. f. width of 251 (abs. 1,1000)
611	0	39	Record/wordp. f. width of 301 (abs. 1,1001)
613	0	40	Record/wordp. f. width of 302 (abs. 1,1002)
615	0	41	Record/wordp. f. width of 303 (abs. 1,1003)
617	0	42	Record/wordp. f. width of 304 (abs. 1,1004)

```
---------|------------------|-------------------------------------------------
Word no  |    Content       |                    Meaning
---------|------------------|-------------------------------------------------
 1241    |   0       101    | Record/wordp. f. width of  616  (abs.  1,1063)
 1243    |   0       102    | Record/wordp. f. width of  617  (abs.  1,1064)
 1245    |   0       103    | Record/wordp. f. width of  618  (abs.  1,1065)
 1247    |   0       104    | Record/wordp. f. width of  619  (abs.  1,1066)
 1249    |   0       105    | Record/wordp. f. width of  620  (abs.  1,1067)
 1251    |   0       106    | Record/wordp. f. width of  621  (abs.  1,1068)
 1253    |   0       107    | Record/wordp. f. width of  622  (abs.  1,1069)
 1255    |   0       108    | Record/wordp. f. width of  623  (abs.  1,1070)
 1257    |   0       109    | Record/wordp. f. width of  624  (abs.  1,1071)
 1259    |   0       110    | Record/wordp. f. width of  625  (abs.  1,1072)
 1261    |   0       111    | Record/wordp. f. width of  626  (abs.  1,1073)
 1263    |   0       112    | Record/wordp. f. width of  627  (abs.  1,1074)
 1265    |   0       113    | Record/wordp. f. width of  628  (abs.  1,1075)
 1267    |   0       114    | Record/wordp. f. width of  629  (abs.  1,1076)
 1269    |   0       115    | Record/wordp. f. width of  630  (abs.  1,1077)
 1271    |   0       116    | Record/wordp. f. width of  631  (abs.  1,1078)
 1273    |   0       117    | Record/wordp. f. width of  632  (abs.  1,1079)
 1275    |   0       118    | Record/wordp. f. width of  633  (abs.  1,1080)
 1277    |   0       119    | Record/wordp. f. width of  634  (abs.  1,1081)
 1315    |   0       120    | Record/wordp. f. width of  653  (abs.  1,1082)
 1317    |   0       121    | Record/wordp. f. width of  654  (abs.  1,1083)
 1405    |   0       122    | Record/wordp. f. width of  698  (abs.  1,1084)
---------|------------------|-------------------------------------------------
         | Spacing information
         | ------------------
 3011    |              0   | Records      Length of table
 3012    |            122   | Words
---------|------------------|-------------------------------------------------
 S., W.  |    Content       |                    Meaning
---------|------------------|-------------------------------------------------
 1  965  |          15000   | Width for the em
 1  966  |          12054   | Width of character   108
 1  967  |           9525   | Width of character   314
 1  968  |          11191   | Width of character   101
 1  969  |          10202   | Width of character   102
 1  970  |          11027   | Width of character   103
 1  971  |          11931   | Width of character   104
 1  972  |           9829   | Width of character   105
 1  973  |           8781   | Width of character   106
 1  974  |          12106   | Width of character   107
 1  975  |           5392   | Width of character   109
 1  976  |           5352   | Width of character   110
 1  977  |          10528   | Width of character   111
 1  978  |           9044   | Width of character   112
 1  979  |          14300   | Width of character   113
 1  980  |          11545   | Width of character   114
 1  981  |          12566   | Width of character   115
 1  982  |           9204   | Width of character   116
 1  983  |          12637   | Width of character   117
 1  984  |          10053   | Width of character   118
 1  985  |           8949   | Width of character   119
 1  986  |           9458   | Width of character   120
 1  987  |          11254   | Width of character   121
 1  988  |          10792   | Width of character   122
 1  989  |          15155   | Width of character   123
 1  990  |           9448   | Width of character   124
 1  991  |           9768   | Width of character   125
 1  992  |           9577   | Width of character   126
---------|------------------|-------------------------------------------------
```

339

S., W.	Content	Meaning
1 993	13903	Width of character 127
1 994	15445	Width of character 128
1 995	12614	Width of character 129
1 996	11241	Width of character 201
1 997	11191	Width of character 208
1 998	11027	Width of character 210
1 999	12566	Width of character 237
1 1000	11254	Width of character 251
1 1001	7710	Width of character 301
1 1002	9637	Width of character 302
1 1003	7407	Width of character 303
1 1004	9475	Width of character 304
1 1005	8141	Width of character 305
1 1006	4421	Width of character 306
1 1007	7569	Width of character 307
1 1008	9667	Width of character 308
1 1009	4369	Width of character 309
1 1010	4051	Width of character 310
1 1011	8877	Width of character 311
1 1012	4400	Width of character 312
1 1013	14511	Width of character 313
1 1014	9004	Width of character 315
1 1015	9426	Width of character 316
1 1016	9521	Width of character 317
1 1017	6154	Width of character 318
1 1018	6984	Width of character 319
1 1019	4994	Width of character 320
1 1020	9303	Width of character 321
1 1021	8377	Width of character 322
1 1022	12784	Width of character 323
1 1023	8058	Width of character 324
1 1024	7881	Width of character 325
1 1025	7681	Width of character 326
1 1026	11845	Width of character 327
1 1027	13430	Width of character 328
1 1028	8985	Width of character 329
1 1029	8788	Width of character 330
1 1030	7710	Width of character 401
1 1031	7710	Width of character 408
1 1032	7395	Width of character 413
1 1033	8985	Width of character 436
1 1034	9403	Width of character 449
1 1035	7500	Width of character 501
1 1036	7500	Width of character 502
1 1037	7500	Width of character 503
1 1038	7500	Width of character 504
1 1039	7500	Width of character 505
1 1040	7501	Width of character 506
1 1041	7500	Width of character 507
1 1042	8000	Width of character 508
1 1043	7500	Width of character 509
1 1044	7500	Width of character 510
1 1045	9647	Width of character 511
1 1046	7500	Width of character 512
1 1047	8000	Width of character 513
1 1048	3500	Width of character 601
1 1049	3500	Width of character 602
1 1050	2185	Width of character 603
1 1051	7000	Width of character 604

S., W.	Content	Meaning
1 1052	7000	Width of character 605
1 1053	10500	Width of character 606
1 1054	3500	Width of character 607
1 1055	3500	Width of character 608
1 1056	3092	Width of character 609
1 1057	3192	Width of character 610
1 1058	5792	Width of character 611
1 1059	5792	Width of character 612
1 1060	5700	Width of character 613
1 1061	3536	Width of character 614
1 1062	3536	Width of character 615
1 1063	5482	Width of character 616
1 1064	5482	Width of character 617
1 1065	5596	Width of character 618
1 1066	5596	Width of character 619
1 1067	4310	Width of character 620
1 1068	4310	Width of character 621
1 1069	6095	Width of character 622
1 1070	4774	Width of character 623
1 1071	5977	Width of character 624
1 1072	7957	Width of character 625
1 1073	4576	Width of character 626
1 1074	4576	Width of character 627
1 1075	4500	Width of character 628
1 1076	4501	Width of character 629
1 1077	11722	Width of character 630
1 1078	6973	Width of character 631
1 1079	6496	Width of character 632
1 1080	6496	Width of character 633
1 1081	5374	Width of character 634
1 1082	3500	Width of character 653
1 1083	3500	Width of character 654
1 1084	8120	Width of character 698

Word no	Content		Meaning
1		1	Records Length of table
2		1991	Words

NAME SECTION

3		3	Length of name section
4		2	Table = short kerning
5		0	Following part number

RECORD INFORMATION

6		5	Length of record information
7		32	Number of columns of correction matrix
8		32	Number of lines of correction matrix
9		1	Unit size is 1/100 mm
10		3	Number of corresponding long kerning table

SPACING INDEX

11		1	Records Length of spacing index
12		954	Words
213	0	579	Record/wordp. f. pairs 101,* (abs. 1,1543)
215	0	675	Record/wordp. f. pairs 102,* (abs. 1,1639)
217	0	387	Record/wordp. f. pairs 103,* (abs. 1,1351)
219	0	707	Record/wordp. f. pairs 104,* (abs. 1,1671)
221	0	675	Record/wordp. f. pairs 105,* (abs. 1,1639)
223	0	419	Record/wordp. f. pairs 106,* (abs. 1,1383)
225	0	739	Record/wordp. f. pairs 107,* (abs. 1,1703)
227	0	451	Record/wordp. f. pairs 108,* (abs. 1,1415)
229	0	451	Record/wordp. f. pairs 109,* (abs. 1,1415)
231	0	483	Record/wordp. f. pairs 110,* (abs. 1,1447)
233	0	227	Record/wordp. f. pairs 111,* (abs. 1,1191)
235	0	131	Record/wordp. f. pairs 112,* (abs. 1,1095)
237	0	451	Record/wordp. f. pairs 113,* (abs. 1,1415)
239	0	483	Record/wordp. f. pairs 114,* (abs. 1,1447)
241	0	707	Record/wordp. f. pairs 115,* (abs. 1,1671)
243	0	419	Record/wordp. f. pairs 116,* (abs. 1,1383)
245	0	803	Record/wordp. f. pairs 117,* (abs. 1,1767)
247	0	835	Record/wordp. f. pairs 118,* (abs. 1,1799)
249	0	931	Record/wordp. f. pairs 119,* (abs. 1,1895)
251	0	419	Record/wordp. f. pairs 120,* (abs. 1,1383)
253	0	483	Record/wordp. f. pairs 121,* (abs. 1,1447)
255	0	323	Record/wordp. f. pairs 122,* (abs. 1,1287)
257	0	323	Record/wordp. f. pairs 123,* (abs. 1,1287)
259	0	227	Record/wordp. f. pairs 124,* (abs. 1,1191)
261	0	323	Record/wordp. f. pairs 125,* (abs. 1,1287)
263	0	963	Record/wordp. f. pairs 126,* (abs. 1,1927)
265	0	675	Record/wordp. f. pairs 127,* (abs. 1,1639)
267	0	675	Record/wordp. f. pairs 128,* (abs. 1,1639)
269	0	707	Record/wordp. f. pairs 129,* (abs. 1,1671)
413	0	579	Record/wordp. f. pairs 201,* (abs. 1,1543)
427	0	195	Record/wordp. f. pairs 208,* (abs. 1,1159)
431	0	291	Record/wordp. f. pairs 210,* (abs. 1,1255)
485	0	707	Record/wordp. f. pairs 237,* (abs. 1,1671)
513	0	483	Record/wordp. f. pairs 251,* (abs. 1,1447)
613	0	67	Record/wordp. f. pairs 301,* (abs. 1,1031)
615	0	163	Record/wordp. f. pairs 302,* (abs. 1,1127)

Word no	Content		Meaning
1255	0	419	Record/wordp. f. pairs 622,* (abs. 1,1383)
1257	0	547	Record/wordp. f. pairs 623,* (abs. 1,1511)
1263	0	547	Record/wordp. f. pairs 626,* (abs. 1,1511)
1265	0	547	Record/wordp. f. pairs 627,* (abs. 1,1511)
1267	0	547	Record/wordp. f. pairs 628,* (abs. 1,1511)
1269	0	547	Record/wordp. f. pairs 629,* (abs. 1,1511)
1271	0	547	Record/wordp. f. pairs 630,* (abs. 1,1511)
1273	0	547	Record/wordp. f. pairs 631,* (abs. 1,1511)
1279	0	643	Record/wordp. f. pairs 634,* (abs. 1,1607)
1407	0	99	Record/wordp. f. pairs 698,* (abs. 1,1063)
2113		18	Word pointer for character pairs *, 101
2114		1	Word pointer for character pairs *, 102
2115		2	Word pointer for character pairs *, 103
2116		1	Word pointer for character pairs *, 104
2117		1	Word pointer for character pairs *, 105
2118		1	Word pointer for character pairs *, 106
2119		2	Word pointer for character pairs *, 107
2120		1	Word pointer for character pairs *, 108
2121		1	Word pointer for character pairs *, 109
2122		30	Word pointer for character pairs *, 110
2123		1	Word pointer for character pairs *, 111
2124		1	Word pointer for character pairs *, 112
2125		1	Word pointer for character pairs *, 113
2126		1	Word pointer for character pairs *, 114
2127		2	Word pointer for character pairs *, 115
2128		1	Word pointer for character pairs *, 116
2129		2	Word pointer for character pairs *, 117
2130		1	Word pointer for character pairs *, 118
2131		30	Word pointer for character pairs *, 119
2132		14	Word pointer for character pairs *, 120
2133		22	Word pointer for character pairs *, 121
2134		23	Word pointer for character pairs *, 122
2135		23	Word pointer for character pairs *, 123
2136		24	Word pointer for character pairs *, 124
2137		23	Word pointer for character pairs *, 125
2138		7	Word pointer for character pairs *, 126
2139		18	Word pointer for character pairs *, 127
2140		2	Word pointer for character pairs *, 128
2141		2	Word pointer for character pairs *, 129
2213		18	Word pointer for character pairs *, 201
2220		4	Word pointer for character pairs *, 208
2222		2	Word pointer for character pairs *, 210
2249		2	Word pointer for character pairs *, 237
2263		22	Word pointer for character pairs *, 251
2313		25	Word pointer for character pairs *, 301
2314		16	Word pointer for character pairs *, 302
2315		11	Word pointer for character pairs *, 303
2316		11	Word pointer for character pairs *, 304
2317		11	Word pointer for character pairs *, 305
2318		27	Word pointer for character pairs *, 306
2319		15	Word pointer for character pairs *, 307
2320		16	Word pointer for character pairs *, 308
2321		3	Word pointer for character pairs *, 309
2322		21	Word pointer for character pairs *, 310
2323		16	Word pointer for character pairs *, 311
2324		16	Word pointer for character pairs *, 312
2325		13	Word pointer for character pairs *, 313
2326		13	Word pointer for character pairs *, 314
2327		11	Word pointer for character pairs *, 315

343

Word no	Content	Meaning

Spacing information

3013	0	Records Length of table
3014	1026	Words

S., W. COLUMN	CORRECTION VALUE

S., W.	COLUMN									
1, 967	0- 9	0	0	0	0	0	0	0	0	0	0
	10- 19	0	0	0	0	0	0	0	0	0	0
	20- 29	0	0	0	0	0	0	0	0	0	0
	30- 31	0	0								
1, 999	0- 9	0	-1248	-1641	-1740	197	-1787	-1795	-1069	-1141	-2266
	10- 19	-2232	-1803	-1569	-1492	-2792	-1435	-1596	-3243	272	-2426
	20- 29	-683	-1025	-1821	-2760	-874	-1305	-2677	-1856	-1598	-1210
	30- 31	-824	-357								
1,1031	0- 9	0	-1255	-946	-1017	-471	-1517	-959	-1206	-1078	-1199
	10- 19	-999	-982	-985	-1015	-1475	-989	-1228	-2086	-444	-1449
	20- 29	-572	-1009	-1378	-1835	-1444	-942	-998	-997	-1412	-1077
	30- 31	-1110	-603								
1,1063	0- 9	0	-1257	-907	-987	-823	-1287	-1841	-1167	-2061	-1276
	10- 19	-899	-842	-928	-1014	-1279	-974	-1177	-1416	-813	-2142
	20- 29	-677	-1013	-1222	-1504	-1373	-865	-875	-929	-1243	-991
	30- 31	-999	-1749								
1,1095	0- 9	0	-1258	-911	-1098	-1029	-1246	-346	-1151	-972	-385
	10- 19	-1026	-829	-1053	-1091	-2198	-1020	-1221	-2291	-829	-551
	20- 29	-714	-1032	-1207	-1672	-1321	-865	-1029	-1033	-1177	-955
	30- 31	-989	-831								
1,1127	0- 9	0	-1257	-766	-949	-517	-1479	-700	-1227	-1016	-1790
	10- 19	-842	-652	-902	-986	-1612	-993	-1129	-1706	-495	-1345
	20- 29	-349	-1054	-1236	-1973	-1502	-851	-806	-884	-1337	-970
	30- 31	-1060	-566								
1,1159	0- 9	0	-1258	-1170	-566	-1044	-1278	-551	-1155	-1132	155
	10- 19	-619	-525	-580	-538	-1458	-487	-727	-2602	-1042	-626
	20- 29	-1077	-518	-1355	-1507	-1292	-478	-655	-581	-1267	-1145
	30- 31	-1128	-1032								
1,1191	0- 9	0	-1258	-1571	-730	-1211	-1248	-1318	-1198	-1217	-559
	10- 19	-1246	-1320	-1346	-1000	-1369	-963	-1002	-1406	-1210	-1348
	20- 29	-1272	-983	-1321	-1356	-1237	-1265	-1431	-1152	-1249	-1229
	30- 31	-1206	-1218								
1,1223	0- 9	0	-1255	-988	-1036	-483	-1522	-1033	-1224	-1146	-1334
	10- 19	-1025	-1045	-1018	-1033	-1299	-1031	-1279	-1931	-456	-1510
	20- 29	-655	-1029	-1284	-1439	-1449	-1028	-1023	-1027	-1452	-1143
	30- 31	-1174	-689								
1,1255	0- 9	0	-1257	-1197	-1183	-1243	-1017	-1215	-1158	-1139	-1451
	10- 19	-1094	-1221	-1101	-1222	-792	-1272	-1467	-844	-1245	-1270
	20- 29	-1103	-1259	-1165	-1102	-1242	-1158	-1050	-1125	-980	-1042
	30- 31	-1064	-1064								
1,1287	0- 9	0	-1259	-1179	-1456	-1513	-1147	-1818	-1250	-1183	-2746
	10- 19	-1469	-1991	-1444	-1703	-998	-1913	-1154	-45	-1924	-1741
	20- 29	-1314	-1642	-1121	-769	-1295	-2016	-1367	-1537	-1102	-1164
	30- 31	-1256	-1359								
1,1319	0- 9	0	-1257	-1000	-945	-507	-1488	-1090	-1189	-1125	-1182
	10- 19	-975	-1182	-961	-957	-1349	-1014	-1249	-1519	-481	-1546
	20- 29	-727	-1003	-1448	-1782	-1449	-1051	-970	-980	-1421	-1131
	30- 31	-1190	-717								
1,1351	0- 9	0	-1257	-1097	-1183	-1243	-1017	-1215	-1158	-1032	-1321

```
----------------|-------------------------------------------------------------
S., W.  COLUMN  |                    CORRECTION VALUE
----------------|-------------------------------------------------------------
1,1831  0-  9   |     0 -1255  -796  -859  -512 -1439  -891 -1179  -990 -1488
        10- 19  |  -799  -890  -813  -901 -1177  -950 -1146 -1436  -488 -1367
        20- 29  |  -527  -950 -1284 -1600 -1470  -888  -766  -835 -1296  -980
        30- 31  | -1077  -565
1,1863  0-  9   |     0 -1258  -663  -695  -609 -1406  -840 -1206  -992 -2260
        10- 19  |  -696  -884  -732  -785 -1034  -975 -1128  -829  -590 -1290
        20- 29  |  -510  -978 -1215 -1453 -1553  -955  -636  -786 -1261  -946
        30- 31  | -1118  -641
1,1895  0-  9   |     0 -1257  -990 -1260 -1150 -1134  -834 -1266 -1034 -1100
        10- 19  | -1165 -1035 -1189 -1267 -1288 -1238 -1422 -1256 -1153 -1007
        20- 29  |  -839 -1274 -1161 -1210 -1383 -1084 -1120 -1179 -1093 -1012
        30- 31  | -1077  -980
1,1927  0-  9   |     0 -1258 -1283  -945 -1102 -1228  -682 -1182 -1047  -730
        10- 19  |  -874  -678  -900  -938 -1252  -866 -1069 -1775 -1102  -880
        20- 29  |  -830  -928 -1185 -1265 -1276  -710  -877  -880 -1178 -1035
        30- 31  | -1083  -937
1,1959  0-  9   |     0 -1260 -1170 -1850 -1515 -1255 -1867 -1214 -1188 -2806
        10- 19  | -1761 -1843 -1802 -1904  -883 -1924 -2092    23 -1526 -1791
        20- 29  | -1504 -1948 -1119 -1043 -1289 -1883 -1714 -1801 -1213 -1314
        30- 31  | -1279 -1403
----------------|-------------------------------------------------------------
--------|-----------------|-------------------------------------------------------
```

Word no	Content	Meaning
1	20 Records	Length of table
2	93 Words	

NAME SECTION

3	3	Length of name section
4	3	Table = long kerning
5	0	Following part number

RECORD INFORMATION

6	19	Length of record information
7	195	Number of columns of correction matrix
8	195	Number of lines of correction matrix
9	1	Unit size is 1/100 mm
10	991	Base upper case (1st spacing letter)
11	992	Base lower case (2nd spacing letter)
12	1850	Left side bearing of 1st spacing letter
13	1850	Right side bearing of 1st spacing letter
14	1400	Left side bearing of 2nd spacing letter
15	1400	Right side bearing of 2nd spacing letter
16	-5000	Minimum distance on the level of baselines
17	-5000	Minimum distance between baselines
18	0	Factor for condensation of white space
19	0	Distance function appropriate to geom. mean
20	0	Italic angle (in 1/10 degree)
21	800	Serif height (in 1/100 mm)
22	10000	Cap height are given
23	7000	x-height specially for
24	-2600	Descender length kerning calculation

SPACING INDEX

25	1 Records	Length of spacing index
26	954 Words	

227	0	198	Record/wordp. f. pairs 101,* (abs. 1,1176)
229	0	393	Record/wordp. f. pairs 102,* (abs. 1,1371)
231	0	588	Record/wordp. f. pairs 103,* (abs. 1,1566)
233	0	783	Record/wordp. f. pairs 104,* (abs. 1,1761)
235	0	978	Record/wordp. f. pairs 105,* (abs. 1,1956)
237	0	1173	Record/wordp. f. pairs 106,* (abs. 2, 103)
239	0	1368	Record/wordp. f. pairs 107,* (abs. 2, 298)
241	0	1563	Record/wordp. f. pairs 108,* (abs. 2, 493)
243	0	1758	Record/wordp. f. pairs 109,* (abs. 2, 688)
245	0	1953	Record/wordp. f. pairs 110,* (abs. 2, 883)
247	1	100	Record/wordp. f. pairs 111,* (abs. 2,1078)
249	1	295	Record/wordp. f. pairs 112,* (abs. 2,1273)
251	1	490	Record/wordp. f. pairs 113,* (abs. 2,1468)
253	1	685	Record/wordp. f. pairs 114,* (abs. 2,1663)
255	1	880	Record/wordp. f. pairs 115,* (abs. 2,1858)
257	1	1075	Record/wordp. f. pairs 116,* (abs. 3, 5)
259	1	1270	Record/wordp. f. pairs 117,* (abs. 3, 200)
261	1	1465	Record/wordp. f. pairs 118,* (abs. 3, 395)
263	1	1660	Record/wordp. f. pairs 119,* (abs. 3, 590)
265	1	1855	Record/wordp. f. pairs 120,* (abs. 3, 785)
267	2	2	Record/wordp. f. pairs 121,* (abs. 3, 980)
269	2	197	Record/wordp. f. pairs 122,* (abs. 3,1175)

Word no	Content		Meaning			
683	7	1657	Record/wordp. f. pairs	329,*	(abs.	9, 587)
685	7	1852	Record/wordp. f. pairs	330,*	(abs.	9, 782)
687	7	2047	Record/wordp. f. pairs	331,*	(abs.	9, 977)
689	8	194	Record/wordp. f. pairs	332,*	(abs.	9,1172)
697	8	389	Record/wordp. f. pairs	336,*	(abs.	9,1367)
699	8	584	Record/wordp. f. pairs	337,*	(abs.	9,1562)
701	8	779	Record/wordp. f. pairs	338,*	(abs.	9,1757)
703	8	974	Record/wordp. f. pairs	339,*	(abs.	9,1952)
705	8	1169	Record/wordp. f. pairs	340,*	(abs.	10, 99)
707	8	1364	Record/wordp. f. pairs	341,*	(abs.	10, 294)
709	8	1559	Record/wordp. f. pairs	342,*	(abs.	10, 489)
711	8	1754	Record/wordp. f. pairs	343,*	(abs.	10, 684)
745	8	1949	Record/wordp. f. pairs	360,*	(abs.	10, 879)
827	9	96	Record/wordp. f. pairs	401,*	(abs.	10,1074)
829	9	291	Record/wordp. f. pairs	402,*	(abs.	10,1269)
831	9	486	Record/wordp. f. pairs	403,*	(abs.	10,1464)
841	9	681	Record/wordp. f. pairs	408,*	(abs.	10,1659)
843	9	876	Record/wordp. f. pairs	409,*	(abs.	10,1854)
851	9	1071	Record/wordp. f. pairs	413,*	(abs.	11, 1)
853	9	1266	Record/wordp. f. pairs	414,*	(abs.	11, 196)
855	9	1461	Record/wordp. f. pairs	415,*	(abs.	11, 391)
859	9	1656	Record/wordp. f. pairs	417,*	(abs.	11, 586)
861	9	1851	Record/wordp. f. pairs	418,*	(abs.	11, 781)
869	9	2046	Record/wordp. f. pairs	422,*	(abs.	11, 976)
879	10	193	Record/wordp. f. pairs	427,*	(abs.	11,1171)
887	10	388	Record/wordp. f. pairs	431,*	(abs.	11,1366)
889	10	583	Record/wordp. f. pairs	432,*	(abs.	11,1561)
897	10	778	Record/wordp. f. pairs	436,*	(abs.	11,1756)
899	10	973	Record/wordp. f. pairs	437,*	(abs.	11,1951)
901	10	1168	Record/wordp. f. pairs	438,*	(abs.	12, 98)
921	10	1363	Record/wordp. f. pairs	448,*	(abs.	12, 293)
923	10	1558	Record/wordp. f. pairs	449,*	(abs.	12, 488)
925	10	1753	Record/wordp. f. pairs	450,*	(abs.	12, 683)
927	10	1948	Record/wordp. f. pairs	451,*	(abs.	12, 878)
943	11	95	Record/wordp. f. pairs	459,*	(abs.	12,1073)
945	11	290	Record/wordp. f. pairs	460,*	(abs.	12,1268)
951	11	485	Record/wordp. f. pairs	463,*	(abs.	12,1463)
965	11	680	Record/wordp. f. pairs	470,*	(abs.	12,1658)
1027	11	875	Record/wordp. f. pairs	501,*	(abs.	12,1853)
1029	11	1070	Record/wordp. f. pairs	502,*	(abs.	12,2048)
1031	11	1265	Record/wordp. f. pairs	503,*	(abs.	13, 195)
1033	11	1460	Record/wordp. f. pairs	504,*	(abs.	13, 390)
1035	11	1655	Record/wordp. f. pairs	505,*	(abs.	13, 585)
1037	11	1850	Record/wordp. f. pairs	506,*	(abs.	13, 780)
1039	11	2045	Record/wordp. f. pairs	507,*	(abs.	13, 975)
1041	12	192	Record/wordp. f. pairs	508,*	(abs.	13,1170)
1043	12	387	Record/wordp. f. pairs	509,*	(abs.	13,1365)
1045	12	582	Record/wordp. f. pairs	510,*	(abs.	13,1560)
1047	12	777	Record/wordp. f. pairs	511,*	(abs.	13,1755)
1049	12	972	Record/wordp. f. pairs	512,*	(abs.	13,1950)
1051	12	1167	Record/wordp. f. pairs	513,*	(abs.	14, 97)
1053	12	1362	Record/wordp. f. pairs	514,*	(abs.	14, 292)
1057	12	1557	Record/wordp. f. pairs	516,*	(abs.	14, 487)
1225	12	1752	Record/wordp. f. pairs	600,*	(abs.	14, 682)
1227	12	1947	Record/wordp. f. pairs	601,*	(abs.	14, 877)
1229	13	94	Record/wordp. f. pairs	602,*	(abs.	14,1072)
1231	13	289	Record/wordp. f. pairs	603,*	(abs.	14,1267)
1233	13	484	Record/wordp. f. pairs	604,*	(abs.	14,1462)
1235	13	679	Record/wordp. f. pairs	605,*	(abs.	14,1657)

Word no	Content		Meaning
1237	13	874	Record/wordp. f. pairs 606,* (abs. 14,1852)
1239	13	1069	Record/wordp. f. pairs 607,* (abs. 14,2047)
1241	13	1264	Record/wordp. f. pairs 608,* (abs. 15, 194)
1243	13	1459	Record/wordp. f. pairs 609,* (abs. 15, 389)
1245	13	1654	Record/wordp. f. pairs 610,* (abs. 15, 584)
1247	13	1849	Record/wordp. f. pairs 611,* (abs. 15, 779)
1249	13	2044	Record/wordp. f. pairs 612,* (abs. 15, 974)
1251	14	191	Record/wordp. f. pairs 613,* (abs. 15,1169)
1253	14	386	Record/wordp. f. pairs 614,* (abs. 15,1364)
1255	14	581	Record/wordp. f. pairs 615,* (abs. 15,1559)
1257	14	776	Record/wordp. f. pairs 616,* (abs. 15,1754)
1259	14	971	Record/wordp. f. pairs 617,* (abs. 15,1949)
1261	14	1166	Record/wordp. f. pairs 618,* (abs. 16, 96)
1263	14	1361	Record/wordp. f. pairs 619,* (abs. 16, 291)
1265	14	1556	Record/wordp. f. pairs 620,* (abs. 16, 486)
1267	14	1751	Record/wordp. f. pairs 621,* (abs. 16, 681)
1269	14	1946	Record/wordp. f. pairs 622,* (abs. 16, 876)
1271	15	93	Record/wordp. f. pairs 623,* (abs. 16,1071)
1273	15	288	Record/wordp. f. pairs 624,* (abs. 16,1266)
1275	15	483	Record/wordp. f. pairs 625,* (abs. 16,1461)
1277	15	678	Record/wordp. f. pairs 626,* (abs. 16,1656)
1279	15	873	Record/wordp. f. pairs 627,* (abs. 16,1851)
1281	15	1068	Record/wordp. f. pairs 628,* (abs. 16,2046)
1283	15	1263	Record/wordp. f. pairs 629,* (abs. 17, 193)
1285	15	1458	Record/wordp. f. pairs 630,* (abs. 17, 388)
1287	15	1653	Record/wordp. f. pairs 631,* (abs. 17, 583)
1289	15	1848	Record/wordp. f. pairs 632,* (abs. 17, 778)
1291	15	2043	Record/wordp. f. pairs 633,* (abs. 17, 973)
1293	16	190	Record/wordp. f. pairs 634,* (abs. 17,1168)
1295	16	385	Record/wordp. f. pairs 635,* (abs. 17,1363)
1297	16	580	Record/wordp. f. pairs 636,* (abs. 17,1558)
1299	16	775	Record/wordp. f. pairs 637,* (abs. 17,1753)
1301	16	970	Record/wordp. f. pairs 638,* (abs. 17,1948)
1303	16	1165	Record/wordp. f. pairs 639,* (abs. 18, 95)
1305	16	1360	Record/wordp. f. pairs 640,* (abs. 18, 290)
1309	16	1555	Record/wordp. f. pairs 642,* (abs. 18, 485)
1311	16	1750	Record/wordp. f. pairs 643,* (abs. 18, 680)
1313	16	1945	Record/wordp. f. pairs 644,* (abs. 18, 875)
1317	17	92	Record/wordp. f. pairs 646,* (abs. 18,1070)
1321	17	287	Record/wordp. f. pairs 648,* (abs. 18,1265)
1323	17	482	Record/wordp. f. pairs 649,* (abs. 18,1460)
1329	17	677	Record/wordp. f. pairs 652,* (abs. 18,1655)
1331	17	872	Record/wordp. f. pairs 653,* (abs. 18,1850)
1333	17	1067	Record/wordp. f. pairs 654,* (abs. 18,2045)
1335	17	1262	Record/wordp. f. pairs 655,* (abs. 19, 192)
1337	17	1457	Record/wordp. f. pairs 656,* (abs. 19, 387)
1381	17	1652	Record/wordp. f. pairs 678,* (abs. 19, 582)
1383	17	1847	Record/wordp. f. pairs 679,* (abs. 19, 777)
1421	17	2042	Record/wordp. f. pairs 698,* (abs. 19, 972)
1423	18	189	Record/wordp. f. pairs 699,* (abs. 19,1167)
2005	18	384	Record/wordp. f. pairs 990,* (abs. 19,1362)
2007	18	579	Record/wordp. f. pairs 991,* (abs. 19,1557)
2009	18	774	Record/wordp. f. pairs 992,* (abs. 19,1752)
2023	18	969	Record/wordp. f. pairs 999,* (abs. 19,1947)
2127		1	Word pointer for character pairs *, 101
2128		2	Word pointer for character pairs *, 102
2129		3	Word pointer for character pairs *, 103
2130		4	Word pointer for character pairs *, 104
2131		5	Word pointer for character pairs *, 105

Word no	Content	Meaning
2679	183	Word pointer for character pairs *, 653
2680	184	Word pointer for character pairs *, 654
2681	185	Word pointer for character pairs *, 655
2682	186	Word pointer for character pairs *, 656
2704	187	Word pointer for character pairs *, 678
2705	188	Word pointer for character pairs *, 679
2724	189	Word pointer for character pairs *, 698
2725	190	Word pointer for character pairs *, 699
3016	191	Word pointer for character pairs *, 990
3017	192	Word pointer for character pairs *, 991
3018	193	Word pointer for character pairs *, 992
3025	194	Word pointer for character pairs *, 999

Spacing information

3027	18	Records Length of table
3028	1163	Words

S., W.	COLUMN	CORRECTION VALUES									
1, 981	0- 9	0	0	0	0	0	0	0	0	0	0
	10- 19	0	0	0	0	0	0	0	0	0	0
for	20- 29	0	0	0	0	0	0	0	0	0	0
1,*	30- 39	0	0	0	0	0	0	0	0	0	0
	40- 49	0	0	0	0	0	0	0	0	0	0
	50- 59	0	0	0	0	0	0	0	0	0	0
	60- 69	0	0	0	0	0	0	0	0	0	0
	70- 79	0	0	0	0	0	0	0	0	0	0
	80- 89	0	0	0	0	0	0	0	0	0	0
	90- 99	0	0	0	0	0	0	0	0	0	0
	100-109	0	0	0	0	0	0	0	0	0	0
	110-119	0	0	0	0	0	0	0	0	0	0
	120-129	0	0	0	0	0	0	0	0	0	0
	130-139	0	0	0	0	0	0	0	0	0	0
	140-149	0	0	0	0	0	0	0	0	0	0
	150-159	0	0	0	0	0	0	0	0	0	0
	160-169	0	0	0	0	0	0	0	0	0	0
	170-179	0	0	0	0	0	0	0	0	0	0
	180-189	0	0	0	0	0	0	0	0	0	0
	190-194	0	0	0	0	0					
1,1176	0- 9	0	-712	-164	-417	-164	-164	-164	-389	-164	-164
	10- 19	-311	-164	-163	-161	-97	-383	-164	-377	-164	2
for	20- 29	-442	-627	-1523	-1224	-58	-1461	208	-322	-414	-383
101,*	30- 39	0	-736	0	0	0	0	0	-1111	0	-417
	40- 49	0	0	0	0	0	0	0	0	0	-383
	50- 59	0	-627	0	0	346	-203	-106	-113	-101	294
	60- 69	42	-60	653	936	40	39	317	317	-92	172
	70- 79	-103	317	242	-39	19	-420	-274	264	3	497
	80- 89	368	-117	-38	617	317	0	0	144	144	144
	90- 99	144	144	144	0	0	346	0	0	346	0
	100-109	-106	0	0	0	0	0	0	0	0	-95
	110-119	0	0	0	169	0	0	0	0	0	0
	120-129	-728	-16	-361	-216	163	27	-500	-273	6	26
	130-139	1302	1401	1136	0	0	0	2007	1608	2146	245
	140-149	1173	3007	1684	1535	-758	-411	-658	-311	2284	556
	150-159	2268	853	1476	841	631	607	133	182	1083	1583
	160-169	1542	890	148	1265	224	643	1375	972	972	-596
	170-179	0	0	0	0	0	0	0	0	0	0

S., W. COLUMN	CORRECTION VALUES									
180-189	0	0	0	2684	2684	0	0	0	0	999
190-194	961	1565	-285	279	0					
1,1371 0- 9	0	-272	373	354	373	373	373	383	373	373
10- 19	344	373	374	372	437	390	373	398	373	635
for 20- 29	790	142	-206	46	481	-205	747	104	358	375
102,* 30- 39	0	-296	0	0	0	0	0	-671	0	354
40- 49	0	0	0	0	0	0	0	0	0	390
50- 59	0	142	0	0	594	29	254	248	259	494
60- 69	174	58	602	985	158	156	349	349	266	433
70- 79	257	349	250	277	329	69	197	171	336	436
80- 89	608	242	294	571	449	0	0	344	344	344
90- 99	344	344	344	0	0	594	0	0	594	0
100-109	254	0	0	0	0	0	0	0	0	263
110-119	0	0	0	498	0	0	0	0	0	0
120-129	-18	555	301	591	818	782	246	498	684	781
130-139	1897	2076	1397	0	0	0	1320	1599	2828	867
140-149	495	2320	991	1547	1185	1556	1285	1656	1591	1191
150-159	2619	1590	1687	843	883	607	386	756	1769	2269
160-169	2218	1642	818	1882	842	1429	1974	1822	1822	1231
170-179	0	0	0	0	0	0	0	0	0	0
180-189	0	0	0	1991	1991	0	0	0	0	1639
190-194	1601	2182	332	345	0					
1,1566 0- 9	0	-271	476	295	476	476	476	318	476	476
10- 19	413	476	477	477	543	334	476	336	488	571
for 20- 29	1163	203	-46	187	632	-15	845	108	307	333
103,* 30- 39	0	-295	0	0	0	0	0	-670	0	295
40- 49	0	0	0	0	0	0	0	0	0	334
50- 59	0	203	0	0	404	-137	41	32	44	472
60- 69	27	-88	576	888	12	11	296	296	53	364
70- 79	41	296	87	225	238	37	160	111	322	332
80- 89	432	27	93	505	396	0	0	322	322	322
90- 99	322	322	322	0	0	404	0	0	404	0
100-109	41	0	0	0	0	0	0	0	0	51
110-119	0	0	0	435	0	0	0	0	0	0
120-129	173	628	344	397	880	704	429	441	805	748
130-139	1905	2140	1081	0	0	0	1182	1526	2570	47
140-149	368	2182	839	1478	1659	2028	1759	2128	1439	1323
150-159	2610	1744	1644	773	595	554	97	786	932	1432
160-169	1337	1580	888	1951	898	1350	1973	1928	1928	1718
170-179	0	0	0	0	0	0	0	0	0	0
180-189	0	0	0	1839	1839	0	0	0	0	1724
190-194	1686	2251	401	162	0					
1,1761 0- 9	0	-544	155	458	155	155	155	480	155	155
10- 19	114	155	156	149	214	492	155	497	155	340
for 20- 29	501	-45	-397	-141	-100	-414	222	-176	454	479
104,* 30- 39	0	-567	0	0	0	0	0	-942	0	458
40- 49	0	0	0	0	0	0	0	0	0	492
50- 59	0	-45	0	0	264	-86	133	123	134	524
60- 69	48	-77	609	828	23	21	262	262	138	368
70- 79	124	262	4	329	279	107	222	44	300	382
80- 89	298	114	161	518	362	0	0	374	374	374
90- 99	374	374	374	0	0	264	0	0	264	0
100-109	133	0	0	0	0	0	0	0	0	140
110-119	0	0	0	546	0	0	0	0	0	0
120-129	-216	286	21	321	618	719	60	229	558	748
130-139	1629	1854	1271	0	0	0	518	1566	3467	741
140-149	-308	1518	190	1508	1153	1490	1253	1590	790	973
150-159	2503	1368	1433	773	749	530	248	494	1907	2407
160-169	2406	1707	593	1751	616	1119	1919	1799	1799	1234

S., W. COLUMN	CORRECTION VALUES									
130-139	2069	1793	1092	0	0	0	504	960	2297	-154
140-149	-326	1504	184	897	530	767	630	867	784	799
150-159	2230	1010	1608	161	106	-52	-391	608	892	1392
160-169	1382	1085	52	1100	267	1194	1463	1099	1099	398
170-179	0	0	0	0	0	0	0	0	0	0
180-189	0	0	0	1184	1184	0	0	0	0	1307
190-194	1269	1400	-31	1400	0					
19,1947 0- 9	0	0	0	0	0	0	0	0	0	0
10- 19	0	0	0	0	0	0	0	0	0	0
for 20- 29	0	0	0	0	0	0	0	0	0	0
-1,* 30- 39	0	0	0	0	0	0	0	0	0	0
40- 49	0	0	0	0	0	0	0	0	0	0
50- 59	0	0	0	0	0	0	0	0	0	0
60- 69	0	0	0	0	0	0	0	0	0	0
70- 79	0	0	0	0	0	0	0	0	0	0
80- 89	0	0	0	0	0	0	0	0	0	0
90- 99	0	0	0	0	0	0	0	0	0	0
100-109	0	0	0	0	0	0	0	0	0	0
110-119	0	0	0	0	0	0	0	0	0	0
120-129	0	0	0	0	0	0	0	0	0	0
130-139	0	0	0	0	0	0	0	0	0	0
140-149	0	0	0	0	0	0	0	0	0	0
150-159	0	0	0	0	0	0	0	0	0	0
160-169	0	0	0	0	0	0	0	0	0	0
170-179	0	0	0	0	0	0	0	0	0	0
180-189	0	0	0	0	0	0	0	0	0	0
190-194	0	0	0	0	0					

351

```
---------|------------------|-------------------------------------------------
Word no  |    Content       |                  Meaning
---------|------------------|-------------------------------------------------
   1     |              1   | Records     Length of table
   2     |           1357   | Words
---------|------------------|-------------------------------------------------

         NAME SECTION
   3     |              3   | Length of name section
   4     |              6   | Table = left/right side bearings and widths
   5     |              0   | Following part number
---------|------------------|-------------------------------------------------
         RECORD INFORMATION
         ------------------
   6     |              3   | Length of record information
   7     |            131   | Number of LSB, RSB and widths
   8     |              1   | Unit size is 1/100 mm
---------|------------------|-------------------------------------------------
         SPACING INDEX
         -------------
   9     |              1   | Records     Length of spacing index
  10     |            954   | Words

  211    |  0           6   | R/wp. for lsb/rsb/width of  101 (abs.   1, 968)
  213    |  0           9   | R/wp. for lsb/rsb/width of  102 (abs.   1, 971)
  215    |  0          12   | R/wp. for lsb/rsb/width of  103 (abs.   1, 974)
  217    |  0          15   | R/wp. for lsb/rsb/width of  104 (abs.   1, 977)
  219    |  0          18   | R/wp. for lsb/rsb/width of  105 (abs.   1, 980)
  221    |  0          21   | R/wp. for lsb/rsb/width of  106 (abs.   1, 983)
  223    |  0          24   | R/wp. for lsb/rsb/width of  107 (abs.   1, 986)
  225    |  0          27   | R/wp. for lsb/rsb/width of  108 (abs.   1, 989)
  227    |  0          30   | R/wp. for lsb/rsb/width of  109 (abs.   1, 992)
  229    |  0          33   | R/wp. for lsb/rsb/width of  110 (abs.   1, 995)
  231    |  0          36   | R/wp. for lsb/rsb/width of  111 (abs.   1, 998)
  233    |  0          39   | R/wp. for lsb/rsb/width of  112 (abs.   1,1001)
  235    |  0          42   | R/wp. for lsb/rsb/width of  113 (abs.   1,1004)
  237    |  0          45   | R/wp. for lsb/rsb/width of  114 (abs.   1,1007)
  239    |  0          48   | R/wp. for lsb/rsb/width of  115 (abs.   1,1010)
  241    |  0          51   | R/wp. for lsb/rsb/width of  116 (abs.   1,1013)
  243    |  0          54   | R/wp. for lsb/rsb/width of  117 (abs.   1,1016)
  245    |  0          57   | R/wp. for lsb/rsb/width of  118 (abs.   1,1019)
  247    |  0          60   | R/wp. for lsb/rsb/width of  119 (abs.   1,1022)
  249    |  0          63   | R/wp. for lsb/rsb/width of  120 (abs.   1,1025)
  251    |  0          66   | R/wp. for lsb/rsb/width of  121 (abs.   1,1028)
  253    |  0          69   | R/wp. for lsb/rsb/width of  122 (abs.   1,1031)
  255    |  0          72   | R/wp. for lsb/rsb/width of  123 (abs.   1,1034)
  257    |  0          75   | R/wp. for lsb/rsb/width of  124 (abs.   1,1037)
  259    |  0          78   | R/wp. for lsb/rsb/width of  125 (abs.   1,1040)
  261    |  0          81   | R/wp. for lsb/rsb/width of  126 (abs.   1,1043)
  263    |  0          84   | R/wp. for lsb/rsb/width of  127 (abs.   1,1046)
  265    |  0          87   | R/wp. for lsb/rsb/width of  128 (abs.   1,1049)
  267    |  0          90   | R/wp. for lsb/rsb/width of  129 (abs.   1,1052)
  411    |  0          93   | R/wp. for lsb/rsb/width of  201 (abs.   1,1055)
  425    |  0          96   | R/wp. for lsb/rsb/width of  208 (abs.   1,1058)
  429    |  0          99   | R/wp. for lsb/rsb/width of  210 (abs.   1,1061)
  483    |  0         102   | R/wp. for lsb/rsb/width of  237 (abs.   1,1064)
  511    |  0         105   | R/wp. for lsb/rsb/width of  251 (abs.   1,1067)
  611    |  0         108   | R/wp. for lsb/rsb/width of  301 (abs.   1,1070)
  613    |  0         111   | R/wp. for lsb/rsb/width of  302 (abs.   1,1073)
  615    |  0         114   | R/wp. for lsb/rsb/width of  303 (abs.   1,1076)
  617    |  0         117   | R/wp. for lsb/rsb/width of  304 (abs.   1,1079)
---------|------------------|-------------------------------------------------
```

352

Word no	Content		Meaning
1227	0	297	R/wp. for lsb/rsb/width of 609 (abs. 1,1259)
1229	0	300	R/wp. for lsb/rsb/width of 610 (abs. 1,1262)
1231	0	303	R/wp. for lsb/rsb/width of 611 (abs. 1,1265)
1233	0	306	R/wp. for lsb/rsb/width of 612 (abs. 1,1268)
1235	0	309	R/wp. for lsb/rsb/width of 613 (abs. 1,1271)
1237	0	312	R/wp. for lsb/rsb/width of 614 (abs. 1,1274)
1239	0	315	R/wp. for lsb/rsb/width of 615 (abs. 1,1277)
1241	0	318	R/wp. for lsb/rsb/width of 616 (abs. 1,1280)
1243	0	321	R/wp. for lsb/rsb/width of 617 (abs. 1,1283)
1245	0	324	R/wp. for lsb/rsb/width of 618 (abs. 1,1286)
1247	0	327	R/wp. for lsb/rsb/width of 619 (abs. 1,1289)
1249	0	330	R/wp. for lsb/rsb/width of 620 (abs. 1,1292)
1251	0	333	R/wp. for lsb/rsb/width of 621 (abs. 1,1295)
1253	0	336	R/wp. for lsb/rsb/width of 622 (abs. 1,1298)
1255	0	339	R/wp. for lsb/rsb/width of 623 (abs. 1,1301)
1257	0	342	R/wp. for lsb/rsb/width of 624 (abs. 1,1304)
1259	0	345	R/wp. for lsb/rsb/width of 625 (abs. 1,1307)
1261	0	348	R/wp. for lsb/rsb/width of 626 (abs. 1,1310)
1263	0	351	R/wp. for lsb/rsb/width of 627 (abs. 1,1313)
1265	0	354	R/wp. for lsb/rsb/width of 628 (abs. 1,1316)
1267	0	357	R/wp. for lsb/rsb/width of 629 (abs. 1,1319)
1269	0	360	R/wp. for lsb/rsb/width of 630 (abs. 1,1322)
1271	0	363	R/wp. for lsb/rsb/width of 631 (abs. 1,1325)
1273	0	366	R/wp. for lsb/rsb/width of 632 (abs. 1,1328)
1275	0	369	R/wp. for lsb/rsb/width of 633 (abs. 1,1331)
1277	0	372	R/wp. for lsb/rsb/width of 634 (abs. 1,1334)
1315	0	375	R/wp. for lsb/rsb/width of 653 (abs. 1,1337)
1317	0	378	R/wp. for lsb/rsb/width of 654 (abs. 1,1340)
1405	0	381	R/wp. for lsb/rsb/width of 698 (abs. 1,1343)
1407	0	384	R/wp. for lsb/rsb/width of 699 (abs. 1,1346)
1989	0	387	R/wp. for lsb/rsb/width of 990 (abs. 1,1349)
1991	0	390	R/wp. for lsb/rsb/width of 991 (abs. 1,1352)
1993	0	393	R/wp. for lsb/rsb/width of 992 (abs. 1,1355)

Spacing information

3011		0	Records Length of table
3012		395	Words

S., W.	Content		Meaning
1 965	0	0 15000	LSB, RSB and width of character 1
1 968	96	236 11523	LSB, RSB and width of character 101
1 971	1258	1473 11833	LSB, RSB and width of character 102
1 974	1321	1526 12424	LSB, RSB and width of character 103
1 977	1258	1355 13344	LSB, RSB and width of character 104
1 980	1258	1611 11698	LSB, RSB and width of character 105
1 983	1258	1002 10641	LSB, RSB and width of character 106
1 986	1345	861 13511	LSB, RSB and width of character 107
1 989	1258	1258 13770	LSB, RSB and width of character 108
1 992	1258	1258 7108	LSB, RSB and width of character 109
1 995	259	1023 6824	LSB, RSB and width of character 110
1 998	1258	695 12431	LSB, RSB and width of character 111
1 1001	1259	742 10445	LSB, RSB and width of character 112
1 1004	1163	1224 16087	LSB, RSB and width of character 113
1 1007	1179	928 13402	LSB, RSB and width of character 114
1 1010	1356	1354 13676	LSB, RSB and width of character 115
1 1013	1258	1036 10848	LSB, RSB and width of character 116

353

S., W.	Content			Meaning
1 1193	653	765	10821	LSB, RSB and width of character 449
1 1196	1408	858	7843	LSB, RSB and width of character 501
1 1199	1383	1471	9198	LSB, RSB and width of character 502
1 1202	1382	1569	8703	LSB, RSB and width of character 503
1 1205	884	1113	8502	LSB, RSB and width of character 504
1 1208	1792	1523	9051	LSB, RSB and width of character 505
1 1211	1637	1685	9330	LSB, RSB and width of character 506
1 1214	1583	712	8304	LSB, RSB and width of character 507
1 1217	1629	1610	9231	LSB, RSB and width of character 508
1 1220	1672	1640	9319	LSB, RSB and width of character 509
1 1223	1659	1658	9382	LSB, RSB and width of character 510
1 1226	2186	2352	13814	LSB, RSB and width of character 511
1 1229	2884	2748	11906	LSB, RSB and width of character 512
1 1232	2389	2454	10964	LSB, RSB and width of character 513
1 1235	2417	2417	6734	LSB, RSB and width of character 601
1 1238	2951	2951	7802	LSB, RSB and width of character 602
1 1241	3030	3030	8245	LSB, RSB and width of character 603
1 1244	3036	3036	8162	LSB, RSB and width of character 604
1 1247	3416	3416	8542	LSB, RSB and width of character 605
1 1250	3417	3417	15734	LSB, RSB and width of character 606
1 1253	2394	2456	7042	LSB, RSB and width of character 607
1 1256	2910	2845	7947	LSB, RSB and width of character 608
1 1259	2356	2261	6809	LSB, RSB and width of character 609
1 1262	2259	2353	6804	LSB, RSB and width of character 610
1 1265	2356	2261	9609	LSB, RSB and width of character 611
1 1268	2259	2353	9604	LSB, RSB and width of character 612
1 1271	2394	2456	9842	LSB, RSB and width of character 613
1 1274	3002	3017	8005	LSB, RSB and width of character 614
1 1277	2835	2819	7640	LSB, RSB and width of character 615
1 1280	2561	2137	9480	LSB, RSB and width of character 616
1 1283	1905	2366	9053	LSB, RSB and width of character 617
1 1286	1910	1434	7640	LSB, RSB and width of character 618
1 1289	1434	1910	7640	LSB, RSB and width of character 619
1 1292	1684	1434	5628	LSB, RSB and width of character 620
1 1295	1435	1682	5627	LSB, RSB and width of character 621
1 1298	1601	1615	8311	LSB, RSB and width of character 622
1 1301	2129	2129	8032	LSB, RSB and width of character 623
1 1304	2129	2129	10235	LSB, RSB and width of character 624
1 1307	2117	2117	12191	LSB, RSB and width of character 625
1 1310	2504	1465	7545	LSB, RSB and width of character 626
1 1313	1423	2503	7502	LSB, RSB and width of character 627
1 1316	3179	1633	7812	LSB, RSB and width of character 628
1 1319	1632	3176	7809	LSB, RSB and width of character 629
1 1322	2061	2487	15180	LSB, RSB and width of character 630
1 1325	2879	2990	11432	LSB, RSB and width of character 631
1 1328	2236	2243	10575	LSB, RSB and width of character 632
1 1331	2236	2243	10575	LSB, RSB and width of character 633
1 1334	2168	2168	8710	LSB, RSB and width of character 634
1 1337	3394	3456	9042	LSB, RSB and width of character 653
1 1340	3394	3456	9042	LSB, RSB and width of character 654
1 1343	1893	1856	12202	LSB, RSB and width of character 698
1 1346	1893	2121	19014	LSB, RSB and width of character 699
1 1349	2479	2479	19958	LSB, RSB and width of character 990
1 1352	629	629	16258	LSB, RSB and width of character 991
1 1355	521	521	16042	LSB, RSB and width of character 992

Appendix U
Touching tables

Touching tables do not differ in structure from the kerning tables (see appendix T).

Touching tables are of importance to typesetting for two reasons. In the first place one can find correction values for the actual touching, and also gain additional information to help with the kerning of large cap heights – e.g. in window display text.

We assume in outside-advertising text that the kerning works to a good effect provided that the typesetting is carried out with cap heights of up to 10 cm. One has to mention, however, that such text lines are generally seen from a distance of approx. 5 meters. This corresponds with the viewing of a 1 cm character from 50 cm distance.

With larger characters a closer arrangement is sometimes desirable. It is as though viewers of large displays consider that the proportionally increased separations make the characters appear isolated.

Our letter spacing in this case has the following conception: The user defines in a parameter how far he wishes to approach the touching values. In this 0% means only kerning and 100% means only touching. Values in between allow appropriate interpolation of the two correction values.

touching
berühren

Examples of touching

Appendix V
Overlapping table

The overlapping tables have the same structure as kerning tables. They contain however such large negative correction values for character pairs that the two letters overlap. This may be used on the one hand for overlapping whereby a white line outlines the character which is intended to overlap another character. On the other hand one can blend the characters into one another, leaving out the white outlines. Blending or overlapping has absolutely nothing to do with normal typesetting of text, and it is normally used in the development of logos and signets or when creating special effects.

überdecken overlapping

verschmelzen blending

Examples of overlapping and blending

Appendix W
Programs for converting IK→DI

This appendix includes subroutines which convert the IKARUS format into the DISPLAY format.

For this, the subroutine BUCHGK must first be called. Prior to calling this subroutine, however, the character must be loaded in the arrays KE (IK identifications), X (X coordinates) and Y (Y coordinates). In addition to this the number of digitizations must be stored in the variable IKTOT. The result of these calculations can then be made available in the fields KEKE (internal DI identifications), XX (X coordinates), YY (Y coordinates) and RAD (radii). In the case of straights the end points are stored, whereas in the case of segments of circles the end points and the radii are stored. The number of digitizations of internal DI format is transferred in IKTOT2. Every straight and every circle counts as a digitization. The call hierarchy for programs below BUCHGK is as follows:

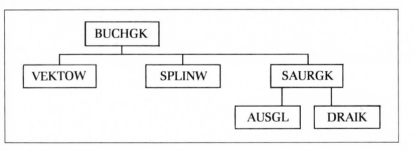

The interaction of the subroutines occurs in such a way that in BUCHGK the straights and curves are separated from one another. First of all VEKTOW calculates the distances, with related unit vectors, for all IK curve points. The unit vector results are stored in fields DS (distances), C0 (X components) and S0 (Y components). Following this the spline interpolation is started. The algorithm was taken from a book (see ref. Späth). From the interpolation we take the tangents as unit vectors represented in the form (cos,sin), which are transferred into field C [X components] and S [Y components] to SAURGK.

The calculation of the circle segment is based on the method as used by the ARISTO company for CAD. The following sketch is intended to show the method of calculation with which one identifies the two radii R1 and R2 of the circle segments.

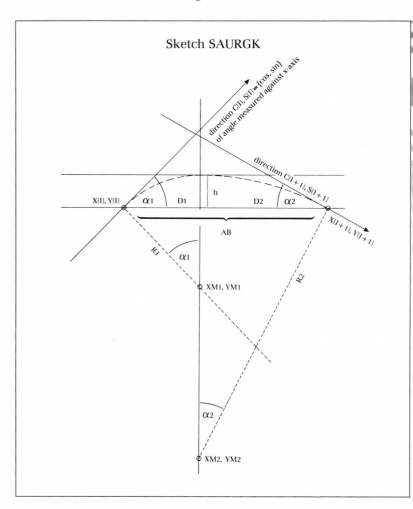

Sketch SAURGK

Method of calculations

Looking for those two circles which have the given directions in the two points respectively and which join with the direction given by the connection of the two points. One can write down the following:

(1) $AB = D1 + D2$

(2) $\sin\alpha_1 = \dfrac{D1}{R1}$

(3) $\sin\alpha_2 = \dfrac{D2}{R2}$

(4) $\cos\alpha_1 = \dfrac{R1 - h}{R1}$

(5) $\cos\alpha_2 = \dfrac{R2 - h}{R2}$

One has five equations for five unknowns: D1, D2, R1, R2, h

(6) → SOLVE: (1)+(2)+(3):
$$AB = R1 \cdot \sin\alpha_1 + R2 \cdot \sin\alpha_2$$

(4)+(5): $h = R1(1 - \cos\alpha_1) = R2(1 - \cos\alpha_2)$

(7)
$$\frac{R1}{R2} = \boxed{DR = \left(\frac{1 - \cos\alpha_2}{1 - \cos\alpha_1}\right)}$$

(8) out of (6) make: $AB = R2 \cdot \dfrac{R1}{R2}\sin\alpha_1 + R2 \cdot \sin\alpha_2$

$$= R2(DR \cdot \sin\alpha_1 + \sin\alpha_2)$$

$\Rightarrow \boxed{R2 = AB/(DR \cdot \sin\alpha_1 + \sin\alpha_2)} \Rightarrow \boxed{R1 = DR \cdot R2}$

The DRAIK routine then has the task of calculating the cos and sin of angles 1 and 2 as pictured in the sketch. The AUSGL routine then has the job of preparing a correction calculation in such cases where two circles of very different radii join with one another. On the following pages we have printed the FORTRAN listing in sequence.

359

INCLUDE-Files for BUCHGK

```
C                         XYCOM.TXT
C
C  Word    Name       Explanation
C -----------------------------------------------------------------------
C   1      IKMAX      Max. number of digs
C   2      IKTOT      Total number of digitisations
C   3/4    H(1)       X minimum
C   5/6    H(2)       X maximum                        of current IK-figure
C   7/8    H(3)       Position of left side mark
C   9/10   H(4)       Position of right side mark
C   11..14 H(5),H(6)  not used
C -----------------------------------------------------------------------
C 1-IKMAX   KE(..)    Markings of IK- digitisations
C -----------------------------------------------------------------------
C 1-2*IKMAX X(..)     X-values  of IK- digitisations
C -----------------------------------------------------------------------
C 1-2*IKMAX Y(..)     Y-values of IK- digitisations
C -----------------------------------------------------------------------
C
        COMMON/HCOM/IKMAX,IKTOT,H(6)
        COMMON/KCOM/KE(1)
        COMMON/XCOM/X(1)          Dimension in main program should be IKMAX
        COMMON/YCOM/Y(1)
C
C                         XY2COM.TXT
C
C  Word    Name       Explanation
C -----------------------------------------------------------------------
C   1      IKMAX2     Max. number of GK points
C   2      IKTOT2     Total number of GK points
C   3/4    HH(1)      X minimum
C   5/6    HH(2)      X maximum                        of GK-figure
C   7/8    HH(3)      Position of left side mark
C   9/10   HH(4)      Position of right side mark
C   11..14 HH(5),HH(6) not used
C -----------------------------------------------------------------------
C 1-IKMAX2  KEKE(..)  Markings of GK- points
C -----------------------------------------------------------------------
C 1-2*IKMAX2 XX(..)   X-values  of GK points
C -----------------------------------------------------------------------
C 1-2*IKMAX2 YY(..)   Y-values of  GK points
C -----------------------------------------------------------------------
C
        COMMON/HHCOM/IKMAX2,IKTOT2,HH(6)
        COMMON/KKCOM/KEKE(1)
        COMMON/XXCOM/XX(1)        Dimension in main program should be IKMAX2
        COMMON/YYCOM/YY(1)
C                         DCSCOM.TXT
        COMMON/COCOM/CO(1)
        COMMON/SOCOM/SO(1)        Dimension in main program should be IKMAX
        COMMON/DSCOM/DS(1)
C                         CSGCOM.TXT
        COMMON/CCOM/C(1)
        COMMON/SCOM/S(1)          Dimension in main program should be IKMAX
        COMMON/GCOM/G(1)
C                         GKCOM.TXT
        COMMON/DXCOM/X(1)
        COMMON/DYCOM/Y(1)         Dimension in main program should be IKMAX2
        COMMON/RADCOM/RAD(1)
```

```
C
C                     ********************************
C                     * I K A R U S - L I B R A R Y *
C                     *     S U B R O U T I N E      *
C                     ********************************
C
C
C
C-  Name:               BUCHGK.FOR
C
C-  Keywords:           IK/GK/CONTOUR/FIGURE/SECTION/CURVE/SPLINE/CALCULATE
C
C-  Short Description:  Converts IK format into GK format
C
C-  Call:               CALL BUCHGK(ISTA)
C
C - - - - - - - - - - - - - - - - - - - - - - - - - - - - - - - - - - - -
C
C-  Input-Parameters:   IKTOT                   - Number of IK digs
C                       H                       - as usual
C                       IKMAX2                  - max. number of GK digs
C-  Input-Data:         X,Y,KE                  - as usual ( IK format)
C-  Output-Parameters:  IKTOT2                  - Number of GK digs
C                       HH                      - Copy of H
C-  Output-Data:        XX,YY,KEKE,DX,DY,RAD    - as usual ( GK format)
C-  Status:             ISTA                    - 0 : OK
C                                                 1 : max. number of GK digs
C                                                     exeeded (Overflow)
C
C
C - - - - - - - - - - - - - - - - - - - - - - - - - - - - - - - - - - - -
C
C-  Subroutine Calls:   VEKTOW,SPLINW,SAURGK
C-  Includes:           XYCOM.TXT,XY2COM.TXT,CSGCOM.TXT
C-  Devices:            -
C-  Author:             R.RADTKE  E.LEHMANN H.STANGE
C-  Date:               00-NOV-84 5-FEB-85  21-AUG-85
C
C - - - - - - - - - - - - - - - - - - - - - - - - - - - - - - - - - - - -
C
C-  Description:        BUCHGK converts IK character into a GK character
C                       ( with straight segments and circle segments
C
C-  Algorithm:          SAUR  method
C-  Commentary:         In VEKTOW,SPLINW and SAURCK the commons  DSCOM, COCOM
C                       and SOCOM, for the GK format the commons DXCOM, DYCOM
C                       and RADCOM  are used. DSCOM, COCOM, SOCOM have to be
C                       dimensioned in the main program with dimension IKMAX
C                       all others with IKMAX2
C-  Interne Variable:   J    - pointer for GK data
C
C*******************************************************************************
C
        SUBROUTINE BUCHGK(ISTA)
C
        IMPLICIT INTEGER*2 (I-N)
        INCLUDE 'XYCOM.TXT'
        INCLUDE 'XY2COM.TXT'
        INCLUDE 'CSGCOM.TXT'
C
        PARAMETER ( KE12=12, KE13=13, KE14=14, KE15=15 )
        PARAMETER ( LA1=1, LA2=2)
```

361

```
C
        ISTA = 0
C
        DO 20 I=1,6
            HH(I) = H(I)
  20    CONTINUE
C
        IF(IKTOT.LE.1) THEN
                IKTOT2 = IKTOT
                IF(IKTOT.EQ.1) THEN
                        XX(1) = X(1)
                        YY(1) = Y(1)
                        KEKE(1) = KE12 + LA1*16
                END IF
                GOTO 500
        END IF
C
        I = 1
        J = 0
C
C - - - - - - - - - - - - - - - - - - - - - - - - - - - - - - - - - - - -
C                 T h e   b i g   l o o p
C
  100   CONTINUE
        IF (KE(I).NE.KE14) THEN                      ! check for curve points
C
C               S t r a i g h t   s e g m e n t s
C
                J = J + 1
                IF(J.EQ.IKMAX2) THEN
                        ISTA = 1
                        GOTO 500
                END IF
C
                IF (KE(I).EQ.KE12) THEN
                        I12 = I                              ! start points
                        KEKE(J) = KE12 + LA1*16
                    ELSE
                        KEKE(J) = KE(I) + LA2*16
                ENDIF
C
                XX(J) = X(I)
                YY(J) = Y(I)
C
            ELSE
C
C               c u r v e   s e g m e n t s
C
                IANF=I-1
  400           CONTINUE
                IF (I.NE.IKTOT) THEN
                    I=I+1                                    ! Loop over curve points
                    IF (KE(I).EQ.KE14) GOTO 400
C
                    IF (KE(I).LT.KE13) I=I-1
                ENDIF
C
                IEND=I
C
C               Calculate distances between IK points
C
                CALL VEKTOW(IANF,IEND,I12,IKTOT,X,Y,KE)
```

362

```
C
C              Calculate tangent directions
C
                   CALL SPLINW(IANF,IEND,I12,IKTOT,X,Y,KE,C,S,G)
C
C              Transformation of a curve into GK format
C
                   CALL SAURGK(IANF,IEND,J,ISTA)
C
                   IF(ISTA.EQ.1) GOTO 500
         END IF
C
         I = I + 1
         IF (I.LE.IKTOT) GOTO 100
C - - - - - - - - - - - - - - - - - - - - - - - - - - - - - - - - - - - -
C
         IKTOT2 = J
C
  500    CONTINUE
         RETURN
         END



C                    ********************************
C                    * I K A R U S - L I B R A R Y *
C                    *   S U B R O U T I N E        *
C                    ********************************
C
C
C
C-   Name:              VEKTOW.FOR
C
C-   Keywords:          SSR/VECTOR/DISTANCE/CALCULATE
C
C-   Short Description: Calculates distances and unit vectors for SPLINW
C
C-   Call:              CALL VEKTOW(IANF,IEND,I12,IKTOT,X,Y,KE)
C
C - - - - - - - - - - - - - - - - - - - - - - - - - - - - - - - - - - - -
C
C-   Input-Parameters:  -
C-   Input-Data:        IANF,IEND  Number of first,last point of contour
C                       I12        Number of last start point
C                       IKTOT      Total number of digs
C                       KE,X,Y     as usual
C-   Output-Parameters: -
C-   Output-Data:       DS         Array with distances
C                       CO,SO      Arrays with unit vectors
C-   Status:            -
C
C - - - - - - - - - - - - - - - - - - - - - - - - - - - - - - - - - - - -
C
C-   Subroutine Calls:  -
C-   Includes:          -
C-   Devices:           -
C-   Author:            R.RADTKE  E.LEHMANN H.STANGE   H.STANGE
C-   Date:              20-NOV-84 30-JAN-85 26-MAR-85 08-MAY-85
C
```

```
C   - - - - - - - - - - - - - - - - - - - - - - - - - - - - - - - - - - - - -
C
C-  Description:          VEKTOW determines the distances and unit vectors between
C                         successive points of a curve of an IK-character
C
C-  Algorithm:            -
C-  Commentary:           The commons DSCOM,COCOM and SOCOM are used . They have
C                         to be dimensioned in the main programm with dimension
C                         IKMAX.
C-  Interne Variable:     -
C
C**********************************************************************************
C
        SUBROUTINE VEKTOW(IANF,IEND,I12,IKTOT,X,Y,KE)
C
        IMPLICIT INTEGER*2 (I-N)
C
        DIMENSION X(1),Y(1),KE(1)
        INCLUDE 'DCSCOM.TXT'
C
        PARAMETER ( KE13 = 13, KE15 = 15)
C
        I=IANF                              ! Start index if first point is or is
        IF (KE(IANF).EQ.KE15) I=I-1         ! not a tangent point
        K=IEND
        GOTO 200
C
  100   CONTINUE
        DXI=X(I1)-X(I)
        DYI=Y(I1)-Y(I)
        DS(I)=SQRT(DXI*DXI+DYI*DYI)         ! distance
        IF (DS(I).LT.1.) THEN
            CO(I)=1.
            SO(I)=0.
        ELSE
            CO(I)=DXI/DS(I)                 ! x-component unit vectors
            SO(I)=DYI/DS(I)                 ! y-component unit vectors
        ENDIF
C
        I=I1
  200   CONTINUE
        I1=I+1
        IF (I.NE.K) GOTO 100
C
        IF (KE(IEND).EQ.KE15.AND.K.EQ.IEND) THEN
C
C           end point is a tangent point
C
            IF (IEND.EQ.IKTOT.OR.KE(IEND+1).LT.KE13) I1=I12+1
            K=I1
            GOTO 100
        ENDIF
        RETURN
C
        END
```

364

```
C
C                    ******************************
C                    * I K A R U S - L I B R A R Y *
C                    *   S U B R O U T I N E   *
C                    ******************************
C
C
C
C-  Name:               SPLINW.FOR
C
C-  Keywords:           SSR/IK/FIGURE/CONTOUR/SPLINE/TANGENT/CALCULATE
C
C-  Short Description:  Calculates tangents
C
C-  Call:               CALL SPLINW(IANF,IEND,I12,IKTOT,X,Y,KE,C,S,G)
C
C - - - - - - - - - - - - - - - - - - - - - - - - - - - - - - - - - - -
C
C-  Input-Parameters:   IANF,IEND    - Number of first/last point of curve
C                       I12          - Number of last start point
C                       IKTOT        - as usual
C-  Input-Data:         X,Y,KE       - as usual
C                       DS           - Array with distance ( from VEKTOW )
C                       CO,SO        - Arrays with unit vectors ( from VEKTOW )
C-  Output-Parameters:  -
C-  Output-Data:        C,S,G        - Unit vectors in direction of tangents
C-  Status:             -
C
C - - - - - - - - - - - - - - - - - - - - - - - - - - - - - - - - - - -
C
C-  Subroutine Calls:   -
C-  Includes:           -
C-  Devices:            -
C-  Author:             R.RADTKE  E.LEHMANN  H.STANGE
C-  Date:               20-NOV-84 30-JAN-85  15-MAY-85
C
C - - - - - - - - - - - - - - - - - - - - - - - - - - - - - - - - - - -
C
C-  Description:        SPLINW determines tangential unit vectors for specified
C                       curve points considering different parameters using
C                       cubic polynom splines.
C
C-  Algorithm:          -
C-  Commentary:         Commons DSCOM,COCOM and SOCOM are used. They have to be
C                       dimensioned in the main program with diemsnion IKMAX
C-  Interne Variable:   TOL = tolerance for closed contours
C
C********************************************************************************
C
        SUBROUTINE SPLINW(IANF,IEND,I12,IKTOT,X,Y,KE,C,S,G)
C
        IMPLICIT INTEGER*2 (I-N)
        DIMENSION X(1),Y(1),KE(1),C(1),S(1),G(1)
        INCLUDE 'DCSCOM.TXT'
C
        PARAMETER ( KE13 = 13, KE14 = 14, KE15 = 15, TOL=100. )
C
        N1=IEND-1
        K=IANF
```

```
C
        IF (KE(IANF).EQ.KE15) THEN        ! First IK-point is a tangent point
            KA=IANF+1
            G(IANF)=0.0
            C(IANF)=CO(IANF-1)
            S(IANF)=SO(IANF-1)
        ELSE                              ! First IK-point is not a tangent point
            KA=IANF
            G(IANF)=0.5
            C(IANF)=1.5*CO(IANF)          ! end curvature in x is 0
            S(IANF)=1.5*SO(IANF)          ! end curvature in y is 0
        ENDIF
C
C       Calculation of tangent directions
C
  100   CONTINUE
        H2=1.
        IF(DS(K).GT.0.1) H2 = 1./DS(K)
        C2=3.*CO(K)*H2
        S2=3.*SO(K)*H2
        IF (K.NE.IANF) THEN
            Z=1./(2.*(H1+H2)-H1*G(K1))
            G(K)=Z*H2
            C(K)=Z*(C1+C2-H1*C(K1))
            S(K)=Z*(S1+S2-H1*S(K1))
            IF (K.GE.N1) THEN
                IF (KE(IEND).EQ.KE15) THEN   ! End point is a tangent point
                    C(IEND)=CO(IEND)
                    S(IEND)=SO(IEND)
                    C1=C(IEND)
                    S1=S(IEND)
                    C(K)=C(K)-G(K)*C1         ! x-component tangent vector
                    S(K)=S(K)-G(K)*S1         ! y-component tangent vector
                    GOTO 200
                ENDIF
            ENDIF
        ENDIF
C
        C1=C2
        S1=S2
        H1=H2
C
        K1=K
        K=K+1
        IF (K.LT.IEND) GOTO 100
C
        Z=1./(2.-G(N1))
        C(IEND)=Z*(3.*CO(N1)-C(N1))       ! end curvature in X is 0
        S(IEND)=Z*(3.*SO(N1)-S(N1))       ! end curvature in Y is 0
C
  200   CONTINUE
        C1=C(K)
        S1=S(K)
        H2=1./SQRT(C1*C1+S1*S1)
        C(K)=C1*H2                        ! normalize x-component
        S(K)=S1*H2                        ! normalize y-component
        K=K-1
        IF (K.GE.KA) THEN
            C(K)=C(K)-G(K)*C1             ! x-component of tangent vector
            S(K)=S(K)-G(K)*S1             ! x-component of tangent vector
            GOTO 200
        ENDIF
```

366

```
C
C          Special treatment for closed curves
C
          IF(KE(IEND).EQ.KE14) THEN
             IF((X(IEND)-X(IANF))**2+(Y(IEND)-Y(IANF))**2.LE.TOL) THEN
C
                   DXK=C(IANF)+C(IEND)                ! average x component
                   DYK=S(IANF)+S(IEND)                ! average y-component
                   H2=1./SQRT(DXK*DXK+DYK*DYK)
                   C(IANF)=DXK*H2                     ! normalize x component
                   S(IANF)=DYK*H2                     ! normalize y component
                   C(IEND)=C(IANF)
                   S(IEND)=S(IANF)
C
             END IF
C
          ELSE IF(KE(IEND).EQ.KE13) THEN
C
C          calculate tangent direction at the end (corner) points
C
                   G(IEND-2)=C(IEND)
                   G(IEND-1)=S(IEND)
C
             IF((IEND.EQ.IKTOT.OR.KE(IEND+1).LT.KE13).AND.
     *          (X(IEND)-X(IANF))**2+(Y(IEND)-Y(IANF))**2.LE.TOL) THEN
C
                        C(IEND) = C(I12)
                        S(IEND) = S(I12)
             END IF
          END IF
C
          RETURN
          END




C
C
C                    *******************************
C                    * I K A R U S - L I B R A R Y *
C                    *    S U B R O U T I N E      *
C                    *******************************
C
C
C-  Name:              SAURGK.FOR
C
C-  Keywords:          SSR/IK/GK/CIRCLES/TANGENT/SECTION/ANGLE/CALCULATE
C
C-  Short Description: Calculates sections of circles or lines between IK points
C
C-  Call:              CALL SAURGK(IANF,IEND,J,ISTA)
C
C - - - - - - - - - - - - - - - - - - - - - - - - - - - - - - - - - - -
C
C-  Input-Parameters:  IANF,IEND      - Number of first/last point of a curve
C                      J              - Pointer for GK  data
C                      IKMAX2         - Max. number of GK  digs
C-  Input-Data:        X,Y,KE         - as usual ( in IK format )
C                      C,S,G          - as usual
C                      DS,CO,SO       - Data from VEKTOW
C-  Output-Parameters: J              - see above
C-  Output-Data:       XX,YY,KEKE,    - Contour ( in GK format )
C                           DX,DY,RAD
```

367

```
C-  Status:         ISTA        - 0 : OK
C                                 1 : Max. number of GK digs exeeded
C
C - - - - - - - - - - - - - - - - - - - - - - - - - - - - - - -
C
C-  Subroutine Calls:  DRAIK (determines cosine and sine of angle between
C                       tangents and link between two sucessive IK points)
C                       AUSGL (corrects skewed triangles)
C
C-  Includes:        XYCOM.TXT,XY2COM.TXT,CSGCOM.TXT,DCSCOM.TXT,GKCOM.TXT
C-  Devices:         -
C-  Author:          R.RADTKE  E.LEHMANN H.STANGE
C-  Date:            00-NOV-84 4-FEB-85  13-MAR-85
C
C - - - - - - - - - - - - - - - - - - - - - - - - - - - - - - -
C
C-  Description:
C-  Beschreibung:    SAURGK displays a curve of an IK character by matching
C                    circle segments in GK format
C
C-  Algorithm:       SAUR  method
C-  Commentary:      Commons DSCOM,COCOM and SOLOM are used. They have to
C                    be dimensioned in the main programm
C-  Interne Variable:  -
C******************************************************************************
C
      SUBROUTINE SAURGK(IANF,IEND,J,ISTA)
C
      IMPLICIT INTEGER*2 (I-N)
      INCLUDE 'XYCOM.TXT'
      INCLUDE 'XY2COM.TXT'
      INCLUDE 'CSGCOM.TXT'
      INCLUDE 'DCSCOM.TXT'
      INCLUDE 'GKCOM.TXT'
C
      PARAMETER (LA2=2, LA3=3, LA4=4)
      ISTA = 0
C- - - - - - - - - - - - - - - - - - - - - - - - - - - - - - - -
      I=IANF+1
      CI1=C(IANF)
      SI1=S(IANF)
      CI=C(I)
      SI=S(I)
      CS=CO(IANF)
      SS=SO(IANF)
      CALL DRAIK(CS,SS,CI1,SI1,CI,SI,SA1,SA2,CA1,CA2,IN)
C- - - - - - - - - - - - - - - - - - - - - - - - - - - - - - - -
C                   New run
  100 CI2=C(I+1)
      SI2=S(I+1)
      CSS=CO(I)
      SSS=SO(I)
      CALL DRAIK(CSS,SSS,CI,SI,CI2,SI2,SA11,SA22,CA11,CA22,INN)
      IF (IN.EQ.0) THEN
          J = J + 1
          IF(J.EQ.IKMAX2) THEN
             ISTA = 1
             RETURN
          END IF
C
```

368

```
        KEKE(J) = KE(I) + LA2*16      ! bad triangle
            XX(J) = X(I)                      ! linear interpolation
            YY(J) = Y(I)
            GOTO 500
        ENDIF
C
        IF(INN.EQ.0) THEN
            CI=CSS
            SI=SSS
            CI2=CSS                          ! second triangle is bad, one
            SI2=SSS                          ! more chance
            GOTO 200
        ENDIF
C
        IF(IN*INN.LT.0) GOTO 400         ! triangles have different sense of
C                                         rotation, no correction possible
        CALL AUSGL(IN,SA1,SA2,SA11,SA22,CI,SI,IAUS)
        IF(IAUS.EQ.0) GOTO 400           ! Correction was not successful
C
C            Apply correction or (200) save second triangle
C
        CALL DRAIK(CSS,SSS,CI,SI,CI2,SI2,SA11,SA22,CA11,CA22,INN)
  200   CALL DRAIK(CS,SS,CI1,SI1,CI,SI,SA1,SA2,CA1,CA2,IN)
  300   CONTINUE
        IF (IN.EQ.0) THEN
            J = J + 1
            IF(J.EQ.IKMAX2) THEN
                ISTA = 1
                RETURN
            END IF
C
            KEKE(J) = KE(I) + LA2*16      ! bad triangle
            XX(J) = X(I)                  ! linear interpolation
            YY(J) = Y(I)
            GOTO 500
        ENDIF
C
C- - - - - - - - - - - - - - - - - - - - - - - - - - - - - - - - - - - -
C     Now it is time to fit the circles (only if radii are reasonable)
C
C---------------------------------------------
  400   DR=(1.-CA2)/(1.-CA1)             !
        R2=DS(I-1)/(DR*SA1+SA2)         !
        R1=DR*R2                        !
C---------------------------------------------
        IF(R2.LT.10..OR.R1.LT.10..OR.R1.GT.5E5.OR.R2.GT.5E5) THEN
            J = J + 1
            IF(J.EQ.IKMAX2) THEN
                ISTA = 1
                RETURN
            END IF
C
            KEKE(J) = KE(I) + LA2*16      ! bad triangle
            XX(J) = X(I)                  ! linear interpolation
            YY(J) = Y(I)
        ELSE
            IF(IN.LE.0) THEN
                R1 = -R1
                R2 = -R2
            ENDIF
```

```
C
C       Point I-1 relativ to centre of first circle
C
        XM1 = X(I-1) - R1*SI1
        YM1 = Y(I-1) + R1*CI1
        DX1 = X(I-1) - XM1
        DY1 = Y(I-1) - YM1
C
C       Auxiliary point
C
        XH=X(I-1)+R1*(SS-SI1)
        YH=Y(I-1)+R1*(CI1-CS)
C
C       Auxiliary point relative to centre of second circle
C
        DX2 = XH - (X(I) - R2*SI)
        DY2 = YH - (Y(I) + R2*CI)
C
        LA = LA3
        IF(IN.GT.0) LA = LA4
C
C       Store auxiliary point and (DX1,DY1)
C
        J = J + 1
        IF(J.EQ.IKMAX2) THEN
            ISTA = 1
            RETURN
        END IF
        KEKE(J) = LA*16
        XX(J) = XH
        YY(J) = YH
        DX(J) = DX1
        DY(J) = DY1
        RAD(J) = ABS(R1)
C
C       Store curve end points and (DX2,DY2)
C
        J = J + 1
        IF(J.EQ.IKMAX2) THEN
            ISTA = 1
            RETURN
        END IF
        KEKE(J) = KE(I) + LA*16
        XX(J) = X(I)
        YY(J) = Y(I)
        DX(J) = DX2
        DY(J) = DY2
        RAD(J) = ABS(R2)
C
      ENDIF
C- - - - - - - - - - - - - - - - - - - - - - - - - - - - - - - - - - -
C             Final procedure
C
  500 IF (I.NE.IEND) THEN
          IN=INN
          SA1=SA11
          SA2=SA22
          CA1=CA11
          CA2=CA22
          CS=CSS
          SS=SSS
          CI1=CI
```

370

```
            SI1=SI
            CI=CI2
            SI=SI2
            I=I+1
            IF (I.LT.IEND) THEN
                GOTO 100
            ELSE
                GOTO 300
            ENDIF
        ENDIF
C- - - - - - - - - - - - - - - - - - - - - - - - - - - - - - - - - - - - - -
        RETURN
        END




C
C
C                        *******************************
C                        * I K A R U S - L I B R A R Y *
C                        *    S U B R O U T I N E      *
C                        *******************************
C
C
C
C-  Name:                  DRAIK.FOR
C
C-  Keywords:              SSR, ANGLE, TRIANGLE, CALCULATE
C
C-  Short Description:     DRAIK checks triangles and calculates base angles
C
C-  Call:                  CALL DRAIK(CS,SS,CI1,SI1,CI,SI,SA1,SA2,CA1,CA2,IDREH)
C
C - - - - - - - - - - - - - - - - - - - - - - - - - - - - - - - - - - - - - -
C
C-  Input-Parameters:    (CS,SS)   -   Direction of triangle basis
C                        (CI1,SI1) -       "          left arm
C                        (CI,SI)   -                  right arm
C-  Input-Data:           -
C-  Output-Parameters:   SA1,SA2   -   Sine of both base angles
C                        CA1,CA2   -   Cosine   "    "     "
C                        IDREH     -   Sense of turn
C-  Output-Data:          -
C-  Status:               -
C - - - - - - - - - - - - - - - - - - - - - - - - - - - - - - - - - - - - - -
C
C-  Subroutine Calls:     -
C-  Includes:             -
C-  Devices:              -
C-  Author:          ?     H.STANGE
C-  Date:         00-JAN-00 02-NOV-84
C
C - - - - - - - - - - - - - - - - - - - - - - - - - - - - - - - - - - - - - -
C
C-  Description:
C-  Beschreibung:    DRAIK checks triangles and calculates base angles
C
C                    IDREH =  1, when triangle o.k., when math. right
C                    IDREH = -1, when triangle o.k., when math. left
C
C                    IDREH =  0, when not o.k.
```

```
C
C-  Algorithm:         -
C-  Commentary:        -
C-  Interne Variable:  -
C
C*******************************************************************************
C
      SUBROUTINE DRAIK(CS,SS,CI1,SI1,CI,SI,SA1,SA2,CA1,CA2,IDREH)
C
C
      IMPLICIT INTEGER*2 (I-N)
C
      PARAMETER ( TOL = 0.0015 )
C
      IDREH=1
C
C
      SA1=CS*SI1-CI1*SS
      SA2=CS*SI - CI*SS
C
      IF(SA1*SA2.LE.O.) THEN
C
              IF(SA1.GT.O.) IDREH = -1
              SA1=ABS(SA1)
              SA2=ABS(SA2)
C
              IF(SA1.GE.TOL.AND.SA2.GE.TOL) THEN
                      CA1=CS*CI1+SS*SI1
                      CA2=CS*CI +SS*SI
                      IF(CA1.LT..1.OR.CA2.LT..1) IDREH = O
                  ELSE
                      IDREH = O
                  END IF
C
            ELSE
                IDREH = O
C
        END IF
C
C
      RETURN
      END



C
C
C                  ******************************
C                  * I K A R U S - L I B R A R Y *
C                  *     S U B R O U T I N E     *
C                  ******************************
C
C
C
C-  Name:              AUSGL.FOR
C
C-  Keywords:          SSR/TRIANGLE/CHANGE/ANGLE
C
C-  Short Description: Corrects triangles for program SAURGK
C
C-  Call:              CALL AUSGL(IDREH,SA1,SA2,SA11,SA22,CI,SI,IAUS)
C
```

```
C - - - - - - - - - - - - - - - - - - - - - - - - - - - - - - - - - - - - -
C
C-   Input-Parameters:   IDREH               Sense of turn for both triangles
C-   Input-Data:
C                        SA1,SA2             Opening angles of first triangle
C                        SA11,SA22           Opening angles of second triangle
C                        CI,SI               Direction of common section
C-   Output-Parameters:  IAUS = 0            If correction is not necessary
C                             = 1            If correction was applied
C-   Output-Data:         CI,SI              New direction of common section
C-   Status:              -
C
C - - - - - - - - - - - - - - - - - - - - - - - - - - - - - - - - - - - - -
C
C-   Subroutine Calls:-
C-   Includes:-
C-   Devices:-
C-   Author: NN        E.LEHMANN
C-   Date: 00-JAN-00  4-FEB-85
C
C - - - - - - - - - - - - - - - - - - - - - - - - - - - - - - - - - - - - -
C-   Description:
C-   Beschreibung:   AUSGL corrects triangles that are not o.k.
C                    One side of both triangles are placed on one line.
C                    This common direction (CI,SI) is corrected, in order to
C                    make both triangles a little more symmetrical.
C
C                    CI,SI  = common line direction (turned if necessary)
C                    -----------------**-----------------
C                    ^          SA2  .. SA11              ^
C                      ^               .   .            ^
C                        ^               .   .        ^
C                          ^             .     .    ^
C                      ^ SA1  .  <<       >>  .  SA22 ^
C                        ^    .       arms      .    ^
C                          ^  .               .   ^
C                            ^.             .    .^
C    *
C                SA1,SA2 ... are sines of angles
C-   Algorithm:-
C-   Commentary:-
C-   Interne Variable:-
C
C*********************************************************************************
      SUBROUTINE AUSGL(IDREH,SA1,SA2,SA11,SA22,CI,SI,IAUS)
      IMPLICIT INTEGER*2 (I-N)
C
      IAUS=0
      DR=IDREH*.7
      DEL1=(SA1-SA2)*DR
      DEL2=(SA11-SA22)*DR
      DEL=(DEL1+DEL2)*.7
C
C  DEL = positiv , turn right
C  DEL = negativ , turn left
C
      DELDR=DEL*DR
```

373

```
C - - - - - - - - - - - - - - - - - - - - - - - - - - - - - - - - - - - - - - - -
        IF(DELDR.GE.O.) THEN
C
C  SA11 becomes smaller
C
          IF(DELDR.LT..O1) RETURN
          IF(DELDR.GT.DEL2*DR) DEL=DEL2
        ELSE
C
C  SA2 becomes smaller
C
          IF(DELDR.GT.-.O1) RETURN
          IF(DELDR.LT.DEL1*DR) DEL=DEL1
        ENDIF
C - - - - - - - - - - - - - - - - - - - - - - - - - - - - - - - - - - - - - - -
C  Rotate (CI,SI)
C
        CDEL=SQRT(1.-DEL*DEL)
        C=CI*CDEL-SI* DEL
        SI=CI* DEL+SI*CDEL
        CI=C
C
        IAUS=1
        RETURN
        END
```

Appendix X
Marking rules

Prior to the proper digitizing procedure, one must prepare the original. This involves marking the digitization points, adjusting the baseline, the left side and right side bearings, and treating of special cases, e.g. digitizing multicolored logotypes.

The results of the digitizing are very dependent upon the number and position of the digitization points. The idea is to achieve the best reproduction of the original with the least number of points. To this end it is recommended to mark the points to be digitized on the original prior to digitization, as follows:

Start points	Show the direction of digitization.
Corner points	— Need not be marked, they are obvious.
Curve points	– Extreme points, two or three points within a 90° change of direction, at points of inflection and auxiliary points.
Tangent points	> Tangent points never occur alone. There are either two tangent points or a neighbouring corner point, in order to define the straight.

First of all the necessary points (e.g. curve extremes and auxiliary points) are marked, followed by the necessary intermediate points, marked as uniformly as possible.

1) Mark in start points

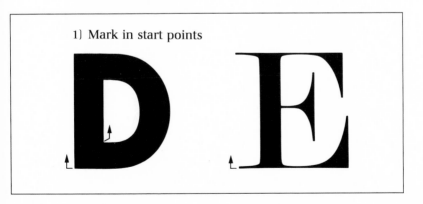

2) Mark in curve extreme points

3) Mark in tangent points

4) Mark in aid points

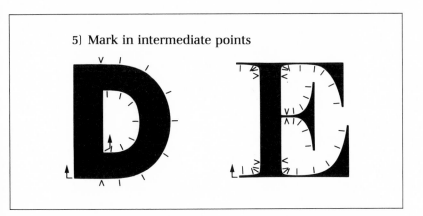

5) Mark in intermediate points

In the following, further marking rules are described using combinations of text and examples.

A circle is marked by its extreme points. These points are at the maximum and minimum extension of a curve. With a full circle four curve points suffice for its display. With deviations from ideal circles additional curve points are necessary; two or three additional curve points per 90 degree turn.

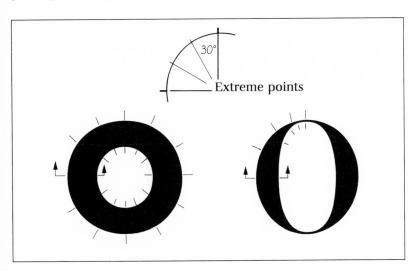

The joint of a curve to a corner requires particular attention. Since only curve points can create a curved line, placing the curved point too far from the joint will produce too flat a curve. For this reason the last curve point must be marked approximately three to five millimeters from the corner point (assuming 100 mm cap height).

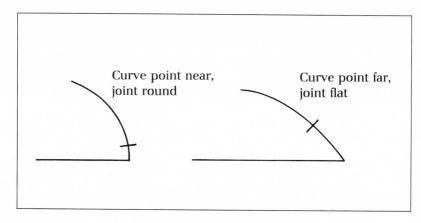

Points of inflection must to be marked with a curve point.

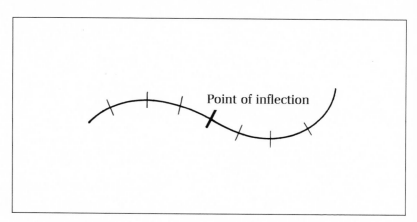

Point of inflection refers to those positions at which a left curve runs into a right curve or a right curve runs into a left curve.

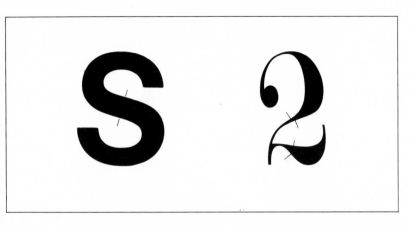

There are examples in graphics where such directional changes do not take place immediately, but where there is a straight segment between two curved sections. In such cases we do not have a point of inflection but a transition from curve into straight and from straight into curve, i.e. tangent points.

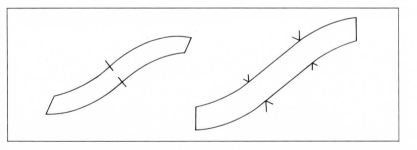

Marking examples

The original below has only straight contours. Correspondingly we have one start and twelve corner points to digitize. The direction of digitization is marked at the start point with an arrow. The corner points do not need to be marked.

The original below right has only tangent and curve points. For the start point, the correct tangent point is selected so that the second point will also be a tangent point.

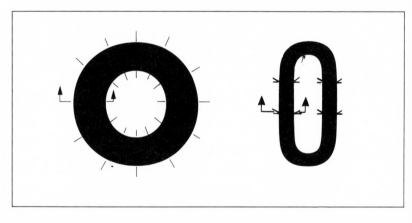

This original above left has only curve points. Points should be marked approximately every 30 degrees.

Below original consists of corner and curve points. Notice that the extreme values of the curves have to be marked, and that at the section joining corner to curve, a curve point should be set approximately 3 to 5 mm from the corner.

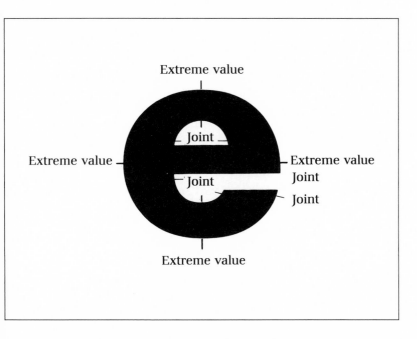

Tangent points are marked with >. When dealing with symmetrical sections of the original for example, make sure that the corresponding tangent points are marked at the same height or width.

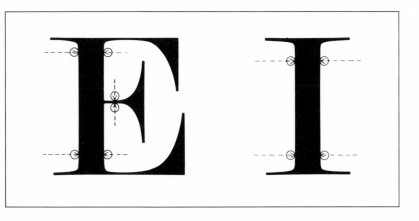

Appendix Y
Digitizing rules

1. Operating the sensor
The sensor of the digitizer has a cross-hair fitted under a magnifying glass, and five sensor keys. It is fitted into a box and interacts electromagnetically with the digitizer tablet. This small device is also popularly known as the "mouse". In order to avoid misunderstandings, it should be mentioned that the commonly used mouse can just return relative displacement information to its host, whereas a digitizer mouse enables absolute measurements of positions.

Cross-hair
The point where the two hairs cross is lined up on the marked point above the black/white transition of the letter outline. Its current position is input into the computer by pressing the appropriate key for the type of point.

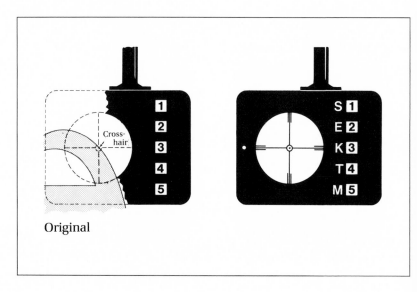

Sensor keys

The upper four sensor keys correspond directly to the four individual types of points used to represent the IKARUS format:

> **s 1** start point
> **e 2** corner point
> **k 3** curve point
> **t 4** tangent point
> The last sensor key
> **m 5** is reserved for the menu field
>   and initiates the menu command.

In order to select from the menu the cross-hair is approximately
lined up with the center of the relevant 1 cm × 1 cm menu box (lining
up exactly with the centre of the box is not necessary) and sensor
key **m 5** pressed.

The menu commands allow 34 different program functions to be
selected for new digitizing and for the correction of digitizations of
originals.

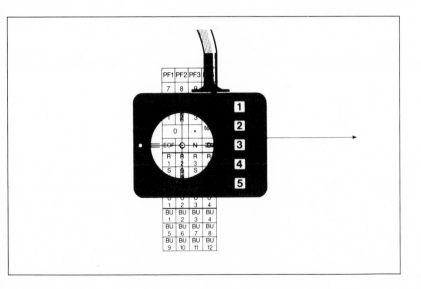

The sensor is held as shown:

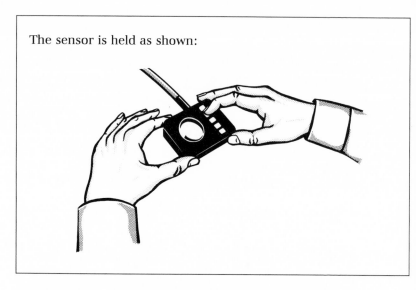

2. Structure of digitizing menu for IKARUS

The axis intersection together with the menu box is marked on a transparent sheet which is placed on the digitizer tablet.

The menu field in the 2nd quadrant can be used as an alternative to the key board when entering character numbers.

The other fields are used with an interactive program which is not described in detail here.

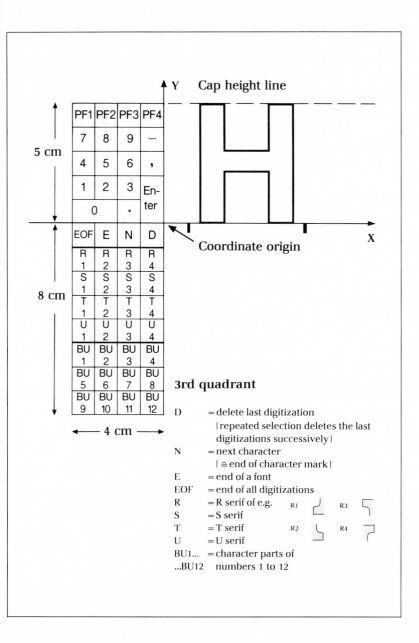

Y   Cap height line

PF1	PF2	PF3	PF4
7	8	9	–
4	5	6	,
1	2	3	En-ter
0		.	

5 cm

Coordinate origin

X

EOF	E	N	D
R 1	R 2	R 3	R 4
S 1	S 2	S 3	S 4
T 1	T 2	T 3	T 4
U 1	U 2	U 3	U 4
BU 1	BU 2	BU 3	BU 4
BU 5	BU 6	BU 7	BU 8
BU 9	BU 10	BU 11	BU 12

8 cm

← 4 cm →

3rd quadrant

D   = delete last digitization
        (repeated selection deletes the last
        digitizations successively)
N   = next character
        (≙ end of character mark)
E   = end of a font
EOF   = end of all digitizations
R   = R serif of e.g.   R1   R3
S   = S serif
T   = T serif   R2   R4
U   = U serif
BU1... = character parts of
...BU12   numbers 1 to 12

385

3. Digitizing

The first character original is fixed under the plastic sheet with adhesive tape or on register pins in such a manner that its baseline rests exactly on the X axis and the left side bearing is about 1 cm to the right of the Y axis. No part of the character may overlap the menu field to the left of the Y axis. Unlike the marking, the digitizing of all characters must take place in a prescribed sequence.

At the start of the digitizing procedure the coordinate origin for the font is determined, which simultaneously defines the position of the IKARUS menu field. The job number is entered using the menu keyboard. If the characters are to be recorded with left and right side bearings these details are digitized first, the data being entered using the key for corner points. The next digitizing step is the start point of the character. This marks the start of the digitizing of a closed outline or a closed curve so that when the character is being output, the writing head (pen, engraving stylus or knife) moves to this point "raised". As already mentioned, the contour (outline) is recorded with the sensor sequentially, point by point. As each key is pressed, the computer stores the type of point and absolut coordinate value for each mark.

After each letter is finished, an "N" (next) is keyed in as a separating mark between characters and the character number of the next character is then entered.

4. Part-serifs and character parts

Up to four different part-serif sets, each with four different part-serifs and up to twelve different character parts can be stored by processing steps.

Storing part-serifs

One needs to digitize only the R1 or S1, T1 or U1 serif, paying attention that one always "digitizes from the serif to the straight", because the program always assumes that all parts of serifs are digitized as if they were positioned on vertical stems. Prior to the recording of part-serifs the appropriate menu command must be given. The program calculates the part-serifs 2, 3 and 4 automatically as mirror images at Y axis, at X axis and as rotation by 180 degrees, and stores them ready for recall via other menu commands.

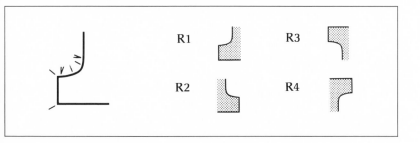

Recording and fitting of character parts

The term "character parts" refers to parts similar to serifs (incomplete, characteristic letter forms, repeated regularly throughout an alphabet), and has relevant commands in the menu positioned directly under those given for the serifs. The procedure for digitizing character parts differs from that of serifs in so far that after the menu command is given for the recording of the character parts, they start with a start point and they are digitized "from the straight to the serif".

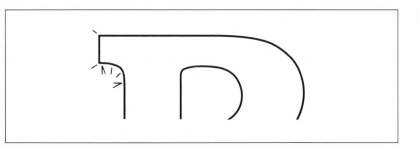

In contrast to serifs, character parts also have to be digitized at the correct Y height. One must make sure that the last point (here a corner point) in the X direction allows the direction of fitting to be recognized. Directions of fitting are "to the right" and "to the left". This shift only takes place in the X direction, i.e. the character part must be digitized for recording at the correct Y height. Prior to digitizing the character part, the appropriate menu command (BU1 to BU12) must be given.

Digitizing part-serifs

Characters are dealt with in the following manner: The digitizing sequence is: Start point, tangent point, menu field R2, corner point, corner point, menu field R1, tangent point, tangent point, menu field R3, corner point, corner point, menu field R4, tangent point. Care must be taken to ensure that the digitizing of a character does not start with a menu command or end with a menu command. In the course of the further processing (channel processing), the two horizontal straights of the "I" (for example) are lined up with the base line and the cap height line respectively. Afterwards the serifs are fitted using the program DV.

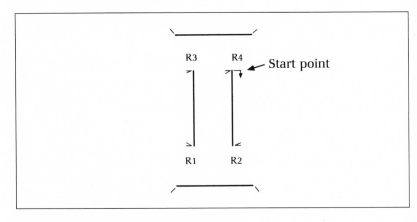

Serif fitting on straight stems

Part-serif a is to be fitted onto character b. Points 5 and 6 are determinant for the length of the serifs, points 3 and 4 are not determinant with respect to their Y position, which is taken from part a (serif height is defined by point 2). The curved segment of the serif is retained, the extension lies between corner and tangent point. The result is character part c.

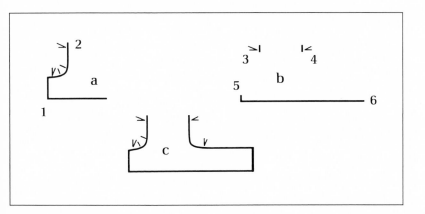

Other fitting results:

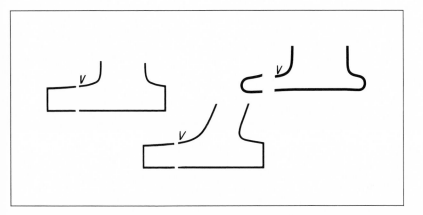

As can be seen in this example, it is imperative that the serifs to be fitted are marked with tangent points.

Serif fitting on sloped strokes
Serifs may be fitted not only to vertical but also to sloped stems. In this case the curve of the serif has to be adjusted to match the diagonal. For this, so-called "alignment points" are required which detail the thickness and direction of the sloping stems.

389

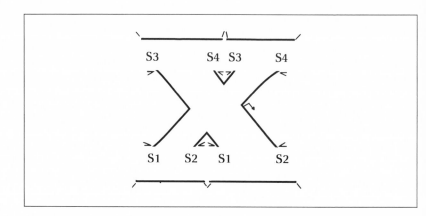

All points in this example also serve as alignment points. In the case of fitting onto straight sloping stems, two alignment points would be sufficient for the program.

When the alignment points are curve points then round fitting is executed.

Three alignment points will always be required to determine and describe a circle.

The last point of the serif part is placed on the circle at its correct Y height. Finally the alignment point which is nearest to the serif is deleted.

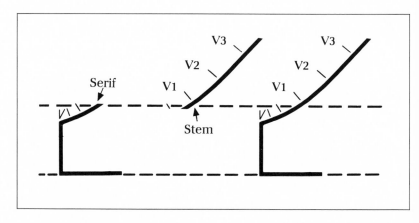

5. Post digitizing

If one only has to execute slight corrections to letters, it is possible to post digitize segments rather than carry out a complete new digitization. In order to match the digitizations to the old character, the character number is entered and the left and right side bearings should also be digitized to act as calibration points. The first and last point of the newly recorded part are fitted to the character. A tolerance circle at the start and end points of the post digitization allows automatic fitting of the respective points to the corrected digitization.

First and last points of the post digitization are deleted. Closed lines can also be similarly fitted. A tolerance circle around the start point allows the appropriate closed line to be found.

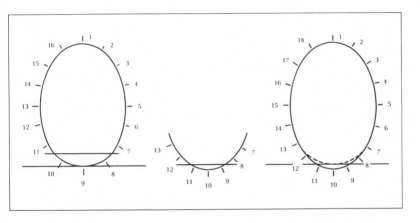

The number and types of points digitized in the old and new parts do not have to correspond with one another. The number of points is recalculated.

Appendix Z
References, on typefaces in particular

1. Typefaces

Bosshard, H. R., "Technische Grundlagen zur Satzherstellung", Band 1, Verlag des Bildungsverbandes Schweizerischer Typografen Bst, Bern, 1980.

Fiebig, D., "Tabellensatz. Programmierte Anleitung für das richtige Setzen von Reihensatz, Formularsatz, Werk-, Akzidenz- und Schreibtabellen", Heft F 11 Fachtechnische Schriftenreihe, Industriegewerkschaft Druck und Papier, Stuttgart, 1971.

Frutiger, A., "Schrift – Ecriture – Lettering. Die Entwicklung der europäischen Schriften, in Holz geschnitten", Verlag des Bildungsverbandes Schweizerischer Buchdrucker, Zürich, 1951.

Goudy, F. W., "The Alphabet and Elements of Lettering", University of California Press, Berkeley/Los Angeles, 1942.

Johnston, E., "Schreibschrift, Zierschrift und angewandte Schrift", Leipzig, 1910, and "Writing and Illuminating and Lettering", London, 1906.

Kapr, A., "Schriftkunst", VEB Verlag der Kunst, Dresden, 1971.

Kindersley, D., "Optical Letter Spacing", in The Penrose Annual, The International Review of the Graphic Arts, Vol. 62, blz. 167–176, Lund Humphries Publishers Ltd., London, 1969.

Morison, S., "First Principles of Typography", Cambridge, 1936. "Letter Forms, Typographic and Scriptorial", London, 1968. "On Script Types", The Fleuron 4, London, 1925.

Ovink, G. W., "Legibility, Atmosphere-value and Forms of Printing Types", A. W. Sijthoff's Uitgeversmaatschappij n.v., Leiden, 1938.

Renner, P., "Die Kunst der Typographie", Bern, 1939.

Treebus, K. F., "Het zetten van vreemde talen. Tips voor het juiste gebruik van accenten, hoofdletters, leestekens e.d. in het Deens, Duits, Engels, Esperanto, Fins, Frans, Fries, Hongaars, Iers, Indonesisch, Italiaans, Latijn, Noors, Pools, Portugees, Roemeens, Servo-Kroatisch, Slowaaks, Sloweens, Spaans, Tsjechisch, Turks, IJslands, Zuidafrikaans en Zweeds, alsmede beknopte regels voor het afbreken van woorden", Staatsuitgeverij, 's-Gravenhage, 1971.

Tschichold, J., "Die neue Typographie", Berlin, 1928. "Geschichte der Schrift in Bildern", Basel, 1946, and "Meisterbuch der Schrift", Ravensburg, 1952.

Zapf, H., "About Alphabets. Some Marginal Notes on Type Design", New York, 1960. German edition: "Über Alphabete", Frankfurt am Main, 1960. "Manuale typographicum I–II", Frankfurt am Main, 1954/1968, and "Typographische Variationen", Frankfurt am Main, 1963.

2. Digital type

Bigelow, C. and Day, D., "Digital Typography", Scientific American, Vol. 249, Number 2, August 1983, pp. 106–119.

Bigelow, C., "Font Design for Personal Workstations", BYTE magazine, January 1985, pp. 255–270.

Coueignoux, P., "Generation of Roman Printed Fonts", Ph. D. Thesis, Massachusetts Institute of Technology, Cambridge, Massachusetts, June 1975.

ISO/TC97/SC18/WG8, "Information Processing – Font and Character Information Interchange"; ANSI American National Standards Institute, 1430 Broadway, New York, NY 10018 c/o Bernadette St.John, Secretariat of ISO/TC97/SC18.

Knudson, D. R., "Digital Encoding of Newspaper Graphics", Massachusetts Institute of Technology, Cambridge, Report ESL-R-616, August 1975.

Knuth, D. E., "Metafont: A System for Alphabet Design", STAN-CS-79-762, Department of Computer Science, Stanford University, Stanford, California, September 1979. "TEX and Metafont", American Mathematical Society and Digital Press, Bedford, Massachusetts, 1979.

Naiman, A., "High-Quality Text for Raster Displays", Department of Computer Science, University of Toronto, January 1985.

Plass, P. and Stone, M., "Curve-Fitting with Piecewise Parametric Cubics", Imaging Sciences Laboratory, Xerox Palo Alto Research Centers, March 1983 (unpublished).

Ruggles, L., "Letterform Design Systems", STAN-CS-83-971, Department of Computer Science, Stanford University, Stanford, California, April 1983.

Späth, H., "Spline-Algorithmen zur Konstruktion glatter Kurven und Flächen", Oldenbourg Verlag München Wien, 1973.

Warnock, J. E., "The Display of Characters Using Gray Level Sample Arrays", Computer Graphics, Volume 14, Number 3, July 1980, pp. 302–307. Siggraph 1980 Proceedings.

3. Journals

"Deutscher Drucker", Unabhängiges Fachmagazin für die Druckindustrie, Verlagsgesellschaft mbH & Co. KG, Stuttgart.

"Der Druckspiegel", Fachzeitschrift für deutsche und internationale Drucktechnik, Druckspiegel Verlagsgesellschaft mbH & Co., Heusenstamm.

"The Seybold Report on Publishing Systems", Seybold Publications Inc., Media (Pa).

"U&lc". Upper and Lower Case, The International Journal of Typographics, International Typeface Corp., New York.

"Visible Language", The Journal for Research on the Visual Media of Language Expression, Visible Language, Cleveland (Ohio).

The author:
I was born a farmer's son in Stargard, Pomerania, on the 11th of November 1940, but in 1945 the family fled as refugees to the vicinity of Hamburg. From school I progressed to university, where I studied high energy physics leading to a dissertation in 1971 concerning meson production through electrons.

My partners Rubow and Weber founded URW (Unternehmensberatung Rubow Weber) in the same year, and I joined them as a third partner early in 1972. Later that year I met with Walter Brendel of Düsseldorf and the company ARISTO in Hamburg as consultant programmer to develop a method of cutting typeface rubyliths with a flatbed plotter.

Had I been told at the time that digital type would become the work of a lifetime, I would never have believed it. This work swiftly became, however, a most enjoyable and exciting task continuing to the present day, full of meetings with the pleasant and interesting people in our little typographic world (maybe only 1000 people on the whole planet), many of whom are friends or members of the ATYPI.

Initially, due to bugs, IKARUS as a program often "fell to earth" as Greek mythology taught us long ago. For the help and support received during each crisis from my two partners Rubow and Weber, help which has continued unchanged throughout the years, I remain very grateful indead.

I am also very grateful to Hermann Zapf for good advice, for introducing me to ATYPI in 1975, and for wholeheartedly supporting our digital approach to type.

Concerning further developments, we, the URW partners, together with Hermann Zapf, have formed a new company this year called URW Master Design GmbH, to design and program so called masters (a little bit more than canned templates) to lend the special qualities of typography to the many varied kinds of text documents presently in use.

Peter Karow

Production

Cover:	Calligraphy by Jovica Veljovic
Translation:	Mike Daines, Dietrich Buglass
Correction:	Andy Newton
Layout:	Christine Utech
Text setting:	Renate Gloor

Typeface

Name:	Marconi roman demi italic
Typesetter:	Digiset 200T1, HELL Gmbh, Kiel